WELSH WOODS AND FORESTS

A HISTORY

WELSH WOODS AND FORESTS
A HISTORY

W. LINNARD

First Impression – 2000

© W. Linnard, 2000

ISBN 1 85902 864 0

Printed in Wales at
Gomer Press, Llandysul, Ceredigion

CONTENTS

PREFACE

Welsh Woods and Forests, first published by the National Museum of Wales in 1982, was well received, soon went out of print, and for years has been unobtainable. Since then, many people have encouraged me to prepare a new and updated edition of the book. The time is now appropriate: the first edition described the history of the woodlands of Wales up to 1919, the year in which the Forestry Commission was formed. In 1999 Wales stands at a new threshold, with the establishment of the National Assembly, and the publication of Wales' own forest strategy.

This new edition of *Welsh Woods and Forests* includes much additional historical material that has come to light since the first publication in 1982. It also contains several completely new chapters, describing the famous trees and big trees of Wales, and summarizing the enormous developments in forestry that have transformed the Welsh countryside during the twentieth century.

The forest historian of Wales faces a dilemma. For the period before 1919 the main problem is a shortage of good documentary sources. After 1919 the problem is the plethora of source material – official publications, unpublished records, and recollections of serving and retired foresters. In the interest of historical balance this book describes only the main developments in Wales during the twentieth century.

The main sources available and which I have used include: the Annual Reports of the Forestry Commissioners (1920 onwards); the Census of Woodlands reports; various House of Commons Reports, Command Papers, Acts of Parliament and associated regulations; the Reports on Forest Research (1949 onwards); the *Journal of the Forestry Commission* (1922-69); and the many Forestry Commission publications, especially those relating specifically to Wales. These include: *Britain's New Forests* (1936); four guides – *Cambrian Forests, Glamorgan Forests, Snowdonia Forest Park* and *Dean Forest & Wye Valley*; leaflets on individual forests: *Rheola* and *Coed y Brenin* (English and Welsh versions); *Forestry in Wales/Coedwigaeth yng Nghymru* (several editions, in English and Welsh); *Tales from the Gwydyr Woods* and *Gwydyr Forest in Snowdonia: A History* (both by D.L. Shaw); *Tree Growth on the South Wales Coalfield* (G.J. Mayhead et al., 1974); *Guide to Site Types in Forests of North and Mid Wales* (D.G. Pyatt, 1970); *Shelterbelts for Welsh Hill Farms* (W.A. Cadman, 1954, 1966); and *Forestry in Wales* (J.W.Ll. Zehetmayr, 1985). Other sources of major importance are: George Ryle's *Forest Service* (1969), a detailed history of the development of the Forestry Commission, especially in South Wales, from 1919 to 1965; George Ryle's unpublished typescript 'Beating About the Bush' (1977); and finally *Broadleaved Woodlands in Wales: the Core Report* (Coed Cymru, 1985), which itself contains an extensive bibliography of relevant published and unpublished material. In 1994 the Forestry Commission published *The First 75 Years*, a brief account of the history of the Forestry Commission 1919-94, by Douglas Pringle.

ACKNOWLEDGEMENTS

I owe a debt of gratitude to many people for their help in the preparation of this book. Firstly, of course, my indebtedness continues to all those persons and institutions named individually in the first edition. Secondly, I am most grateful to the National Museums & Galleries of Wales (as holders of the original copyright) for granting me permission to produce this new, revised and updated edition. I am also grateful to the University of Wales Press for allowing me to use in Chapter I copyright material which I contributed to *Settlement and Society in Wales* (editor D. Huw Owen; UWP, 1989).

Thanks are due also to Dr Graham J. Mayhead (former lecturer, School of Agricultural & Forest Sciences, University of Wales Bangor), Mr John F. Morgan (former Forestry Commission Director for Wales, and Director Forest Enterprise Wales), and Mr J.W.Ll. Zehetmayr (former Forestry Commission Senior Officer Wales, and Conservator South Wales) for helpful discussions and advice. Of course, I am responsible for the opinions expressed in this book, and for any errors of omission or commission.

Above all, I owe very special thanks to Mrs Pauline Ridgway for producing the text of this book. Without her skilled assistance this book would not have seen the light of day.

For illustrations without attributions in the captions, I am grateful to the following for permission to publish: National Library of Wales 9, 19, 40; National Museums & Galleries of Wales 24, 56; Museum of Welsh Life 6, 16, 28-9, 33, 36, 43-5, 48-9, 52-3, 69, 70, 72, 77-9, 81-2, 84-6, 88; Forestry Commission 80, 90, 91, 93, 95; L. & M. Gayton 36; Gwynedd Archives 39; Glamorgan Record Office 47; Abergavenny Museum 41, 51, 75; Torfaen Museum 65; National Trust 71. The other illustrations are from the author's collection.

Finally, I wish to thank the publishers, Gomer Press of Llandysul, for all their skilled care and assistance.

William Linnard
Radyr
6 May 1999

Chapter I

THE WOODLANDS OF WALES:
ICE AGE TO NORMAN CONQUEST

Tree-trunks became visible, standing in the sea . . . and the sea-shore took
on the appearance of a forest grove, cut down at the time of the Flood . . .
Giraldus Cambrensis, *Itinerarium Kambriae*

The general features of the development of the vegetation since the end of the
last glacial (Devensian) period in the territory now known as Wales have been
fairly accurately determined by examination of plant remains from
archaeologically dated sites, and especially by pollen analyses carried out over
the last fifty years, chiefly on samples of peat obtained from bogs at various
places in upland and lowland sites.

Most of our native trees liberate into the air large amounts of pollen which is
blown about by the wind, and some of this pollen 'rain' settles down on
neighbouring lakes and pools or on the surface of peatbogs. The bog mosses, as
they die back, do not decay completely but accumulate, forming deposits of wet
peat which preserve the pollen grains. The species or at least the genera of the
plants releasing pollen grains can be identified microscopically, the ratio of tree
to non-tree pollen ascertained, and the relative proportions of individual species
determined. By analysing samples of peat from various depths, the changes in
the composition of the local flora over time can be followed.

The results of these pollen analyses may differ in local details, and in the later
stages of the pollen record they often indicate divergent vegetation histories
attributable in greater or lesser degree to the influence of man. However, taken
together, they reveal a great measure of agreement, and a fairly consistent picture
of vegetation history emerges which conforms broadly to that shown by parallel
studies carried out in other parts of Britain and Northern Europe.[1]

The general outline of vegetation development in relation to climatic phases,
pollen zones, and human economic activity was summarized diagrammatically
by Hyde over a quarter of a century ago.[2] This summary diagram remains
substantially correct, though certain modifications have become necessary in the
light of recent research which has revealed deviations from the established
continental Holocene climatic periods in the maritime climates of the British
Isles, and alterations have been made too in the chronologies of the culture
periods of Neolithic, Bronze Age and Iron Age in the British Isles. Radiocarbon
dating corrected by dendrochronology has already caused modifications in the
accepted picture, and future work will inevitably lead to further refinement.

Fig.1 attempts to update Hyde's diagram on the basis of the most recent data summarized and reviewed by Taylor.[3] This diagram summarizes the general situation for Wales as a whole, but it is necessary to distinguish three broad regional environments or zones having distinct bioclimates. The first, which may be termed the maritime or Atlantic zone, comprises Anglesey, coastal Gwynedd including Llŷn, coastal Ceredigion, Pembrokeshire and Carmarthenshire and especially the extreme south-west peninsula, the lower Vale of Tywi, Gower, and the southern coastal fringe of Glamorgan. This zone merges rapidly inland into the second zone, the central mass of the Welsh uplands, an area of high rainfall and shorter growing season, which responds late to a warming but early to a cooling climate. The third zone is the Welsh borderland, with the least maritime

Calendar Years	Climatic Periods	Pollen Zones	Cultures	Trees percent	Vegetation	Economy
2000					Reforestation	Industrialization
			Historical			
1000	Sub-/ Atlantic	VIII			Forest shrinkage	
					oak - birch -	
AD/BC			Iron Age		beech - alder	Agricultural and Pastoral Farming
1000						
			Bronze Age			
	Sub-Boreal	VIIb				
2000					Mixed oak forest and alder woods	Shifting Agriculture and Pastoral Farming
3000			Neolithic			
4000	Atlantic	VIIa				
5000						
			Mesolithic		Oak - alder	
6000					Pine - hazel	Gathering, Hunting Fowling and Fishing
7000	Boreal	VI			Pine-hazel-birch	
		V				
		IV			Birch - pine	
8000		III				
9000	Late Glacial	II	Upper Palaeolithic		'park - tundra'	
		I			Tundra	
10,000						

1. Diagram showing vegetation development in Wales in relation to climatic phases, pollen zones, and human economic activity.

climate, extending from the Dee estuary to the coast of Gwent and including the eastern parts of the Welsh border counties. Within these three major zones, local topography and soils impose further variation, in turn affecting the natural vegetation.

Natural vegetation itself is not static, and develops according to the climate and soil of the area. Bare ground is first occupied by pioneer plants, which are eventually displaced by a natural succession of species occupying the site more intensively, until finally the climax vegetation becomes established, this being the most highly developed form of plant community which the area can support. Over much of Wales, and indeed the greater part of Britain and western Europe, the climax vegetation is broadleaved deciduous forest.

The last glacial period, the Devensian (Weichselian), drew to an end some 12,000 years ago, and in general, and in its simplest terms, the climatic picture since then has been one of gradual warming for some three and a half thousand years until 6500 BC, followed by a period of 'optimum' climate of similar duration, until 3000 BC, and then a cooling period extending to the present. Of course, numerous shorter- and longer-term climatic fluctuations and cycles have occurred within these major periods.

Following the retreat of the ice at the end of the glacial period, a sparse tundra or 'park-tundra' vegetation of herbs and subshrubs gradually developed, similar to that seen in northern Scandinavia today. As the climate improved in the early Boreal period (Pollen Zone IV), the first trees to colonize large areas were the birches – light-seeded pioneer species, dispersed by the wind, capable of rapid spread and relatively undemanding as to site. The birches comprised the dwarf species (*Betula nana* L.), not now part of the Welsh flora, and the two common native species *Betula pendula* L. and *B. pubescens* Ehrh., which cannot be separated by pollen analyses. The pollen record shows that birch was for a time the sole tree present, but it was soon followed by the next invading species, another light-demanding tree, Scots pine (*Pinus sylvestris* L.), a conifer which has a very wide Eurasian distribution. Birch and pine continued to dominate the tree vegetation throughout the Pre-Boreal and early Boreal, apparently alternating in relative importance.

Pine continued to be an important element of the Welsh vegetation throughout the Boreal, with birch declining somewhat in importance and other broadleaved species such as hazel (*Corylus avellana* L.), elm (presumably only *Ulmus glabra* Huds., see below), and oak becoming established. Oak was soon to become the dominant native tree throughout Wales, and to remain so for seven millennia, up until the very recent period of extensive planting of exotic species, mainly conifers, in the nineteenth and twentieth centuries.[4] In Wales, oak is represented by two species, the pedunculate oak (*Quercus robur* L.) and the sessile oak (*Q. petraea* (Matt.) Liebl.), but these are indistinguishable in pollen analyses or by examination of the wood. *Q. robur* is the main species in the lowlands and on the heavier soils of the borderland, while *Q. petraea* is the main species in the uplands in areas of high rainfall and on the older siliceous rocks. Natural hybrids between the two native oak species are frequent.

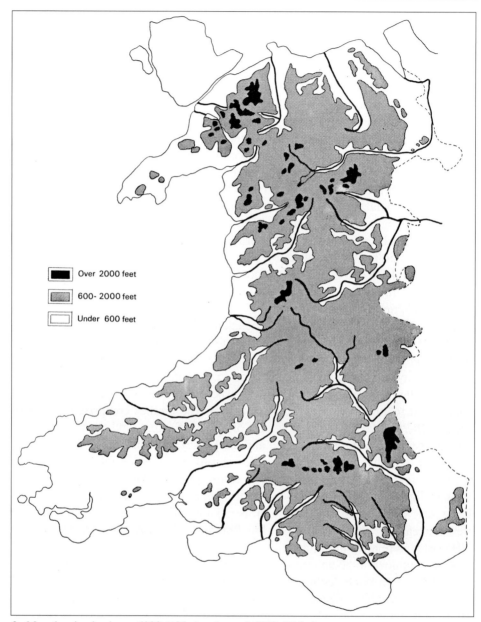

2. Map showing land over 600ft (185m) and over 2,000ft (615m).

In Taylor's ecosystem model for the Early Mesolithic,[5] Pollen Zone VI is divided into VIa with a hazel maximum in both uplands and lowlands, birch declining in favour of oak, elm and pine in the lowlands and promoting a major expansion of pine in the uplands. Thus, early Mesolithic man would have found mixed broadleaved forests in the lowlands, and birch/pine in the uplands. In Zone VIb, hazel became reduced everywhere, surviving as an understorey beneath oak and elm; pine survived especially in the uplands, where birch declined. In Zone

VIc, oak and pine expanded, especially in the uplands, with pine increasing particularly at higher altitudes; hazel decreased in the lowlands, the relatively thermophilous small-leaved lime (*Tilia cordata* Mill.) arrived, as did the common or black alder (*Alnus glutinosa* Gaertn.). The latter, a nitrogen-fixing species, spread rapidly everywhere. During the Boreal, with rising sea levels and submergence, the land links with Ireland were broken, and somewhat later the British Isles became detached from continental Europe. Forest probably reached its greatest altitudinal extent during the climatic optimum of the Atlantic period, but conditions in the preceding Boreal and in the succeeding Sub-Boreal may also have enabled trees to colonize land at high altitudes. At the time of maximum forest expansion, forest would have covered most of the land area of Wales apart from the very highest mountains. Subfossil tree roots and stems, commonly known as bog-wood and identified as pine, oak and birch, are found in peat at many places at altitudes up to about 2,000ft, which coincidentally is the general upper limit of planting by the Forestry Commission in Wales today. Only 1% of the land area of Wales lies above 2,000ft, i.e. above the probable upper forest limit, and some 6% of the land area lies between 1,500 and 2,000ft, at altitudes where tree growth is possible, though rates of increment would not be rapid. Naturally, areas of marine sands, lakes, rock and scree, and special sites such as salt-marsh or very exposed areas would not have carried forest vegetation. Wind too is a limiting factor of great importance, especially on west- and north-facing slopes.

After the Boreal, the climate became wetter during the Atlantic period, with a warmth maximum. Mixed deciduous woodland is generally believed to have attained its maximum expansion and vigour, except at higher altitudes and in exposed locations. The proportion of alder increased substantially, and that of pine decreased quite sharply to a very low but fairly steady level, persisting in the uplands where competition with other tree species was least. During this climatic optimum, small-leaved lime formed a small but important element of mixed oak forests, especially on lower and warmer sites. Alder was dominant on wet marshy sites, and occurred with oak in valleys, and on plains and slopes. Some elm was present at all altitudes, but oak forest became the characteristic and major vegetation of the lowlands in the Atlantic and later periods, and of the highland zone too in the later Sub-Boreal period.

Tŷ Canol Wood, on the north slope of the Presely Hills, is today an area of primary sessile oak/ash/hazel with a rich bryophyte flora, where there has almost certainly been some woodland cover since Atlantic times.[6] Other fragments of ancient woodlands with a particularly rich flora of epiphytic lichens occur in the Gwaun Valley in Pembrokeshire and Coed Rheidol in Ceredigion, and in Coed Cymerau, Coed Ganllwyd and Coed y Rhygen in Gwynedd (now National Nature Reserves).

During the Atlantic period, with its wetter and windier climate, peat mosses gradually invaded the plateaux and upper slopes. The effect of the small Mesolithic population of food-gatherers, hunters and fishers on the vegetation in this period has been generally thought to be slight, but recent research suggests that human influence was more important and, in conjunction with climatic change, could have brought about significant modification of forest, at least locally. The ability of small numbers of men with hand-axes and the deliberate use of fire to modify or destroy forests can be considerable.

Towards the end of the Atlantic period, with a cooler and then drier climate, Mesolithic nomadism was replaced by the more settled Neolithic system. Areas of heath and upland peats spread, but extensive mixed deciduous woodlands dominated by oak persisted at lower altitudes and on steep slopes. Ash (*Fraxinus excelsior* L.) arrived *c.*3000 BC and spread locally. Heath and bog expansion favoured birch and pine, especially on drying sites.

Though extrapolated from fragmentary evidence, the pollen maps produced by Birks et al.[7] for pine, birch, oak, elm, alder, hazel and lime in Wales at 3000 BC, just before the start of marked decline in elm pollen and before the most extensive of the Neolithic clearances, show that pine was by then very rare everywhere, and not an important element in the Welsh forests; oak was the principal component of the forests; birch was not a major forest species, though occasional high pollen values are recorded in south Wales; elm was moderately important in parts of south Wales but very rare in the north; alder was frequent in north, mid and south Wales, but not the south-west; hazel was common everywhere except Snowdonia; and lime was important only in mid Wales. At this time the first weeds of grazing and cultivation appear in the pollen record, and also cereal pollen. Scrub and forest-margin species such as bracken also become more prominent, reflecting the increasing clearance of forest.

The question of elm decline associated with the advent of Neolithic farmers is still unresolved. The timing and extent of the decline varied, apparently being less dramatic in Wales than in Ireland and lowland England, and being accompanied by the appearance of typical weed species such as plantains and nettles. Though the possibility of a catastrophic epidemic such as occurred during the 1970s cannot be dismissed, the decline of elm is generally ascribed to the selective influence of man, in felling or lopping trees particularly suitable for leaf fodder for pounded livestock during winter, and seems to have restricted what was previously a quite widely distributed tree to certain favoured areas, in particular the middle stretches of the larger rivers in eastern Wales, and some small regions in the south, west and north of the country. Lime and perhaps also ash are believed to have been affected in the same way.

Early in the Sub-Boreal (early VIIb) the ecological equilibrium of the Mesolithic begins to be lost, and Neolithic and later Bronze Age people with metal tools and more sophisticated use of fire caused selective and locally massive deforestation. Peat growth continued on the higher, wetter plateaux, but pine and birch reasserted themselves somewhat. Elm disappeared from many areas, as did lime.

All the native broadleaved species of Wales are capable of regenerating more or less vigorously by coppice sprouting from the stump after felling. The vigour depends on tree species, age and light, and the subsequent survival and growth of the coppice shoots depend on freedom from browsing and other damage. The procedures of clearance of natural woodland by shifting cultivation or slash-and-burn agriculture of Neolithic and later farmers are recalled succinctly in the Mabinogion tale of Culhwch and Olwen, where Ysbaddaden sets his first task for Culhwch: 'Dost see the great thicket yonder? . . . I must have it uprooted out of the earth and burnt on the face of the ground so that the cinders and ashes thereof be its manure, and that it be ploughed and sown . . .'[8]

In practice, initial site selection was a skilled job, to avoid frost hollows, stony terrain and areas prone to seasonal waterlogging. Open woodland rather than dense hardwood forest would obviously be preferred for ease of clearance. Trees were dealt with in two ways: the large trees, especially hard-wooded species such as oak, were killed by girdling the bark and chopping away some of the sapwood, while smaller trees were felled. Large stumps would probably be left *in situ*, as complete clearance of the site by uprooting would be excessively laborious for only short-term agricultural utilization. The forests cleared were often open upland woodlands of oak and/or birch, as for example on sites studied in Powys,[9] and in the lower Conwy valley.[10] The felled material would be spread over the area and left to dry out, for burning to be done in one operation, probably in spring, and repeated if necessary. Crops would be sown under dead standing trees. Each slash-and-burn site, perhaps a few acres in size, would be cropped for only a few years before its fertility was exhausted and another site would have to be used. This would result in a regular programme of tree girdling and felling, drying out and burning, and then cultivation. Felling would have to be done at least a year before crop sowing took place. Some of the root suckers and coppice regeneration from stumps in and around the cleared areas would be destroyed by grazing animals, while surviving sprouts from successive clearings would tend to form an age sequence similar to managed coppice. Excavations in the Somerset Levels have revealed numerous wooden trackways of Neolithic age, and of various types, the evidence indicating quite sophisticated methods of production and utilization of the local woody species, with ample evidence of coppiced hazel stands. The understanding of coppicing and its systematic application has probably been a regular form of woodland management ever since Neolithic times, and in the mixed arable and livestock husbandry of the Neolithic farmers, sheep were an ideal means of exploiting open oakwoods, and would have had a significant effect in eliminating tree regeneration around settlements.

During the Middle and Late Bronze Age, the climatic and anthropogenic effects on the forests continued, with peat accumulation, and the spread of heath, moorland grasses, bracken and scrub. The plateau woodlands were mainly birch/hazel/pine, with alder prominent in wet habitats at low and intermediate altitudes. Oak forest still occupied large areas on slopes and lower lands.

The abandonment of small areas used for shifting cultivation would often be followed by natural succession back to secondary forest. This process of alternating clearance and natural forest regrowth is also described in the tale of Culhwch and Olwen, by the Owl of Cwm Cawlwyd: 'the great valley you can see was a wooded glen, and a race of men came thereto and it was laid waste. And the second wood grew up therein, and this wood is the third . . .'[11]

With the cooler and wetter climate of the Sub-Atlantic (at the start of Zone VIII) during the Iron Age the tree-line and agricultural and settlement limits were all reduced in altitude. Peat formation increased in the uplands, especially on deforested areas and wet soils, with the development of extensive *Sphagnum* moss and *Eriophorum* (cotton grass) communities, which Leland later described so graphically as 'wilde pastures . . . sogges and quikke'.[12] The improved tools and more settled mode of life at lower altitudes marked the start of major clearance of the dense low-altitude forests in Wales.

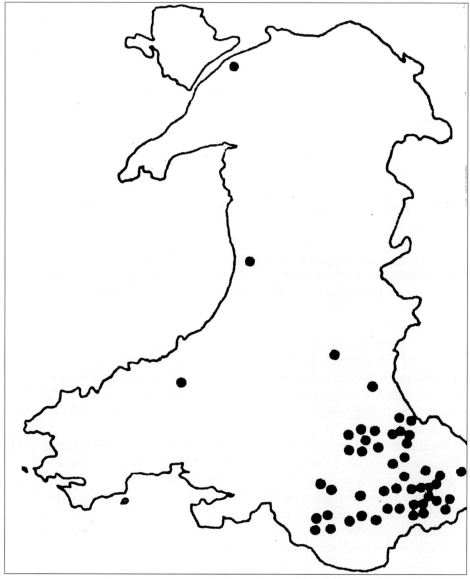

3. Map showing location of place-names which include the Welsh words for beech (*ffawydd, ffawydden, ffawyddog*). The three dots in north and west Wales represent names of eighteenth-century origin.

This period also saw the immigration into Wales of beech (*Fagus sylvatica* L.) and probably hornbeam (*Carpinus betulus* L.), the last tree species to form part of the native flora before the period of proven introduction by man. Beech is native in Wales only in south-east Powys, Monmouthshire and east Glamorgan, where numerous relict beech woods and place-names incorporating the Welsh name for beech (*ffawydd, ffawydden, ffawyddog*) are found within or immediately outside the eastern fringe of the coalfield.[13] The pollen evidence for the presence of beech in Wales before the Roman invasion is not conclusive, but the discovery of quantities of beech charcoal in an Iron Age hearth at Radyr (Glamorgan) dated at or before the first century AD proves the nativity of beech

4. A beech tree growing on the Iron Age hearth at Radyr (Glamorgan).

in Wales.[14] The charcoal in this hearth was in the form of short thick sticks, some evidently cut with an axe, and indicated that the forest environment there was ash/oak/beech woodland, with elm (probably *Ulmus glabra*) an important accessory species, and also occasional birch, field maple (*Acer campestre*) and holly, with hazel the main shrub. Apart from birch, all these species still occur in the present-day woodlands at the hearth site, together with sycamore and lime.

The natural area of beech in south-east Wales apparently remained relatively stable for nearly 2,000 years. Numerous documentary references and place-names attest to beech as a timber species in south-eastern Wales from the thirteenth century onward, but it remained confined to the south-east corner, its failure to spread further northward and westward naturally being apparently attributable to its intolerance of the wetter and cooler conditions prevailing there. A charter of 1223 mentions beech (*nigrum fagum*) in Glasgoed, Gwent.

Jury evidence for a general survey of the estates of the Earl of Pembroke in 1570 gives a clear statement of the local geographical distribution of beech in Glamorgan at that time: 'within the said Foreste called Forreste Keven y Vyd and Forest Keven Onn there ys for the most parte Beache of sundry sortes and no oeke or Tymber at all'; 'Forest Maes yr allt . . . in which there ys oeke and beaches'; 'Llowyd Koyd is replenyshed most with oke, glyn Kynon moste with beache and some with okes, glyn Tave with bothe and Koed Marchan all with okes'.[15] The natural distribution of beech in Wales, which was not obscured by planting in the west and north until the eighteenth century, was noted at the end of the seventeenth century by Edward Lhuyd in correspondence; 'In noe part of Northwales is found any flint or chalk, nor beech trees' (1 July 1690), and again: 'In South Wales I found several plants common which I had never seen in North Wales, such as . . . Fagus' (24 November 1696).[16]

The post-Boreal status of Scots pine (*Pinus sylvestris* L.) in Wales is much more doubtful.[17] Pollen records from north and south Wales show pine present at all levels from the Pre-Boreal onwards, but from the end of the Atlantic period (*c*.3000 BC) at levels so low that the pollen may have been carried in by the wind from far away, for example Ireland. Hyde concludes that pine died out 'almost if not quite completely' in Wales. Remains of pine trees in submerged forests off the coast between Penmaen-mawr and Priestholm were recorded by John Ray in 1662, and pines have also been identified off the coast at Borth and Ynys-las. Godwin believed that a relict stock of native pine might have persisted in Wales in special bog and mountain sites, for example, at Borth Bog near the pine trees found in the submerged forest. Pine charcoal found in a Neolithic cairn at Bryn-celli-ddu (Anglesey) was dated at *c*.1500 BC. Pine trunks and stumps have frequently been found in peat beds in various parts of Wales, for example at Llyn Llwydiart in Anglesey, in Cwm Bychan (Merioneth), and 'in the deeps of Monmouth, where turfe is digged'. This subfossilized resinous bog-wood was used by Welsh peasants in later centuries for splints and torches.

Significantly, the earliest Welsh literary reference to pine, in the form of torches or fires of pine, comes not from Wales itself but from the country of Gododdin, between the Forth and the Tyne, in a sixth-century poem by Aneirin.[18]

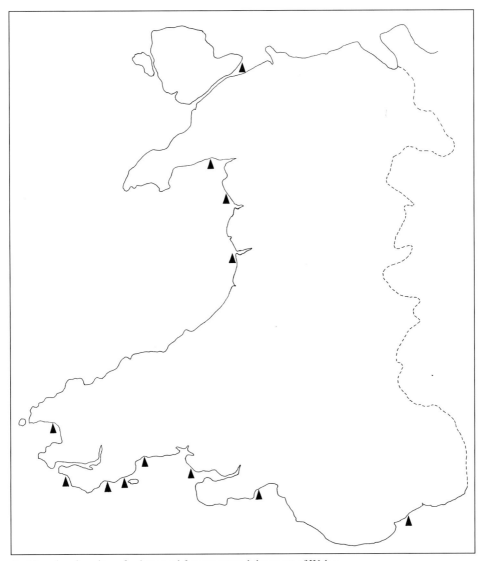

5. Map showing sites of submerged forests around the coast of Wales.

Other early literary references to pine (*ffenitwydd, ffinydwydd*) occur in the thirteenth-century manuscripts of the *Kat Godeu* (*Cad Goddau*) and Mabinogion (White and Red Books), but although the original sources of the surviving manuscripts are from even earlier periods, they cannot be regarded as providing definite evidence of the existence of living pine in Wales. The same applies to later poetical references to pine, for example by Madog Benfras in the fourteenth century,[19] and Lewys Glyn Cothi (*fl.* 1447-89) who described a bow. This bow was, of course, made of yew, but its ends were of pine: *Ei ddau ben oedd o binus*. Lewys describes the bow as being of four colours, namely red, white, blue and black, these symbolizing fire, snow, sky and earth, respectively. The actual

6. Submerged tree stumps exposed at low tide, near Goldcliff (Monmouthshire).

elements of the bow gave the colours: the yew heartwood being red, the yew sapwood white, the string blue, and the two ends of pine being black – possibly bog pine. Place-name evidence is even more uncertain, and there are no early place-names that incorporate a pine/fir element, though it has been suggested that names such as Coed Du or Coed Duon (= black wood) may refer to former pine-dominated woodland. The absence of pine from the lists of tree values in the Welsh Laws attributed to Hywel Dda is strong evidence that it had completely died out; such a uniquely useful species would surely have been mentioned in lists reflecting relative usefulness to man. Scots pine was planted widely in Wales from the seventeenth century onward, but there is no positive evidence of the existence of living pine in Wales before then. Therefore, the possibility of the uninterrupted survival of the species in Wales since Boreal times must remain open and doubtful.

Using sophisticated biometrical methods of analysis, Richens has made a detailed study of the variation and distribution of elms throughout England, and discusses their history in relation to man.[20] He argues that in England the earliest introduction of elms by man may be of Late Bronze Age date, and that thereafter the elm in the pollen profiles is not necessarily *U. glabra*. In a further special study devoted to Wales, Richens and Jeffers[21] show that elm of any sort is now rare over much of Wales, and that the only elm certainly native is the wych elm, *U. glabra*, which is now frequent in nineteen regions, the largest of these lying along the English border in the basins of the Dee, Severn, Usk and middle Wye. The other regions of *U. glabra* in the south, west and north are much smaller.

The relatively poor native flora formed only few natural forest types. Oak, the most valuable and most extensive tree, formed two main vegetation types, viz. pedunculate oakwood dominated by *Quercus robur*, and sessile oakwood dominated by *Quercus petraea*. The two oaks produce pollen that is not distinguishable, and readily interbreed to produce a number of hybrid forms intermediate between the two parent species. The pedunculate oakwood occurs in the lowlands, with associate species including wych elm, small-leaved lime, field maple, cherry, aspen, holly and yew, and often hazel underwood; only remnants of this type of woodland now exist, as the soils on which it developed are well suited to agricultural use. The ground flora includes dog's mercury, wood sanicle or primrose on the heavier soils, and bluebell and wood anemone on the lighter ones. The sessile oakwood, for millennia the typical native woodland over the large part of upland Wales, with older acidic rocks and higher rainfall, still covers quite considerable areas on steeper slopes. Birch and rowan are the typical associates, the birch forming pure stands in places, especially at higher altitudes. Bracken commonly dominates the field layer, persisting after the woods are felled, and bluebell, bramble and foxglove are frequent.

On particular sites, other forest types predominated, and some fragments still persist today. Alder woods, dominated by common alder (*Alnus glutinosa*) together with various willows (especially *Salix caprea* and *S. cinerea*), occupy marshy, valley-bottom sites. On gentle slopes alder also forms woods with ash and oak.

Ash woods, dominated by common ash (*Fraxinus excelsior*), and mixed ash/oak woods occur on Carboniferous Limestone in south Wales, on steep slopes, with aspen and wych elm as associated species. Shrubs such as dogwood, spindle and wayfaring tree are a particular feature of limestone woodlands. The field layer may comprise ramsons (*Allium ursinum*), dog's mercury or hart's-tongue fern. Ashwoods also occur on basic igneous rocks in Gwynedd, and some residual ash/oak/field-maple woods are found on the Lias limestone in Glamorgan.

Beechwoods, dominated by beech (*Fagus sylvatica*) and with some associated oak, ash and wych elm, occur in south-east Wales. The ground flora is very thin, and in the densest woods the soil may be quite bare (*Fagetum nudum*), but with more light the ground flora includes ramsons, bluebell, dog's mercury and bramble. Two of the best remaining semi-natural beechwoods are in the Cwm Clydach National Nature Reserve, south-west of Abergavenny.

New archaeological discoveries are constantly adding to our picture of human settlement and influence on the woodlands.[22] Recent years have seen the discovery of worked oak timbers of Neolithic age at a site *c.* 350m above sea level in the Tal-y-bont valley (Brecon Beacons) and wooden trackways of the Bronze Age at Caldicot and Goldcliff. Most striking of all is the giant wooden henge structure discovered at Sarn y Bryn Caled (near Welshpool), consisting of an outer circle of 20 massive oak columns with six more columns in the centre, dated at *c.*2100 BC. A replica of this spectacular monument has been constructed at the Museum of Welsh Life, St Fagans.

7. Replica of wooden henge structure at St Fagans.

Roman Wales

A town among the Britons is nothing more than a thick wood
Caesar, *De Bello Gallico*, V, 12

Wales at the start of the Roman invasion in the first century AD consisted of small areas of settlement and cleared land in a matrix of mainly oak forests extending up to altitudes of around 1,250ft, or higher in sheltered valleys. The native oakwoods were of two main types, the pedunculate oak forest (dominated by *Quercus robur*) of the lowlands, with associate species including wych elm, lime, maple, cherry, aspen, holly and yew, and often hazel underwood; and the sessile oakwood (dominated by *Quercus petraea*) of the uplands on the dominantly acidic rocks and in the higher rainfall, with birch and bracken as typical associates. On particular sites, other forest types would have predominated: alder woods with willows on marshy, valley-bottom sites; beechwoods with some oak and elm in restricted areas on limestone and Old Red Sandstone in the south-east; and ashwoods and ash/oak mainly on steep slopes on Carboniferous Limestone in the south.

The pattern of land use around settlements consisted of temporary or semi-permanent clearings for agriculture, areas of grazed forests or open woodlands, with occasional selective fellings and perhaps regularly coppiced woods. Away from the settlements, the structure of the primeval forests, unmodified by man's activity, consisted of a relatively high proportion of very old and large trees with little underwood, and large quantities of rotten stems and other debris on the ground.

The conquest and subsequent partial settlement of Wales by the Romans brought profound changes to the country and the people, and these changes extended to the forests, where certain important modifications were initiated, notably in management, utilization, and the introduction of exotic species. Original sources give only tantalizingly brief references to Wales, but archaeology is adding rapidly and substantially to the picture, modifying the earlier idea of a primarily military presence and indicating more and more a settled and civilian influence. Little direct information is available on the forests, or on the practice of forestry in the country during the Roman period, but inferences can be made from accounts of military campaigns, reports of archaeological excavations, and analogies with other parts of the Roman empire.

Caesar stated that a town among the Britons is nothing more than a thick wood, fortified with a ditch and rampart, to serve as a place of retreat against the incursions of their enemies.[23] The piecemeal conquest of the tribes in Wales started soon after AD 43 and ended with the final crushing defeat of the Ordovices in AD 78. The Welsh tribes, for the most part bitterly hostile to the invaders, used their native forests as places of ambush, and for the Romans the conquest was partly a matter of attrition and partly of gradual encroachment, until the tribe concerned was forced into the final pitched battle in which military organization and arms prevailed.

The Roman attack on Anglesey in AD 60 began the destruction of Druidical power on the island. Druidism probably represented a forest cult, and the popular etymology of the word druid is from δρυζ (oak). Pliny the Elder said of the druids that 'they hold nothing more sacred than the mistletoe and the tree on which it grows provided that it is a *robur*. They choose the robur to form oak groves, and they do not perform any religious rites without its foliage ... Anything growing on those trees they regard as sent from heaven and a sign that this tree has been chosen by god himself'.[24] It is uncertain how much credence should be given to this, or how far the forest is an original feature to the background of druidism, but one of the first actions by the victorious governor, Suetonius Paulinus, was to fell the groves 'dedicated to sanguinary superstitions'.[25]

The military problems of advance against hostile tribes in rugged and well wooded terrain in Wales were similar to those described by Tacitus in the Roman campaigns in Scotland: 'When we used to plunge into the woods and thickets, all the hostile tribesmen charged straight at us', but after a battle, when the enemy reached the woods 'they rallied and profited by their local knowledge to ambush the first rash pursuers'.[26]

The Roman military campaigns required timber. Wood was needed for the flat-bottomed landing craft hurriedly built for the assault on Anglesey, and for the defences and structures of the original camps and forts. The Romans carried essential supplies, including timber assortments, with them from base, but local timber would have been cut and used wherever possible. The network of military roads involved considerable forest clearances, not only for the actual roadways but also for clear ways on either side, in order to reduce the possibility of ambush or sniping. These roads represented the first step in the break-up of the great Welsh forest tract.

Large amounts of wood were used in the construction of the forts, and extensive fellings in the locality supplied most if not all of the requirements. At Y Gaer at Coelbren, for example, large numbers of logs were used in the rampart foundations. They were mainly oak, unbarked, 17ft long and 8-9 inches in diameter. Some logs were split lengthways. Above them was a layer of earth, topped by small logs and branches, mainly birch. In some places boards over a foot wide were used in the ramparts and as pavements.[27] Obviously oak and birch forest grew in the vicinity of the camp, at about 800ft in altitude. In the main, small trees were used in the form of roundwood, but the capability for working larger trees was evidently available. At Segontium, overlooking Caernarfon, the first fort, built *c.* AD 75, was of timber. It was replaced by a stone building in the second century. Archaeological excavations have revealed oak-lined wells and pits, wooden booths and hutments, postholes for gateways prepared for timbers nearly a foot square, and other postholes for buildings, generally 3-5 inches square, but sometimes round.[28] Similar evidence can be adduced for many other forts, large and small, and indicates an organized timber industry. A wide range of skill in carpentry is evident in the way both roundwood and squared timber from local resources (chiefly oak) were used in constructing timber-framed buildings.

In their own homeland, the Romans had a highly developed forest administration and system of forest legislation, and this extended to parts of their empire, though no evidence is available to indicate the actual details or extent in Wales. In France, two major forest systems were distinguished during the Gallo-Roman period: *silvae materiariae* (high forest) and *silvae caeduae* (coppice). Forests were also classified according to utilization: *silvae glandiferae* where pannage for pigs was the most important, and *silvae vulgares* where wood was the most important product.[29]

Economic exploitation and development followed closely on the military conquest. The Romans frequently annexed the estates of their conquered enemies, and worked the forests for timber, charcoal and other forest products. In Wales, the value of metalliferous ores – gold, copper, lead, silver and iron – was swiftly realized, and the subsequent development of mining and smelting involved the consumption of considerable amounts of wood for the mines and for the manufacture of charcoal.

Rural development of Britain by the Romans included the introduction of a number of important species of trees. Fruit trees such as the cultivated cherry, medlar, mulberry, fig, walnut and sweet chestnut, and possibly also the horse chestnut (*Aesculus hippocastanum*) and holm oak (*Quercus ilex*) were introduced. Sycamore (*Acer pseudoplatanus*), sometimes thought to have been brought into Britain at this time, is probably a later introduction.

In their utilization of the forest resources of Wales, the Romans had the advantage of superior technology. Serrated flint saws had existed since at least the Neolithic period and were copied in copper and bronze and iron in the

Bronze Age and Iron Age, but the Romans developed tooth setting and frame-saws, used long two-handled saws for the conversion of felled timber, and first developed mechanization of reciprocating saws.[30] In addition to saws, the range of their implements included the basic *securis*, the woodman's axe with convex cutting edge, the sides of the blade more or less concave in profile, and with the blade wedge-shaped in section (Fig. 8). Axes varied considerably in size, weight and shape, the woodman's axe being wider and more convex than those used by the carpenter or butcher. Heavy long-handled axes were used for felling, and lighter short-handled types for splitting logs, chopping out roots, making stakes, etc. The double-bladed type (*securis dolabrata*), with a vertical cutting edge on one arm and a horizontal one on the other, closely resembled the mattock and was ideal for tree-felling and chopping out roots. The shape and method of axe hafting have remained largely unaltered to the present day. The *dolabra* (hatchet), a double-headed tool with a narrow axe-blade on one side and a straight or curved pick on the other, was used for grubbing out stumps and roots, and also for splitting and shaping logs. The type with the upward-curving pick was apparently used for rolling logs into position. Other tools were the *dolabella*, a small short-handled hatchet; the *serrula*, a small saw, often a pruning saw; the *falx arboraria*, the common billhook with a curved blade, used for lopping trees; the *falx lumaria,* a thorn cutter or slasher; the *falx putatoria*, a tree-pruning billhook; and various tools for cutting bracken, brambles, etc.[31] It is likely that one of the main uses of the billhooks and slashers was for lopping branches of selected broadleaved trees to provide winter cattle feed.

8. The Roman woodman's axe (*securis*), and the double-headed *dolabra* used for grubbing out stumps and roots, and also for cleaving wood.

The Dark Ages

> The Owl of Cwm Cawlwyd: When I first came hither, the great valley you
> see was a wooded glen, and a race of men came thereto and it was laid
> waste. And the second wood grew up therein, and this wood is the third.
> *The Mabinogion*

The five or six centuries following the end of the Roman occupation in the last quarter of the fourth century AD are truly 'Dark Ages' in the history of Wales. Few contemporary sources of documentary evidence exist, and the development of the forests during this period must be largely a matter of conjecture and of inference of general trends from archaeological studies of individual sites. The main characteristics of the period are an overall growth of population, a general movement of population towards valley settlements, penetration and colonization of new areas by settlers, the growth of ecclesiastical settlements, intermittent tribal warfare, and ravaging of the border region and coastal areas by Anglo-Saxons and sea-raiders. The pollen record exhibits a continuing decrease in the proportion of tree pollen. With the withdrawal of the Romans the arable area probably decreased, but the formerly prevalent idea of a predominantly pastoral society during the Dark Ages has been considerably modified by recent scholarship.

Culhwch and Olwen, the earliest Arthurian tale in Welsh, gives glimpses of a primitive social code, with subject matter 'perhaps coeval with the dawn of the Celtic world', including a graphic description of forest clearance by slash-and-burn agriculture.[32] Ysbaddaden the Chief Giant sets his first task for Culhwch: 'Dost see the great thicket yonder? . . . I must have it uprooted out of the earth and burnt on the face of the ground so that the cinders and ashes thereof be its manure; and that it be ploughed and sown so that it be ripe in the morning against the drying of the dew'. Clearance for temporary or permanent agricultural usage had an immediate effect, but livestock grazing too would have adversely affected the forest over a long period for much of the grazing would have been in open woodland or wood pasture, its long-term result being the elimination of regeneration and the eventual degradation and destruction of the forest.

Some hill-forts remained in use in the post-Roman period, but the valley-ward settlement following lines of least resistance would have involved clearance first of the valley sides with smaller trees and later the valley bottoms carrying oak of large diameter. At Dinas Emrys, a hill-fort near the southern end of Nant Gwynant, pollen analysis indicates that the natural woodland of the valley had already been cleared fairly extensively in the early Dark Ages. This early clearance was followed by a period of reduced human activity or recolonization by forest vegetation, before further clearance in the later Dark Ages.[33] The timing of these phases is not precise, but this alternating pattern of clearance and abandonment must have been repeated many times at various places throughout the country, often as a result of tribal warfare. The process is vividly described in another passage in *Culhwch and Olwen*, when the ancient Owl of Cwm Cawlwyd says: 'When first I came hither, the great valley you see was a wooded glen, and a race of men came thereto and it was laid waste. And the second wood grew up therein, and this wood is the third'.[34]

At Dinas Powys, apparently the court of an important ruler in the fifth and sixth centuries, stock-raising was the main basis of the economy, but arable cultivation was also important. The existence of large numbers of pigs implies extensive woodland nearby, providing pannage and also hunting territory.[35]

At Aberduhonw (Breconshire) Irish immigrants cleared and settled the area after the departure of the Romans, and repeated human interference caused degradation of the woodland until it eventually failed to regenerate. The valleys were used for corn and pasture, and trees were left on slopes only where steepness made ploughing impossible. Grazing animals moved through these woods, seeking upland and lowland pastures and doubtless destroying any natural regeneration *en route*.[36]

Cyril Fox, in his field survey and interpretation of Offa's Dyke, concluded that irregular or sinuous parts indicate the presence of forest when the bank was built late in the eighth century, whereas straight sections indicate cleared and cultivated areas of a settled agriculture, and wide gaps in the dyke are likely to indicate areas of very dense damp oak forest. In this way the dyke may be used as a transect indicating land use in the late eighth century, from the Dee to the lower Severn. As an illustration, a section of the dyke in Montgomery-shire is interpreted as follows: 'the area between the Vyrnwy and Severn was arable and meadowland; a narrow belt bordering the Severn near Buttington up to the 300-ft contour was arable, above that was woodland, above that again forest (waste); the short straight stretches at the 800-1,000-ft level in Leighton parish represent . . . open downland . . . From Rownal to within a thousand yards of the Caebitra there was thick woodland; thence to the Caebitra was arable. Passing upwards through another belt of woodland the crest of the Mellington Hall spur is reached'.[37] (See Fig. 9) This picture, which can be repeated by analysis of other sections, shows that by the eighth century the extensive coherent tracts of forest had already been broken up into smaller units, individual woods and forests. Maps of woodland recession and settlement advance in Cheshire, Shropshire and Herefordshire, based on place-name elements such as leah, grove and hurst, show that most of the Welsh border was woodland until the late Anglian period.[38] From the place-name and archaeological evidence, it appears that the Angles almost

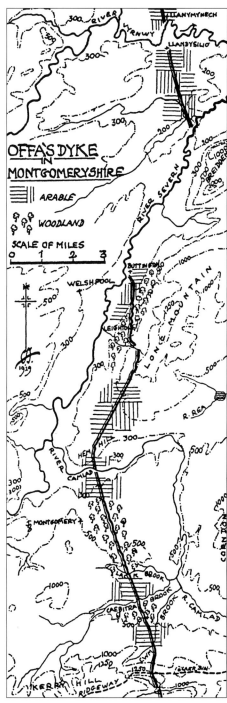

9. Map of the course of Offa's Dyke through Montgomeryshire, showing suggested distribution of arable and low-level woodland in the eighth century (after Fox, *Offa's Dyke*, p. 122).

certainly first settled in those parts of the Borderland where the initial work of clearing the primeval woodlands had already been done by the Brythonic tribes.

The basic territorial framework of human settlement was probably already established before the Roman occupation, and the territorial organization of Wales in the period between the Roman occupation and the Normans was far more stable than believed earlier. Even the poorest land was unlikely to have been regarded as a free commodity, and by the mid ninth century settled rights in land were already old established, with three main types of land-holding. The *tir gwelyog* or hereditary land was the normal land tenure, the right to which passed to descendants in equal shares and the rights of the 'owner' were limited to his lifetime. A hereditary proprietor would have a personal holding of appropriated land (*tir priod*) and a share of joint land (*cytir*) which would embrace wood, pasture and waste subject to joint control but within which the proprietor exercised proportional rights calculated in terms of his acreage of appropriated land. The other types of holding were *tir cyfrif* (reckoned land), the tenure appropriate to villeins, and *tir corddlan* (nucleal land) shared as 'gardens' or strips.[39]

Some light is shed on the forests in the Dark Ages by the Book of Llandaff and the Welsh Laws. The Book of Llandaff,[40] in its present form mainly a compilation of the second half of the twelfth century, was written to magnify the greatness of the diocese of Llandaff and to underline its claims to territory and privileges, and its references to earlier centuries cannot necessarily be taken at face value.

The land boundaries described in the Book of Llandaff include numerous references to groves, woods and forests (*luin, guid, coit*), and indicate that much of the south-east was still well wooded. The boundaries frequently went through a wood, and sometimes along a dyke or bank through a wood, but in many cases the margin of the wood itself served as the boundary. The role of wood-banks as ancient boundary markers has been explained by Rackham.[41] The tree species mentioned as boundary features, marker trees or as woods, include apple, broom, alder, willow, ash and yew. Many woods are mentioned but very few are named, these including Coit Guent (Wentwood), Luin Ili (Ely Wood), and Luhin Latron (Thieves Wood, Gower, ?Clyne Wood).

The Welsh Laws

> Here is a lawbook which Hywel Dda made at the White House on Taf,
> though there be also other things in it, by way of good laws which were
> made both before that and after that.
> Dafydd Jenkins, *The Law of Hywel Dda*, 1986, xxiii

The earliest surviving Latin and Welsh versions of the Laws attributed to Hywel Dda date from the late twelfth or early thirteenth centuries. Though the Laws include matter that is not incompatible with conditions in the tenth century, the information they contain cannot be assigned with certainty to that century, but it does relate in a general way to forest conditions in Wales in the tenth to twelfth century.

10. The earliest illustration of Welsh trees, in a thirteenth-century Latin text of the Welsh Laws (Peniarth MS 28). The tree on the left has been coppiced, the tree on the right has been lopped.

The Welsh Laws suggest that there was little systematic exploitation of the forests which were largely free for tribal use for hunting and as a source of fuel and other forest products. Various regulations and restrictions were aimed broadly at game conservation and, indirectly, at forest conservation.[42] Repeated cutting of underwood for fuel and occasional removal of larger trees (oak) for construction timber would tend to produce coppice, or perhaps coppice with standards, in the neighbourhood of settlements, or an irregular selection forest further afield.

The value of woodland was recognized in the definition of the legal *rhandir*, a tribal unit of land which consisted of 312 acres, of which 300 were arable, grazing and fuelwood, and 12 acres for the buildings of a settlement. Woodland is generally mentioned in the Laws simply as *coed*, without qualification. Reference is also made to *coed cadw* (preserved woodland), a descriptive legal term for a particular category of woodland reserved for pannage and for regulated harvesting of forest products. Woodland (*tir coed*) was distinguished from waste (*tir guyd*). The term for reserved woodland developed from describing a particular category of woodland into a place-name Coed Cadw, surviving to the present day in several places in Wales.[43]

The Welsh Laws also refer to *fforest y brenin* (king's forest), the term *fforest* being used in the legal sense of land reserved for royal hunting and originally largely wooded but not necessarily still woodland. Three categories of timber that could be cut free in the king's forest were wood for the roof of a church, spear shafts to be used in the king's service, and timber for a funeral bier. Large timber was extracted by horses or oxen, a horse-load being equivalent to that of two oxen; smaller assortments, especially fuelwood, were carried as man-loads.

The Laws also contain references to forests apparently in some degree of private ownership, but even here construction timber for a ridge beam and two crucks could be cut with or without the permission of the owner. Owners were allowed to kill swine doing damage in the woods, and received a recompense of one penny for each horse-load or double-oxen load of timber felled without permission.

Deforestation or assarting was not allowed except by agreement of co-proprietors. When a person cleared woodland with the owner's permission, he could hold the land for four or five years but it then reverted free to the owner. No brother was allowed to clear woods belonging to another brother without giving equal wood or equivalent compensation. The period of time for which the cleared land could be held is similar to the duration of occupation of areas cleared in slash-and-burn agriculture, before manuring became necessary.

Pannage in the preserved woods (*coed cadw*) was reserved for the animals of authorized persons during a defined season in autumn and early winter, from a few days before the feast of St Michael until the fifteenth day after Epiphany. These woods were guarded, and the entry of unauthorized swine during this close season was an act of trespass to be compensated for or punished as such; generally the specified penalty was to kill every tenth swine up to a total of nine, and every one thereafter. The increasing value of pigs was defined by the age at which they were turned into the woods, and by the pannage periods.

The office of forester in the modern sense did not exist. The falconer and the chief huntsman held high positions in the court hierarchy, indicating the value placed on hunting as a royal and courtly pastime. The woodman or fuel-gatherer was a low-grade official, not included in the twenty-four officers of the court, though he held his land free. The worth of a native slave was one pound, and if the slave was employed as a woodman, his billhook or hatchet was valued at one penny. The Laws show that wood, not peat, was still the main source of fuel in this period.

Eleven species are explicitly mentioned in the Laws: alder, apple, ash, beech, crabapple, elm, hazel, oak, thorn, willow and yew. The values of most of these are specified, but some differ in the various extant versions of the Laws, and the figures are therefore of interest primarily for comparative purposes.

Oak, the commonest species, providing durable timber, tanbark, and acorns for pannage, was always the most valuable forest tree, its worth at 120 pence being twice that of a standard cow. When an oak had two boles, each was valued at sixty pence and a main branch or branch reaching the heart of the tree was valued at thirty pence. If an oak was cut open in search of wild honey, the payment due was twenty-four or sixty pence to the owner. The Laws do not distinguish between the two native species, *Quercus robur* and *Quercus petraea*, but some versions do mention scrub oak not bearing fruit and worth four legal pence only.

A beech tree was generally valued at sixty pence, half the value of an oak; beech was not included in versions of the Laws from north Wales because it did not grow there, and in two versions from the south-east it was equated with oak in value. An apple tree was valued at sixty pence and a fruiting crabapple half as much. A crabapple before it fruited was worth only four pence. A hazel was valued at fifteen pence and a thorn half as much. In another version, a hazel grove was valued at twenty-four pence, and one hazel from the grove at four pence; any tree bearing fruit (except oak and apple) was valued the same as the hazel grove. Any other tree not bearing edible fruit, such as ash, willow or alder, was worth four or six pence, if it was alive and growing. Main branches of these inferior trees, reaching the heart of the tree, were valued at one penny. A holy or churchyard yew was worth a pound whereas a woodland yew was worth only fifteen or thirty pence. Birch, aspen, lime, maple, holly and poplar, the other common native trees, are not named but would have been valued as trees not bearing edible fruit. Significantly, pine is not mentioned at all, and this strongly suggests that it had become completely extinct in Wales by the time the Laws came to be compiled. Similarly, the absence of sycamore supports the view that this species was not introduced until the Middle Ages.

Trees planted for shade or shelter as windbreaks were specially valued in the Laws, which contain one of the earliest references to deliberate tree planting in Wales: 'Every tree planted for shelter is of twenty-four pence value to its owner, whether planted within a garden, or as a shelter to his house'. Towards the end of his reign, Gruffydd ap Cynan (*c*.1055-1137), king of Gwynedd, is said to have improved the husbandry in his kingdom by 'planting old woods' and making orchards and gardens.[44] This somewhat ambiguous reference apparently indicates the renewal of old woodland (exhausted coppices or senescent high forest) by underplanting or replanting.

Techniques of vegetative propagation were known and practised. A graft, presumably apple, was worth four pence until the end of the year in which it was grafted; thereafter it increased in value by two pence each year until it started to fruit, whereupon it was valued at sixty pence.

The valuation of the trees in the Laws was in general based on their usefulness or economic importance to man, and the production of fruit and mast were very significant factors in determining the relative values. The same pattern is seen in the Irish Tree List of the eighth century which ranks trees into four value-classes, namely nobles, commoners, lower divisions and bushes, and in the Laws of the Visigoths which specified tree values or fines for illegal felling of various species of trees.[45]

Worked constructional timber was highly valued. For example, in the winter dwelling of a transhumance system (the *hendre*), the following items were valued: each cruck twenty pence, the roof-tree (ridge-beam) forty pence, and four legal pence for each of the pillars, benches, stanchions, door-posts, sills, lintels, side-posts and doors. The crucks were prepared by selecting an oak with a branch at the correct angle, and cutting it longitudinally in two (perhaps before felling) so as to produce two identical cruck blades (Fig. 11). Examination of medieval crucks in Monmouthshire houses indicates that the curve of the cruck follows the natural grain of the wood, and that the crucks are placed upside-down in the building, i.e. the branch forms the short base leg of the cruck blade

11. A method of obtaining naturally curved roof
    timbers (crucks) from an oak tree (after Fox
    & Raglan, *Monmouthshire Houses*, I, p. 38).

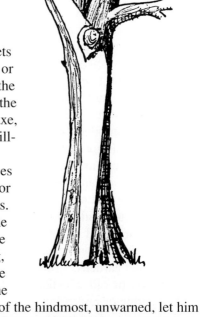

and the butt end of the tree is at the
ridge of the roof.[46] Other wooden articles
mentioned in the Laws include willow buckets
and pails, yew pails, elm-bark rope, and vats or
tubs made of solid wood or of staves. In the
quite detailed lists of tools and implements in the
Laws, the main forest tools were the broad axe,
fuel axe, hand axe, adze, hedging bill, and billhook.

Scattered references to forests and trees
occur in other sections of the Laws, for
example, those dealing with personal injuries.
If someone was killed by a falling tree, the
feller was liable to pay compensation to the
victim's kindred if he had given no warning,
but not if he had. Similarly if 'two persons be
walking through a wood, and a branch, by the
passing of the foremost, should strike the eye of the hindmost, unwarned, let him
be paid for his eye, if he lose it; but, if the other warned him, he is not to pay'.
Trees were important as boundary markers and were therefore involved in
boundary disputes. If a tree fell across a river that formed the boundary between
the lands of two persons, the owner of the land on which the tree grew had the
right to it. Disputes over woodland were frequent enough to make it worth the
lawyer's while to have a model plaint of cutting timber in his precedent book
(see p. 41).

Domesday

> This forest is 10 leagues long and 3 leagues wide
>
> (Domesday: Sutone)

The Domesday survey of England in 1086 covered some parts that are now in
the Welsh border counties.[47] Of the many dozens of entries for such places, the
following are typical examples:

> **Ros and Reweniou** (Rhos and Rhufoniog, Denbighshire): 'There is land enough
> for 20 ploughs only . . . All the rest of the land is woods and moors, and cannot
> be ploughed'.

Biscopestreu (Bistre, Flintshire): 'There is a wood 1 league in length and half a league in width. There is a hawk's eyry. The earl has this wood which has been placed in his forest'.

Sutone (Soughton, Flintshire): 'There is wood half a league long and 4 acres wide. In these 20 hides the earl has all the woods which he has put into his forest, whereby the manors are much depreciated. This forest is 10 leagues long and 3 leagues wide. There are 4 eyries of hawks'.

Lestune (Leighton, Montgomeryshire): 'wood there 2 leagues long, and it is sufficient for fattening 200 swine'.

Cirestoc (Churchstoke, Montgomeryshire): 'wood there for fattening 100 swine'.

Chenistetone (Knighton, Radnorshire): 'a great wood is there'.

Woodlands were generally measured in terms of length alone, or length and breadth, the units of measurement being the league (probably = 1½ miles), furlong and perch. Some woods were measured in acres, others accorded cash valuations, and others measured by their swine fattening capacity. Some underwood was noted, but not consistently. Little or no descriptive detail was given on the species, age-classes, management or products of the woods. The terms used include woods, small woods, very small woods, large woods, woods yielding . . . shillings or pence, unproductive woods, pasturable woods, brushwood, spinney, underwoods, etc.

Names of woods are not given. It is not possible to correlate the dimensions expressed in leagues, acres and swine measures, and it would be rash to make any assumption about the superficial extent of woodland measured in terms of length only, or even length and breadth. 'Waste' in Domesday implies not the natural waste of mountain, marsh or heath, but land that had gone out of cultivation, mainly as a result of deliberate devastation. Considerable areas of waste were recorded along the Welsh border. 'Forest' is used in the sense of hunting ground where forest law applied.

An absence of woodland entries in Domesday does not necessarily mean an absence of actual woodland. For example, the Forest of Dean is not clearly demarcated because of the small population in and around the forest, and no woodland is recorded for the territory of Gwent, which was certainly well wooded at the time and has remained the best wooded of all the Welsh counties. However, Domesday does indicate the existence of an established timber export via the Wye, for tolls were paid at Chepstow castle by ships going to the wood.

In a part of the border now in Radnorshire, the Domesday entry reads 'on these waste lands there have grown up woods in which Osbern hunts, and thence he has whatever he can take'. This natural succession of woods on abandoned and devastated lands was probably the result of Welsh raids in 1055, and the woods therefore would have been some thirty years old at the time of the survey.

The general picture of the Welsh borderland as given by Domesday confirms the earlier interpretation, for example of Offa's Dyke, that there was certainly still a good deal of woodland, some of it secondary, along the whole length of the border from the Dee to the lower Severn. Large hunting forests existed, some 10 x 3 leagues in extent, but woods or woodlands were generally smaller, for example 1 x 1 league, and sometimes very small indeed, only one acre or 40 x 40 perches. This indicates that even in the unstable conditions of the border at this period, fixed and distinct areas of woods and forests were already a feature of the landscape. Woodland management, where it existed at all, may be assumed to have been mainly the utilization of dead fallen wood, underwood and small coppice stems, with occasional felling of larger coppice stems or maiden trees for special purposes, especially building.

Chapter II

MILITARY SIGNIFICANCE OF FORESTS IN THE NORMAN CONQUEST

> The axe and the flame were his weapons as much as the lance and the
> bow.   J.E. Morris, *The Welsh Wars of Edward I*

After his conquest of England, William I set up the earldoms of Hereford, Shrewsbury and Chester, and the Normans soon turned their attention to Wales, conquering large territories in the east and south. In some areas the remaining forests were still sufficiently extensive and dense to prove a formidable barrier to invading forces, and were of considerable strategic importance. Repeatedly over some two centuries, at various places throughout the country, forests featured as scenes of battles, being used by the Welsh both as places of ambush and guerrilla warfare against invaders, and also as places of refuge and shelter from enemies, whether foreign or indigenous. The military and political history of the two centuries of Norman encroachment, occupation and intermittent forest warfare are well known, but the role of the Welsh forests has never been considered *per se*, even though their extent and military importance were clearly realized and described in the middle of this period by Giraldus Cambrensis in his *Itinerarium Kambriae* of 1188 and *Descriptio Kambriae* of 1194.[1]

Giraldus described Wales as a country 'very strongly defended by high mountains, deep valleys, extensive woods, rivers, and marshes'. The Welsh 'neither inhabit towns, villages nor castles, but lead a solitary life in the woods, on the borders of which they . . . content themselves with small huts made of the boughs of trees twisted together, constructed with little labour and expense, and sufficient to endure throughout the year'. Apart from these general references, Giraldus specifically mentioned woods in the territory between the Wye and the Usk. At Llanthony the monks 'would not suffer the thick and wooded parts of the valley to be cultivated and levelled'; these woods were 'well stored with swine and goats' though the tops of the surrounding mountains were 'covered with grass'. His description reflects the marked lowering of the treeline due to the combined effects of climatic change and human influence, and shows that the lower slopes and valley bottoms were still densely wooded. In the Grwyne valley there was a narrow woody tract called 'the bad pass of Coed Grono', where Richard de Clare was ambushed and killed in 1135; between the Rhymney and Taff lay the 'mountainous and woody country' of Ifor Bach. Further west, Maurice de Londres had a hunting forest near Cydweli; Carmarthen was surrounded by woods and pastures, the Cantref Mawr being a safe refuge 'on account of its thick woods', and the castle of Dinefwr was 'strongly situated in the deep recesses of its woods'. The coastal area around St Davids had no woods, but at the sands of Newgale Giraldus recorded the remains of a submerged forest: 'the trunks of trees cut off standing in the very sea itself, the strokes of the hatchet appearing as if made only yesterday . . . the wood like ebony'. In north Wales, the only wood specifically mentioned was 'the wood of Coleshulle' (Coleshill), scene of a defeat of Henry II in 1157.

Giraldus also noted that battles in Wales take place in forests, and pointed out the superiority of light infantry over cavalry 'when the engagement is in narrow defiles, in woods and marshes', and the advantages of a winter campaign 'when the trees are void of leaves'. In fact, these measures were adopted successfully a century later, and it was during these two centuries of intermittent forest warfare that successive kings of England formulated and implemented the first 'forest policy' for Wales: systematic felling and permanent clearance of passes and of large tracts of woodland to form safe areas, and the subsequent introduction of a selective logging industry providing large quantities of hardwood timber for the building and maintenance of castles.

The need to eliminate certain forests as places of ambush and shelter was brought home to the Normans by the events of 1094, 1095 and 1097.[2] In 1094, when under William II, they were defeated with great slaughter at the wood of Coedysbys (the site of which has not been identified); a year later, in 1095, because the Welsh 'sought a defence in their woods and wildernesses' William had apparently intended to cut down all the woods and groves, but was obliged to return to England after a fruitless campaign. The same thing happened again in 1097 with the Normans 'not daring to invade the woods or the wilderness against the Britons'. In 1157, in a campaign against Owain, prince of Gwynedd, Henry II was ambushed in the wood of Hawarden, and after severe losses only narrowly escaped to the open country. The scene of this battle has traditionally been called the wood of Coleshill, but recent reassessment of the evidence suggests a site somewhere between Ewloe and Hawarden, a region which is noted in the Domesday Book as containing considerable areas of woodland.[3]

Though King Magnus had felled trees in Anglesey during a raid there in 1102 in order to provide timber for building castles on the Isle of Man, the first recorded felling of forests by invading forces as a matter of deliberate strategic policy since the Roman conquest was in 1165 when Henry II, in an effort to resolve a military stalemate, 'moved his host into the wood of Dyffryn Ceiriog, and he had that wood cut down, and felled to the ground'.[4] This was the first act of a policy that was continued for well over a century and was to have a profound effect on the forest areas. In 1223, Henry III ordered that effective help be given in the cutting down of forests and the clearing of passes to provide free and safe passage and access for merchants and others to the townships of Cardigan and Carmarthen.[5] In 1224 Henry, for strategic reasons, commanded all soldiers and others owning woods near tracks and public roads around the castle of Montgomery to cut them down and assart them without delay. Henry further warned that if owners failed to obey, their woods would be cut down, assarted and converted to royal ownership.[6] Montgomery occupied a key strategic position, and extensive and repeated fellings were made in this area throughout the thirteenth century. In 1228 the Welsh forced the invaders to retreat, but not before extensive felling had taken place near Montgomery, probably at Ceri where the king 'went to the said wood which was verie large, being five leagues in length and, by reason of the thicke growthe of the wood, verie hard to be stocked [i.e. cleared]; howbeit, the king caused the same, with great diligence and trauell, to be assarted and consumed with fire'.[7]

Again in 1251 the king ordered an inspection of the forest passes at Ceri and Cedewain, west of Montgomery, but if the passes were sufficiently wide, the men of Montgomery were forbidden to lay waste those forests or those of free tenants.[8] This is one of the first regulations specifically prohibiting the excessive felling of forests in Wales. In 1278, Bogo de Knovill was appointed 'to cause to be cut down all hays and thickets in the ways in the parts of Mundgomery, Kery, and Kedewy, which give rise to danger to the passers by, homicides and robberies and other enormities committed there, and . . . to admonish . . . the lords of those lands to cut them down, and, in case of their refusal to do so, to cause it to be done at their cost'.[9]

The abuse caused by felling in places other than those required for military passes also occurred elsewhere. For example, at the pass of Swerdewood near Mold, people of the Wirral and Chester 'cut throughout and everywhere at their will, And thus they waste this wood, and cut it, beside the passes, and not at all in the pass'.[10]

It is impossible to make even a rough estimate of the total area permanently or temporarily cleared in Wales as a result of fellings during and between the various campaigns, though it is certain that the clearances were extensive. Most of the places specifically named as areas where clearances took place in the twelfth and thirteenth centuries are shown in Fig. 12. In addition, general orders were given to numerous individuals to make clearances on the lands for which they were responsible, and the clearances were, in fact, much more widespread than can be indicated on a map.

Something of the organization and scale of these operations can be deduced from accounts of the campaigns of 1277, 1282-83 and 1294-95, and records of the intervening periods.[11] The axe and the flame were weapons just as important as the lance and the bow.

In the 1277 campaign, Edward's plan was to advance into Wales from a strong base, guarding his workmen as they cut through the forest, and then to create a new base from which to repeat the process. This involved the cutting of an invasion roadway for over thirty miles from Chester to the river Conwy, at great speed, between April and August 1277. The road was cut in three sections: from Chester to Flint; from Flint to Rhuddlan; and from Rhuddlan to Degannwy. The felling and building operations were carried out by large numbers of specialist workmen, recruited from the English border and Midland counties. They included sawyers, wood-cutters, carpenters, diggers, masons, and charcoal-burners, some of the latter coming from the Forest of Dean.

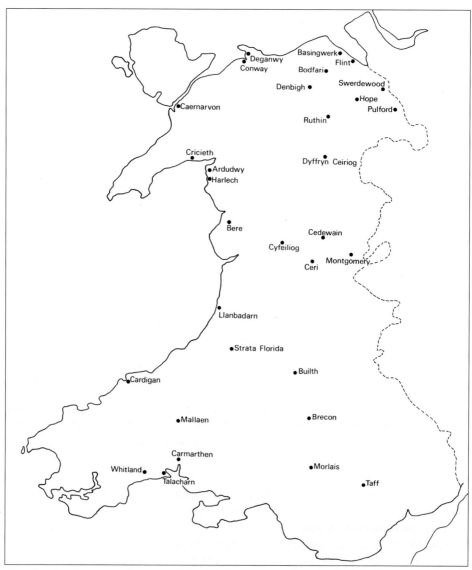

12. Map showing areas of known military fellings in Wales in the twelfth and thirteenth centuries.

Active felling was in process throughout April at the pass of Pulford, on the modern border, as shown by letters from William de Beauchamp to Edward I. These state that the men were cutting as hard as they could, and that the pass had been cut across completely at a place which had never previously been cut. Efforts were made to sell as much as possible of the timber at the best possible price, but large amounts of smaller trees, slash, brush and stumps must have been burnt. On the section from Flint to Rhuddlan, between 1,500 and 1,800 woodmen were engaged, and between 700 and 1,000 on the section from Rhuddlan to Degannwy. The men were carefully guarded, not only for protection but also to prevent desertions, though the men were always paid. Their number varied from week to week, as a result of injuries, desertions, movement of labour, and new recruiting. Some of the timber felled was doubtless used in the temporary strong-posts built at Flint, Rhuddlan and Rhuthun, but large amounts of specially prepared timber assortments were also shipped in for this purpose from Chester.

It is possible to make a very rough estimate of the actual amount of clearance work involved in the making of this particular road. In the Edwardian campaigns, whenever the road clearance width was specified, it was one bowshot in breadth. Expert estimates put this at 200-250 yards, and this is in broad agreement with the clearance of 200ft on either side of the actual roadway laid down by the Statute of Winton (1285). Assuming a minimum width of 150 yards and a maximum of 250, and assuming that clearance was needed on approximately half the length of the route, then the probability is that between 1,000 and 2,000 acres of woodland were felled and cleared in the space of four or five months taken to make this one road.

The years following the 1277 campaign saw a series of royal instructions for systematic felling of Welsh forests to safeguard the lines of communication. The stated justification for felling was that the forests harboured robbers and murderers, but the fellings were resented by the Welsh, and the grievance was partly responsible for subsequent uprisings.

Fellings were made in 1278 in the Montgomery region, between Carmarthen and Brecon, in the territories of Strata Florida and Talacharn, the Bohun territory (Brecon), and at Swerdewood (between Mold and Kinnerton). In 1280, felling and assarting was ordered at Strata Florida, Whitland, and between Carmarthen and Brecon; in the same year, Gelli wood at Whitford (Flint) was given to the Abbot of Basingwerk on the condition that it was cleared within three years, and the king granted his woods in the Rhuddlan area to be rooted up, the people doing the clearance to have the land rent-free for three years. This rent-free period for holding the cleared land again recalls the period specified in the Welsh Laws and the duration of land utilization in primitive slash-and-burn agriculture.

The freedom and encouragement given to destroy forests may be seen from a proclamation, dated 5 February 1278. Foresters were prohibited from exacting any fee 'for trees felled or to be felled or to be rooted up' in Swerdewood and in the woods of the adjacent area, and 'all who wish may take and have freely at their pleasure of the woods in those passes until the passes be fully cleared, and when the passes shall be thus cleared, then from the woods beyond the passes at their will; and that all who wish thus to take or carry away from the woods shall have free passage in going and coming and in removing and carrying away the wood . . . and that no one shall hinder them . . . until the king shall otherwise order'. This proclamation in fact gave a free hand for the clearance of woods on the strategic route into north Wales.

The main plan of campaign in the war of 1282-83 was the same as in 1277, though it was more difficult to carry out. Again, forest clearance played a vital part in the war. Large numbers of hand-picked woodcutters and charcoal-burners were recruited: 'the most powerful, agile and most accustomed to the execution of these offices'. Each was to have a good strong axe or hatchet suitable for felling large and small trees, and paid 3d. a day. A force of 1,000 woodcutters was ordered to be assembled at Chester to proceed to Rhuddlan, and another of 300 picked tree-fellers and charcoal-burners from Hereford and the Forest of Dean was ordered to Brecon for a renewed assault on the forests of west Wales.

General orders were issued for passes a bowshot wide to be cleared of trees and widened in west Wales, and in central Wales between Montgomery and Llanbadarn and in Cyfeiliog.

In December 1282, orders were given for another force of 800 woodcutters to be assembled at Chester for forest-clearance operations in north Wales. This campaign was pursued through the winter, in leafless forests. Bere castle (Merioneth) was taken in April 1283, with a hundred woodmen in the besieging forces, and more passes were cleared through the forests in that area. At Bodfari, between Rhuddlan and Rhuthun, 1,300 men were engaged in felling in order to clear the passes in early May, 1283.

This war too was followed by a period of systematic felling to clear passes. For example, in 1284 the monks of Strata Florida were commanded to fell the woods and enlarge the passes in the county of Cardigan. In the same year, the burgesses and others of Carmarthen were granted free common in the woods of Mahachan (Mallaen) and were permitted to fell and carry away underwood, oaks for timber, and other trees, without any let or hindrance, as a matter of deliberate policy to clear dense woods where robberies and murders were frequent. These fellings were one of the causes of the rising of Rhys ap Maredudd, a native lord in the Vale of Tywi, in 1287. This rising was suppressed by forces that included very large numbers of woodmen. For example, 200 wood-cutters from Chester were ordered to be assembled at Llanbadarn Fawr, and at the same time 400 wood-cutters from the Forest of Dean were to group at Monmouth, while 2,000 diggers and wood-cutters from Salop and Stafford were ordered to Brecon. These were engaged on felling west of Brecon, in the Llywel area. Meanwhile, another body of woodmen 600 strong, rising to 650 and then dropping to 300, was employed in cutting another path from Glamorgan to Brecknock via the Taff valley and Morlais.

The felling policy was continued well after the 1287 rising had been put down. Some authorities were apparently dilatory in carrying out royal instructions, and in May 1288 general instructions were issued to the justices of Chester, north Wales, and west Wales, and to the marcher lords: 'to cause . . . the trees and underwood to be felled in such passes through every wood . . . and to cause the passes to be enlarged and widened in the said woods without any further delay, wherever this shall be necessary in the said woods'. A phase of intensive forest clearance in west-central Wales, attributed to these military fellings in the late thirteenth century, is clearly illustrated in the pollen record preserved in various bogs.

Felling of forests formed a vital part of military strategy, even in the last Welsh rising against Edward I, in 1294-95. Evidence is preserved in a letter to the king, from a writer in a wood called 'Ketthlieconhan', reputedly the strongest place in the whole of Ardudwy, being 'lodged therein to cut down the wood'. The actual site, possibly Gellicynan, has not been identified.

Apart from the clearances, the other major element in the forest policy of the Normans was the introduction of an organized logging industry to provide timber for the building and repair of castles. Castle-building represented operations on a scale never before seen in Wales. Initially, much of the timber used came from assortments shipped in from England, but as soon as local organization could be established, Welsh forests were selectively logged for the desired assortments. These ranged from the smaller material such as poles, shingles and laths, to various sizes of boards and the great joists and beams, some over 30ft long and 1½ft square.

Welsh timber had been used for castle-building in the Isle of Man in 1102, and Abbot Faritius (1100-35) brought the beams and rafters for the rebuilding of Abingdon abbey from the Welsh border by six ox-wains.[12] The timber used in major building works in Wales was rarely specified as regards species, but in most places it was undoubtedly and exclusively oak, the commonest and often the only timber tree available. In the native beech area of the south-east, beech was used occasionally as well as, or perhaps even in preference to, oak. At Llangibby castle in Monmouthshire, for example, beech trees were felled, topped and squared for sawing for castle repairs in 1286-87.[13]

The castles represented enormous engineering works requiring large amounts of selected timber, not only for the initial building but also for regular replacement of decayed wood – a demand which persisted throughout the useful life of the castles, to the sixteenth century and later. The forests in the vicinity of the castles, and especially those convenient for transport of timber by water, were selectively logged for trees suitable for particular uses. Lengthwise sawing was generally avoided except for boards. Timbers were normally used in buildings in the form of a whole log roughly squared by adze. Scantlings were obtained from small oaks, and the larger beams from straight standard trees, presumably growing in natural or semi-natural forest. Selection was a skilled job, and specialists were entrusted with the job of seeking out and marking suitable trees. Felling was by axe, and marking irons were used to identify the felled timber for sale and to prevent misappropriation. Trees were trimmed, topped and usually squared at stump, before extraction. Sometimes the stems were sawn into boards at saw-pits in the forests. Large pieces of timber were extracted by horse or ox teams, and river floating in the form of loose logs or in rafts or shipment in small coastal vessels was employed wherever possible. For example, in 1185 a fleet of ships were used to convey timber from the king's woods at Striguil (Chepstow) to Kenfig castle in Glamorgan,[14] and there are many references to the coastal shipment of wood and timber to Caernarfon, Beaumaris and Harlech castles. The ships were of various sizes and were drawn from very varied sources; they carried loads of timber expressed in terms of tuns of wine, ranging from 8 to 150 tons.

The forest operations associated with castle-building were similar for all the major castles in Wales, but only fragmentary records survive, and a few examples will suffice to illustrate the types of materials produced from the forests. For Carmarthen castle, carpenters were paid for making joists and other timbers 'in the wood', and in the thirteenth and subsequent centuries much timber was bought from local forests, for example laths, small boards, large boards (some 20ft long), wallplates, and large squared timber. The Carmarthen castle accounts for 1430-32 reveal substantial expenditure on timber for the repair of the King's barge, the assortments including long 'shipboards', 'half-boards', logs for rollers and for making treenails, a prow beam, 'wrangs' (deck timbers), and trees for making 'hodyngis' (stern planks), 'carlyngs' (short timbers running between the deckbeams), 'knevis' (knees), a 'folocke', etc.[15]

At Caernarfon, timber was first imported from Cheshire and Lancashire but from the late thirteenth century various assortments were brought from woods in the Conwy valley, these woods supplying large numbers of great joists each 18 royal feet long, 1½ft wide and 2ft thick, and also large beams 32ft long by 1½ft square.[16] This timber had to be transported some thirty miles to the castle, and the transport was by water. Throughout its life, Caernarfon castle was maintained and repaired with timber felled in the Conwy valley and in Cheshire.

Flint castle was regularly supplied with forest products from the wood of Ewloe, as shown for example by the Chamberlain's Accounts for 1302-04, the items furnished including 'legges' (wooden ties), great and thick planks, boards, various roundwood assortments called 'spurlaces', 'steppes', 'courbes' and 'soles' (30ft in length), great posts, beams, 'sperra' (spars) and laths.[17] The primary conversion of the roundwood, including squaring by adzing and pit-sawing to boards, was regularly carried out in the wood.

13. Caernarfon castle within its walls enclosing the original settlement.

Even as late as the sixteenth century, the castles in north Wales incurred heavy expenditure on timber, as indicated by the following selected items from the accounts for Harlech castle for 1539-40:[18]

20 trees at 8p. each	13s. 4d.
felling these trees and 2 great somers [beams]	3s. 4d.
carriage of 18 of these trees	13s. 6d.
carriage of 2 great somers, 22d. and 5s	6s.10d.
carriage of sawn boards of 3 trees from the wood	1s. 8d.
22 'oks' [oaks]	22s. 8d.
felling these trees	4s. 8d.
2 carpenters for 2 days choosing this timber	12d.
5 men working 10 days on this timber	4s.10d.
carriage of 2 great trees from Dolgellau by water to Abermo	2s. 8d.

The details show that transport, especially land transport, was relatively expensive, costing more than the value of the standing timber.

Chapter III

FORESTS AND WOODS IN MEDIEVAL TIMES

the greater part of their sustenance is derived from the woods
Calendar of Ancient Petitions Relating to Wales, p. 74

The rules governing hunting and falconry, the value of the hounds and hawks, and the status of the chief huntsman and falconer as given in the Welsh Laws show the importance attached to hunting and game management. Much of the hunting ground was still well wooded in the early Middle Ages. With the conquest of territories in eastern and southern Wales, the Marcher lords set up 'forests' in their lordships, with the appropriate organization, imitating those of the Norman kings of England. Afforestation (in this legal sense) involved the creation of permanent hunting preserves with defined boundaries, under the highly restrictive and oppressive 'forest law' administered by forest courts.[1]

The forests were partly but not necessarily woodlands, and consisted of 'vert and venison'. Venison meant the game animals. Vert included all trees, coppices and vegetation forming the coverts and feeding grounds of the deer and other game, and the gravest offences were those involving the game, especially the deer. The main offences against vert were purpresture (enclosure of or encroachment upon land), waste (felling of trees) and assart (grubbing up and permanent clearance of woodland to form arable land). The officers appointed for the administration of forests were the justice in eyre (*justiciarius itinerans*), verderers (*viridarii*), regarders (*regardatores*), foresters (*forestarii*), woodwards (*woodwardii*) and agisters (*agistatores*). The regarders supervised the general work of local executive officers. The verderers and foresters protected the vert and venison, and made attachments and presentments in the case of offences. The woodwards appeared at a comparatively late date, when the importance of the timber resources had increased relative to that of the game, and they performed miscellaneous duties relating to vert, such as marking for felling, superintending felling, etc. The agisters collected the grazing dues (agistments) and supervised livestock grazing.

The forest courts, which had jurisdiction over the territory and inhabitants of the forest and replaced the ordinary courts, dealt with all matters concerning the forest, viz. all infringements of the law, the collection of rents and customary dues, arrangements for agistment and pannage, collection of fines and tolls, etc. The courts consisted of the Eyre of the Forest, the Swainmote and the Woodmote. The Woodmote was a court of preliminary enquiry. The Swainmote tried the cases committed from the Woodmote, the verderers being the judges, and freeholders of the forest forming the jury. The Eyre of the Forest was the high court.

14. The Foresters' Oaks at Wentwood, where the Forest Courts were held (from a drawing by Mrs Digby Wyatt in 1839).

In England, in the eleventh and twelfth centuries afforestations had been extensive and the administration of the forest law very severe, with penalties of mutilation and death for offences against game. Several clauses of *Magna Carta* (1215) related specifically to the forests, and gave relief from some of the most oppressive of the forest laws. In 1217 the *Carta Forestae* was enacted, disafforesting many lands, regulating the administration and substituting fines for more severe punishments.

In 1306 an *Ordinatio Forestae* was passed containing six short sections:

      1. How offences done in the forest shall be presented.
      2. An officer dying, or being absent, another shall be put in his place.
      3. No forest shall be put in assizes or juries out of the forest.
      4. The punishment of officers surcharging the forest.
      5. Grounds disafforested.
      6. Common in the forest.

The *Magna Carta* and the *Carta Forestae* were confirmed repeatedly through the fourteenth century. English statutes did not automatically apply in the Crown lands of Wales, where government was sufficiently flexible to recognize various native rights and usages, though English law was administered by English methods where the vital interests of the Crown were involved, especially in the maintenance of order. The establishment of special forest areas was new to Wales, and was resented by the people, because it involved the suspension of common law within a forest, and restrictions on or complete withdrawal of substantial areas of the common pasture. People dwelling in or near a forest were largely at the mercy of the forest officers in whom were vested arbitrary powers under the forest law, and who frequently abused these powers by petty tyranny and extortion.

The first of the Norman hunting forests in Wales were established in the late eleventh century by the Marcher lords, and are referred to in the Domesday Book. For example, the Earl of Chester's forest at Soughton (Flintshire) was 10 leagues long and 3 leagues wide. Many more forests were created in the twelfth and thirteenth centuries, the largest of which was the Great Forest of Brecknock. Bernard de Newmarch, after his conquest of Brecon late in the eleventh century, reserved to himself the large unenclosed tracts in the south-west of the lordship as a great upland game reserve covering over fifty square miles of country, most of it well over 800ft above sea level. By the thirteenth century part of this had been leased off as a separate unit, the Little Forest; the rest was known as the Great Forest, and comprised moorland and scrub waste, with extensive wooded areas, especially in the valleys. The Brecon lordship, including the Forest, was taken over by the Crown in 1521 and remained in Crown possession until 1815, when it was still 40,000 acres in extent.[2]

The location and often the name of many of these hunting forests are known from surviving contemporary manuscripts. For example, in the southern part of Wales and the Marches in the first half of the fourteenth century, the locations of over a hundred forests as well as nearly fifty woods have been mapped, although their actual boundaries and extent can only be known very approximately. The locations of over a hundred commons and twenty-one deer parks are also known.[3] These commons were often largely woodland or scrubland at this time. Parks were deer enclosures, surrounded by a strong and high wooden pale or palisade and sometimes also with a ditch, and the area emparked contained a substantial proportion of woodland and thicket to provide shelter for the deer.

A number of the hunting forests established in north Wales have also been identified, as well as the names and often the locations of many woods, parks and commons. The largest and most famous of these was the Forest of Snowdon, which lay mainly in Caernarfonshire and perhaps also part of north Merioneth, though the date of its establishment, its boundaries and extent are uncertain. From their names, the Foresters of Snowdon were all Englishmen, from men such as John de Clanbow (who took office in 1384-85), John Wakerley, John Bande, John Chetwynd, Robert Ovell, Anthony Revers and Rudolph Egerton, to Robert Dudley, Earl of Leicester, to whom Queen Elizabeth I granted the Forest in 1575. The forest persisted as a legal entity until the seventeenth century, the forest laws being repealed in 1640.[4]

The administration of some of the forests in Wales is known in detail. The Forest of Glyncothi was established by Edward I after the failure of Rhys ap Maredudd's rebellion in 1291. This forest was established in the Cantref Mawr, and comprised the whole of the upper Cothi valley in north Carmarthenshire, coming under the jurisdiction of the castle of Carmarthen. In the mid fifteenth century the celebrated Lewys Glyn Cothi, a poet fond of woodland imagery, described the wooded territory of the royal forest of Glyncothi in a *cywydd* to Rhys ap Dafydd of Blaen Tren.[4a] Rhys's dense and ancient oakwoods were both valuable and extensive. They were likened to Brasil wood, and to the famous forests of Windsor, Caledonia (Scotland), Nien (in the Weser valley of north Germany), and the 'earls of the east', that is to say the Marches.

Derw ieuainc hyd yr awyr	(Young oaks all reaching up
O'u bon oll heb un yn wyr	Straight from their base, not one crooked
Glasterw yn ganerw i gyd	Green oaks, hundred of acres)

These woods contained young oak trees, densely grown and straight-stemmed, and also stately spreading old oak trees (*caterw*), a prolific source of acorns for pannage. These woods were valuable also for swarms and nests of wild bees, and as a haunt of roe and red deer and of squirrels, and songbirds and herons.

The names, periods of office and brief details of many of the foresters, deputy foresters, sub-foresters and beadles of the forests of Glyncothi and Pennant have been listed, from Einion ap Trahaiarn and Cadwgan ab Ieuan in 1301-02 to Hywel ap Guto in 1533-34.[5] The foresters held the forests in one of two ways, either by farming (i.e. renting) them from the lord, or by receiving a fixed stipend, sometimes supplemented according to local custom by fees from various sources. In the lordship of Rhuthun, the foresters and parkers were initially Anglo-Norman, but they were succeeded by Welshmen; the acreage of woodland in the lordship is not known, but the thirty-three pieces of seigneurial demesne throughout the lordship were protected by at least ten foresters and seven parkers.[6]

After the Edwardian settlement of north Wales and the establishment of royal forests, offences of the vert were punished in the hundred court but always formed a class by themselves. Examples of vert offences are given from the court rolls of the lordship of Rhuthun,[7] for example at the Court of Llannerch, 12 August 1295:

Offence	*Fine*
cutting green wood in the forest	6d.
cattle feeding in the forest	6d.
cutting one tree	6d.
carrying away old wood	6d.
cutting down boughs of oak for oxen	12d.
cutting rods in the forest	2d.
cutting and carrying away green wood	2s.

Details of many offences are also given in the proceedings of the small hundred court of the commote of Ardudwy (Merioneth) for the period October 1325 to September 1326.[8] The offences mainly concerned the unauthorized felling and removal of loads of underwood (*subboscus*) and rods (*virgarum*), but species of tree were often also specified, for example one young oak, one green hazel, two large branches from two oak trees, one ash and three hazels, and one crabapple tree.

Common woods, and commons that were largely or partly woodland, were indispensable to every community. The common woods yielded wood for the repair of buildings (housebote), agricultural implements (ploughbote) and hedges (haybote); also fuelwood, grazing for livestock, mast for fattening pigs in the autumn, honey and wax from wild bees, and miscellaneous products such as bracken and litter. The lord had a certain amount of control over the common woods, the degree of control varying locally. The conflicting interests and abuse of the commons and common woods over the centuries led to degradation of the woodlands, and also to encroachments. A good example of the pressure on the common woods can be seen from the Caernarfon Court Rolls for 1361-1402.[9] On 28 March 1368, thirty-five different people were fined (amerced) for various felling offences in the common wood: nineteen men were fined small sums ranging from 6d. to 12d. (in one case 5s.) for cutting fuelwood in the common wood, and sixteen men were fined sums ranging from 3d. to 10s. for felling specified numbers of trees. The amercements were at a standard rate of 1d. per tree, except in the case of the worst offender, Laurence de Wynston, who felled 100 trees and was fined 10s. The total number of trees felled in these offences was 449. Many other similar offences in the common wood, by men and by women, are recorded in the rolls. Despite depredations of this kind over a long period, some common woods have persisted to the present day. One rare example of a substantial area of woodland still subject to common rights is the common wood at Allt-y-rhiw, Coity Wallia, which covers 124 acres in the Ogwr valley in Glamorgan (Fig. 15). A.G. Tansley described this wood in the 1920s,

15. Contorted sessile oak trees in Allt-y-rhiw common wood, near Blackmill, Glamorgan.

and his description still applies today: virtually pure sessile oak, of varying ages and with a wide range of diameters, but only 15-30ft high. Natural regeneration is present, but the older stems are twisted, bushy and misshapen, as a result of frequent coppicing and/or lopping.[10]

Coppicing and lopping were the normal methods of management in the Middle Ages. Coppicing provided a regular recurring crop of small relatively uniform material. Lopping provided a supply of fuelwood and fodder for livestock, without killing the tree. Both these techniques of managing trees for the production of required material are illustrated in a manuscript of the Welsh Laws, dated to early in the thirteenth century (Fig. 10).

Pleas and petitions concerning disputes over woodland were numerous throughout the Middle Ages. For example, in 1279 a dispute over felling timber in the wood of Coedgaer between Llywelyn Vychan, a Welsh baron, and the King's men of Oswestry resulted in bloodshed.[11] Other examples of abuse on a large scale are known. In 1309 the burgesses of Overton (Flintshire) complained of the almost complete destruction of 500 acres of wood, and in 1386 complaints were made of the felling of 3,000 green oaks in the woods of Coydrath and Rodewode (Pembrokeshire), worth 200 marks (£133 6s. 8d.) and the decay of the underwood there through lack of custody and enclosure.[12] Indeed, disputes over woodland were frequent enough to make it worth the medieval lawyer's while to have a model plaint of cutting timber in his precedent book:

> David, son of Llywelyn, is preferring lawful plaint to the lord of this session against the present Morgan Vychan . . . The matter and cause of my plaint is that the present Morgan came within a certain day, the Tuesday next after the feast day of St. Dewi last past within this year, to where I was owner of wood, within the maenor of Gwinvai [Gwynfe, Carmarthenshire] . . . And that the present Morgan came with a fuel hatchet of steel and iron, and did cut two branching oaks, that would have been worth six score curt pence, each of them; and twelve white hazels, that would be worth fifteen curt pence, each of them; and six black thorns, that would be worth seven pence halfpenny, each of them; and nine willows, and ash, and alder, that would be worth sixpence of the curt pennies, each of them. And that the present Morgan is holding that by covert and detention . . . causing injury to a person, or to his property, without doing either right or peace therefor . . .[13]

Strict supervision of forests by foresters and woodwards, multiple-use of woodlands, and complete utilization of woodland products were the main features of the peasant economy of medieval Wales. The vital importance of the forest resource and its products is stressed in the wording of countless pleas and petitions through the thirteenth and fourteenth centuries. One such petition to the King in the first decade of the fourteenth century by the men of Hopedale and Kinnerton (Flintshire) makes it clear that 'the greater part of their sustenance is derived from the woods'.[14]

Initially, the forests were primarily hunting preserves, and management was directed to game conservation, for example deer were fed with hay during winter. However, by the fourteenth century the forests were no longer regarded primarily as game preserves in many parts of Wales, though in the border lordships the preserves were better cared for and hunting was carried on to a greater extent than elsewhere. With the decline of hunting the other forest functions and products increased in importance, and the forest was now regarded as a revenue-producing part of the lordship. Apart from the game animals, the main products (not necessarily in order of importance) were: large timber and logging debris; underwood; bark; windthrown trees and dead wood; charcoal; tree foliage; fruits, berries and nuts; mast; herbage; honey and wax; hawks; and wood ashes and dyestuffs. Examples of each of these products are discussed briefly below.[15] Sometimes coal and metal ores were considered as issues of the forest, and also materials such as peat, bracken, litter, furze, broom, reeds and rushes, but these items are not considered here.

Large Timber and Logging Debris Large and small assortments of hardwood timber were available for a variety of uses. The main species of timber was oak, but elm and ash were also important, and beech in south-east Wales. Large quantities of big timber were required for the major building works of medieval Wales, especially the castles. Timber was also required for bridges, mills, fishing weirs, halls, churches, houses, and the enclosure of deer parks, and also for making ships, carts, ploughs, furniture and a host of smaller items and utensils. Large stems suitable for the particular purpose were sought out and felled selectively, so that an informal irregular selection system of management existed. This, combined with repeated cutting of underwood on a coppice rotation, would have tended to result in coppice with some standards, but in many areas simple coppice was the general rule.

Some fine timber halls, after the English fashion, were erected in the early fourteenth century in Wales, and those at Henblas (Llandderfel) and Penarth Fawr (Llanarmon, near Llanystumdwy) illustrate the skilled use of large amounts of timber. Water-driven corn mills were vital in the life of each community, and the building and maintenance of the mills, wheels and sluices involved the selection of particular species for particular uses. For example, in 1481/82 the repairs to the mills of Pembroke and Castlemartin involved '1 asshe to make ladles for the wheels' and '1 elme tree to make chinkes'. Wood was also imported, for the same mills required a dozen Irish boards for 'chugkyng wegges' and five English boards.[16]

The carriage of timber represented a considerable problem where river floating was not feasible, and obligatory services for the carrying of large timber and stones for the mill were often owed by the local population to the lord. These carrying services were probably survivals and extensions of Welsh tribal customs and generally related to large timber, for example timber that could not be drawn by one horse, but also sometimes to boards, firewood and charcoal. In later periods, these carrying services were often commuted to the payment of cash *in lieu*.

Enclosure of deer parks required large amounts of good-quality timber to make and maintain a perimeter fence. Emparking was generally done with a pale, a palisade of cleft oak stakes, as for example at the park of Llwydcoed

16. Oak timber frame of Hendre'r-ywydd Uchaf, dated *c.* 1470-1500, during re-erection at St Fagans in 1950s.

(Flintshire) which in 1347-48 was enclosed with 'palings from the timber of the same park, 559 perches at 6d. per perch'.[17]

Wood was also required for the fishing weirs that were built on all the rivers. Some of the weirs were large, and complaints were made in 1340 that the weir of Cilgerran on the Teifi prevented the movement of timber and other necessities to the town and castle of Cardigan, and also prevented fish swimming upstream to the King's weirs at Llechryd and Cenarth.[18]

Slash, i.e. branchwood and other logging debris, was never wasted as it represented a valuable additional source of timber and fuelwood. For example, when eight oak trees were felled in 1351-52 for the building of a bridge over the river Dee, the branches were sold separately for 7s.[19]

As part of the policy to obtain revenue from controlled exploitation of resources, licences were issued to carpenters and turners to work for specified periods in the forest, making various wooden utensils for sale. The articles made were usually domestic and agricultural items such as furniture, chests or ploughs; barrels, casks, buckets, pails, tubs and vats made from oak and hooped with ash or willow; and bowls and dishes turned from sycamore, beech or birch. These utensils were sometimes given the general name of *woodasken* or *wodeway*. For example, the accounts of Senghennydd for 1281 record revenue from men working on dead wood and making chests in the forest, and from a wood-turner.[20]

Underwood Most of the native broadleaved tree and shrub species of Wales are capable of regenerating vigorously by coppice sprouts, and it was the repeated cutting of the underwood that yielded the regular supply of fuel, small roundwood assortments such as poles, posts and rods, material for the repair of fences and hedges and for making numerous smaller domestic and agricultural utensils, as well as much of the raw material for the manufacture of charcoal for smelting or lime-burning. Thus, the underwood, cut regularly on a coppice rotation, governed the *annual* value of a wood. Dense high forest, i.e. woods consisting entirely or mainly of standard trees with little or no underwood, was of no annual value as regards wood. This is clearly shown by the example of the wood of Coydragheyn in the Lordship of Denbigh in 1334.[21] This wood contained 158 acres 1½ roods, but the lord received no yearly profit because of the density of the great oaks and because all the tenants claimed common of pasture there.

The principles of coppice management with protection of the stools to ensure regrowth had been long established. The length of the coppice rotation depended on site, tree species and presumably the pressure of demand, the usual rotation being about 10-14 years. Pendinas wood in the Lordship of Denbigh is an example of a coppice rotation in 1334.[22] This wood had a sparse underwood and contained 33 acres 3 roods; it could be cut every twelve years and was then worth 4s. per acre; if the underwood was divided into twelve equal parts it was worth 11s. 3d. per annum; the annual value of the pasture in the wood was 2s. 9d., making a total annual value of 14s.

The need to cut regularly to maintain the supply of the desired small assortments was recognized. The wood of Rusty (Hopedale, Flintshire) was stated in 1347 to be beginning to spoil because it had not been cut in due season. The chamberlain was instructed to cut, and to enclose the felled areas to prevent livestock from entering and destroying the young growth. A few years later, in 1351, a coppicing experiment to determine optimum stool height was tried in Hopedale: a part of the wood was to be 'cut down to the ground, and a part not so far, so that it may be possible to see which part grows best'.[23] This is the first recorded forestry experiment in Wales, and perhaps in Britain as a whole.

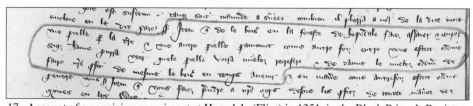

17. Account of a coppicing experiment at Hopedale (Flint) in 1351, in the Black Prince's Register.

The combination of coppice management of underwood with grazing and game is illustrated in the figures of land-use and financial returns for three parks in the commote of Rhufoniog Isaled in the Lordship of Denbigh in 1334 (see p. 53-4). The total annual return was £32 14s. from coppice and pasture.[24]

Bark Oak bark was widely harvested from felled trees and used for tanning leather. In the mid thirteenth century the monks of the Cistercian abbey of Tintern were allowed to buy all the bark from Wentwood Forest for 2d. per load, for use in the monks' tannery.[25] In 1272 the Forester of Wentwood included in his receipts £4 16s. 4½d. for bark and thatch.[26] Bark from felled trees also made a regular contribution in the mid fourteenth century to the revenue from the woods of Baghegre and le Rust and the park of Llwydcoed in Hope and Hopedale, Flintshire.[27]

Windthrown Trees and Dead Wood Dead wood, windthrown trees and debris together formed a regular source of wood that could be used without the labour of felling and without damage to the forest. For example, in Flintshire the Ministers Accounts in the fourteenth century show that windthrown trees, mainly oak and sometimes described as old trees, in the woods of Rusty, Baghegre and Ewloe and in the park of Llwydcoed were sold every year. Good stems were sold as timber; the branches, twigs and stumps of windthrown trees were generally used as fuel or for making charcoal, and even the roots of windthrown trees were utilized.[28]

Charcoal The making of charcoal to supply the lord's castle, to fuel the local metal-smelting enterprises and to burn lime, was important in certain areas. Large numbers of professional charcoal-burners were specifically recruited for tree-felling in military campaigns, and in times of peace the amounts of charcoal produced were sometimes very considerable. In 1284 the burgesses of Flint were granted all the necessities for mining and smelting lead ore from the wood and underwood in the woods in the Northop area and as far as Ewloe;[29] in the following century *Les Leis et Custumes de la Minere* (the local laws and customs of the mines) allowed the lead-miners all manner of wood for use in the mines – as building timber, pitwood and wood for making charcoal;[30] branchwood and underwood were regularly used for smelting, the lord receiving a sixth of the lead smelted with his underwood.[31] In the iron-smelting area of Gwent, large amounts of charcoal were made and sold. At Machen Forest in 1316 for example, 9,969 loads of charcoal were made and sold at 6d. a dozen to give £20 15s. 4½d. In the forest and park of Trelech the sales in 1330 were:

> £56 19s. 9d. charcoal sold at Penallt
> £30 13s. 9d. charcoal sold in the forest of Trelech
> £43 8s. 0d. charcoal sold by the charcoal burner
> £ 7 18s. 6d. charcoal sold by the charcoal burner

The wages of the supervisor of the charcoal burning, 19 weeks, and two assistants (*carbonatores*) were 21s. 2d., plus some of the waste wood. The weekly accounts of sales at Trelech show receipts in certain weeks as high as 64s.[32] The charcoal was measured in hodds, loads and dozens (1 dozen = 12 loads; 1 load = 4 hodds). Iron forges were operated on charcoal made from the windthrown material and underwood in the forest of Rusty and other woods in Hopedale (Flintshire) in the mid fourteenth century.[33]

Tree Foliage The cutting of leafy branches to provide winter fodder for cattle was apparently practised in places in Wales, though it is not possible to assess how widespread the practice was or how long it persisted. In 1295, Anian Cryyth was fined 12d. at the Court of Llannerch in the Lordship of Rhuthun for cutting down boughs of oak for his oxen without licence.[34] Several other people were fined on the same occasion for cutting and carrying away green wood, though the purpose was not specified. The lopping of elm to provide fodder for livestock has been suggested as a cause of elm decline in prehistoric times. Holly foliage was regularly used as winter fodder for livestock. The Mabinogion tale *The Dream of Rhonabwy* describes 'boughs of holly spread over the floor, whereof the cattle had browsed the sprigs'.

Fruits, Berries and Nuts Forest fruits, berries and nuts were collected in season for human consumption, but such records as survive are ambiguous and may sometimes refer to mast collected for or eaten by swine. In Bromfield and Yale (Flintshire), a levy of 1½d. or 1d. a year was made for the right to gather nuts in 1315,[35] and in the 200-acre forest of Lloydarth (Pembrokeshire) the fruit, both acorns and nuts, was worth annually 2s. in 1326.[36] No revenue from nuts in 1356-57 was recorded from the forest of Maelienydd (Radnorshire) because the wood was let to the Abbot of Cwm-hir.[37] In the Lordship of Abergavenny, fifteen trugs or baskets of nuts were sold in 1256/57.[38]

Mast Acorns, hazel nuts and beechmast provided the means of fattening swine in the autumn. Income from pannage was one of the most widespread and important, though irregular, sources of revenue from the forest.[39] Pannage dues were of two kinds, namely payments by freemen who chose to feed their swine in the forest, and payments levied on the bondmen. In the more Anglicized manors of south and east Wales, pannage payment was required at a fixed sum, for example 1d. per pig, but in the Welsh system of west Wales pannage was paid in kind, i.e. one pig from every tenant feeding more than a certain fixed number of swine in the woods. For example, in the commote of Catheiniog (Cantref Mawr) in 1305-06 the pannage due was specified as 'each man who has four pigs or more in the said forests or woods rendering one pig to be chosen in accordance with the custom in those parts,

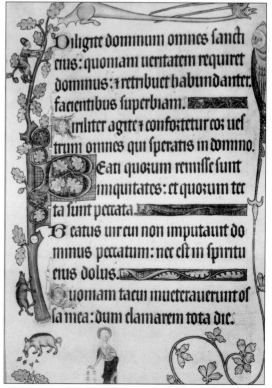

18. Pannage for pigs (illuminated medieval manuscript).

and if he have less than four he shall pay nothing'.[40] Under the Welsh system the pannage dues were assessed and collected at a swine-mote, an appointed place to which all owners were obliged to bring their pigs at the end of the pannage season. Non-attendance or failure to produce the swine involved a fine. The pigs selected were sold on the spot, sent to market, or killed for the castle larder. Pannage revenue obviously depended on the abundance and frequency of mast years, and oak mast years are irregular in Wales. For example, the pannage of the woods of Ewloe and Baghegre yielded 12s. and 30s. respectively in 1328, but nothing in 1335-36 'because there were no acorns there this year'.[41] Feeding of pigs in oakwoods persisted in places until the present century, as for example in the common wood at Allt-y-rhiw in Glamorgan.

Herbage Providing pasture for livestock was one of the most important of all the functions of forests and woods, and indeed remained so until comparatively recently. The practice of grazing and the sale of pasture were termed agistment, the grazing dues too being called agistments. In his private woods and parks, the lord could dispose of pasture at will, but in forests the long-standing communal rights and claims were frequently so strong as to compel compromise, and were long a source of dispute. The grazing rights of the free tenants were frequently described in terms of numbers of livestock, i.e. cattle, oxen, sheep, horses and swine, and the practice of agistment was often subject to local variations.[42] Where the lord was in full possession of the pasture it was customary to sell rights of agistment for the year, usually for a cash sum, though in the forest of Cantref Selyf the grazing dues were paid in capons and hens. The 'farming' (leasing) of forests was mainly responsible for the loss of common rights, and subsequently involved much dispute and litigation.

The Black Book of St Davids describes agistment for the forests of Atpar and Lloydarth in 1326. At Atpar the Bishop of St Davids had a forest of 40 acres 'and each acre with the fruit and herbage is worth 3d. [per annum]. And if there was no agistment in the forest the Lord would be able to keep there 12 great beasts, 100 sheep, and 24 pigs'. In the 300 acres at Lloydarth 'they are able to keep there 20 mares in foal, 40 great beasts and 200 sheep, and the grazing of each great beast is worth 1d. and of every 10 sheep 1d. [per annum]'.[43] Grazing was obviously responsible for the degradation of woodland, and the amount and quality of the herbage improved as the condition of the woods deteriorated.

Honey and Wax Beekeeping in natural holes or holes artificially made in standing trees, or in hollowed out logs hung up in the forest, was common in eastern Europe and may also have been practised in Wales. Certainly, honey and wax from wild bees' nests and from hives kept in the forest were important sources of revenue, and the amounts involved were sometimes large. The accounts and inventory for the castles of Llanbadarn, Dinefwr, Dryslwyn and Emlyn for 1298-1300 showed 11 casks 168 gallons of honey.[44] In 1303-04 the proceeds of a hive in the forest of Glyncothi yielded two gallons of honey, worth 12d.[45] In 1349-50, two gallons of honey of woodland bees in the Park of

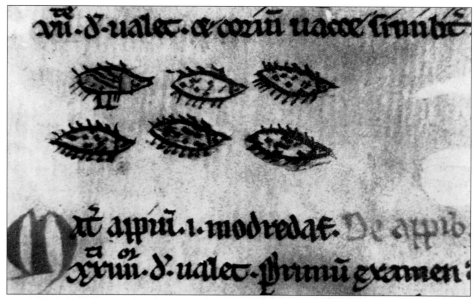

19. Bees in a thirteenth-century manuscript of the Welsh Laws, giving the values of swarms and of honey.

Llwydcoed (Hope, Flintshire) were valued at 1s. 8d.[46] The accounts of the castle and Lordship of Llansteffan (Carmarthenshire) for 1410-11 record 13d. received for honey, but by 1500-01 the accounts state 'of forest honey and wax there this year, nothing, because there is no wood there, neither are the trees grown where such honey and wax may be had'.[47] Hollow trees containing bees' nests were specially valued items in the Welsh Laws, which also covered the theft of honey and specified the fines for stealing honey from a wild nest in a tree. The Laws also laid down the value of swarms and wild colonies of bees, and this indicates that bees were already being kept in hives by early medieval times when the Laws were formulated. Honey collection from wild nests must have coexisted with hive beekeeping for a long time in Wales.

Several poets mentioned bees and honey as valued products of the woodlands. For instance, Lewys Glyn Cothi referred to the swarms and nests of wild bees in the woodlands of Glyncothi in the middle of the fifteenth century. Disputes over the stealing of honey were quite frequent. In one celebrated case, Ieuan Gethin (fl.1410-55) complained in a poem *Cywydd y Bydafe* of three rogues deliberately seeking out wild bees' nests in the hollow trees on his land in the Vale of Neath, and stealing all the honey.[47a] These bee-hunters, Llywelyn, Gruffydd and Ieuan, were described as agile climbers, and came stealthily, early in the morning, equipped with axes, spades, picks and rope. Gruffydd even had the visage of a typical beekeeper – swollen cheeks, large nose and thick eyebrows.

Hawks The provision of hawks for falconry was an important function of the forest, and nests were guarded until the young hawks could be taken. The presence of hawks' nests was often specified in the Domesday survey, and the

Welsh Laws gave the value of a hawk's eyrie as £1. The Welsh forests were a good source and many hawks were exported – for example, two falcons and seven sparrow-hawks from eyries in Wales were taken from Carmarthen to Dover in June 1305,[48] and in 1484 a warrant was issued to take at reasonable price 'such goshawks, tarcells, fawcons, laneretts and other hawks as can be gotten within the principality of Wales . . . as shall be necessary for the king's disport'.[49]

Wood Ashes and Dyestuffs Wood ashes, rich in potash, were used in soap-making in the Middle Ages, and dyer's ashes formed another minor source of revenue.[50] Dye woods were sought in Wyeswood and Bernardswood (Gwent) by the monks of Tintern in 1387-88.[51]

In summary, then, the main categories of revenue were: sales of wood and other materials; pannage payments; agistments or grazing fees; amercements or fines for various offences such as felling without a licence; tolls exacted on strangers passing through the forest; confiscation of stray livestock; and licences issued to woodworkers.

*   *   *

The rights of tenants to take firewood (firebote), and timber for the repair of buildings (housebote), hedges and fences (haybote or hedgebote), agricultural implements (ploughbote), and carts (cartbote) were known as rights of estover. They varied locally but often included dead wood as well as green wood and usually applied on condition that none of the wood be sold or given to anyone having no rights of common. The term *estover* has become fossilized as a place-name for several woods in Wales, as for example Coed y Stover at Leckwith near Cardiff. The rights were frequently included in the earliest town charters, and were repeated or modified when the charters were renewed. For example, in his charter to the burgesses of Rhuthun *c.*1285, Lord Grey granted them housebote and hedgebote in his wood called Garthlegfa, as well as common pasture for beasts and permission to take dead wood without the supervision of his foresters.[52] Two centuries later, in 1496, the Lord's charter of the Borough of Rhuthun allowed the burgesses to

> have and take without the supervision of my foresters housebote and haybote in my wood which is called Garthlegfa and have common pasture in the wood for their animals until I make them reasonable provision in a suitable place; and that they shall have and take dead wood without the supervision of my foresters in my foreign woods . . . and that when there is mast in my woods they shall give for their pigs feeding in the same the tenth pig by name of pannage, or the seventh if they do not have so many, and a penny for each pig when there are fewer than seven.[53]

If genuine, the charter of William, Earl of Warwick (1153-84) to the burgesses of Swansea granted them pasture for their animals in the woods as far as they could go during the day, provided that they returned to their homes by nightfall, and allowed them to keep swine in the woods, and also firewood and oaks for making their houses, fences and ships, as well as small game, but excluding deer, wild boar and martens.[54] Most of these features reappear in the detailed and liberal charter granted to the burgesses of Swansea in 1305-06 by William de Breos. The charter shows, *inter alia,* the desire to utilize the woodlands to stimulate commerce by fostering the local shipbuilding industry:

> We do grant unto them [the Burgesses] reasonable Estovers in all and singular our woods above The Wood, except the wood of Predewen, to be taken in places most convenient for them (to wit, dead wood for fuel, and oak wood for building and repairing their houses within the Liberty of our Borough of Swansea, and for building and repairing their ships and boats) by the view and delivery of our Forester. So nevertheless, if having been once, twice, or thrice warned, he shall neglect or will not fulfil his office (yet so long as he may be conveniently found), then at length by reason of his default let every one take out of the same [woods] what shall seem unto him necessary for the purposes aforesaid. And they may, likewise, have and take the rest of the woods when they will for their necessary use in form before mentioned. But it shall not be lawful for them to sell or give anything out of the aforesaid woods to any stranger, except to guests and travellers coming to our said Borough during the time of their tarrying, yet they may be welcome to give or sell to one another. And they may make and have, if they will, out of the woods aforesaid, four great ships or fewer together and successively; but we grant to them that they may out of the said woods build as many boats as they will, able to carry twenty casks of wine or less, paying to us and our heirs for every new-built ship or boat 12d . . . Nor shall it be lawful for them to take anything out of the said woods, but in the daytime, and that in form, aforesaid.[55]

Supervision of felling and removal of forest products by the foresters was an important feature, and the rules concerning it were often explicit. For example, in the charter of William de Breos to the English and Welsh of Gower in 1306, wood could be taken under the watch of the forester, but if the forester was not present, the applicant had to blow a horn three times or, if he had no horn, strike a tree three times with an axe and await the arrival of the forester. If the forester did not arrive within a reasonable time, the necessary wood could be taken without let or hindrance.[56]

The development of a forest industry during the fourteenth century was seriously affected by intermittent rebellions and by pestilence. In Glamorgan, for example, the revolt of Llewelyn Bren resulted in disruption of operations in the upland forests. The yields of the forest of Senghennydd in 1316 were reduced because workers in the charcoal pits fled the forest in the war, and in Machen Forest many men who used to work the forest were killed during the war.[57]

The Black Death came into Wales in 1349 and the effects of the plague were felt well into the 1350s, with depopulation, tenements in decay, and loss of tenants and rents. A second though milder pestilence struck Wales in 1361-62. The effects were greatest on the manors, which were being reduced to a state of decadence. The practice of letting the demesne land became widespread, and profits from pannage and timber declined, but the drastic effects of the Black

Death on the rural economy were overshadowed by an event even more disruptive to the economic life in Wales, the Owain Glyndŵr rebellion, which started in 1400 and continued for a decade or more. The devastation caused by this war resulted in a breakdown of organization and doubtless in an extension of the area of scrub and secondary woodland on abandoned farmland. The results were graphically described by Sir John Wynn of Gwydyr: 'all the wholle countrey then was but a forrest, rough and spacious as it is still, but then wast of inhabitants, and all over growen with woods, for Owen Glyndwrs warres beginninge in Anno 1400, contynewed fifteene yeares w'ch brought such a desolacion, that greene grasse grewe one the market place in llanroost [Llanrwst] called Brin y Botten'.[58]

Though economic conditions improved generally in the fifteenth century, the Wars of the Roses caused further devastation in some places, which Wynn again described: 'Yow are to understand that in those dayes the countrey of Nanconway was not onelie wooded, but also all Car'r' [Caernarfonshire], Merionythshire, and Denbigheshire seemed to be but one forrest and wood, having few inhabitants'.[59]

Chapter IV

DEER PARKS

Medieval *deer park*, SENGHENNYDD. A large oval embanked area, about 4.3 km long from N. to S. by 3 km wide, enclosing the upper part of the valley of the Nant yr Aber and the surrounding hills . . . The enclosed area is about 2,500 acres.   *RCAHM*

Following the Anglo-Norman conquest of Wales, many of the new landowners soon followed the English fashion and established their own deer parks. William Rees mapped 21 deer parks in south Wales and the March in the fourteenth century, and there are documentary references to the creation of several others in north Wales. Many other deer parks were subsequently established as fashionable adjuncts to castles and large houses, though these parks were often quite small and did not survive for very long.

Some of the medieval deer parks can still be easily traced today by field archaeology. For example, two of the largest and oldest deer parks in Wales were Senghennydd in eastern Glamorgan and Parc Le Breos in mid Gower. Both of these were surveyed by RCAHM Wales for the *Inventory of the Ancient Monuments in Glamorgan*.[1]

At Senghennydd the medieval deer park was a large oval upland area, much of it above 1000ft on Mynydd Eglwysilan, forming the catchment of Nant yr Aber and its several tributaries, the steep-sided valleys of which would then have been thickly wooded and indeed still are to some extent, despite later mining activity. The park was over 2½ miles long from north to south, and nearly 2 miles wide, with a total area of some 2,500 acres. It was enclosed by a bank and internal ditch, designed to prevent the escape of deer.

Much of the bank and ditch enclosing the park still survives in the northern half of the circuit, the bank being between 10 and 20ft wide and up to 4ft high, with a gentle outer scarp and steep inner slope to a flat-bottomed ditch 3-4ft

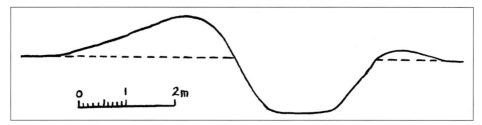

20. Typical cross-section of the mound and ditch enclosing Senghennydd deer park.

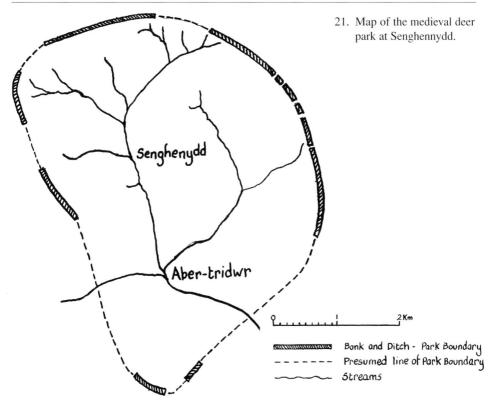

21. Map of the medieval deer park at Senghennydd.

deep and 5ft wide at the bottom. In the south only fragments of the bank and ditch survive, and for long stretches they are absent altogether. The park entrance was presumably in the main valley where the boundary crossed the stream near Craig-y-fedw. The perimeter of this park was eight miles, and if the bank was completely paled around, a total of 50,000 cleft oak palings would have been required to protect the whole circuit.

The area is marked as common on Rees's map of south Wales in the fourteenth century, and there are no documentary references to the earthworks forming the park perimeter, which passes close to several Bronze Age tumuli, but significant place-names Parc Newydd, Parc Mawr and Nant Cwm-parc occur near Senghennydd within the old park boundary.

Only slightly inferior in area to Senghennydd and similar in shape was Parc Le Breos deer park, an oval area over 2½ miles long from east to west and 1½ miles wide, enclosing the valley catchments of Llethrid and Ilston. This park, containing a good deal of (modern) woodland, was first mentioned as 'silva de Bruiz' (1230), 'Park-de-Breoz' (1306) and 'parcus de Bruz' (1319). It was disparked in the fifteenth century, and in the 1580s Rice Merrick referred to 'Park y Price ... sometime emparked with a wall and pale but long time past disparked'.

The main entrance was probably near Parkmill, at the confluence of the two valleys. The boundary perimeter is over seven miles, enclosing some 1,972 acres, and for most of its circuit the boundary is a dyke consisting of an earth bank with a core of stones, varying in scale and state of preservation but normally 10-20ft wide and a yard high, which must have been topped with a pale or hedge. Numerous place-names still testify to the medieval deer park: Parc le Breos, Park Woods, Park Place and Parkmill.

Typically, medieval deer parks contained a good proportion of woodland cover, as well as launds or open grassland areas. This is shown by the following comparison of land-use and financial returns for three small parks in the commote of Rhufoniog Isaled in the Lordship of Denbigh in 1334:

Table 1. Land-use and revenue in three medieval parks[2]

	Little Park (Parvus Parcus)	Galghull' Park	Moillewyk' Park
Enclosure	ditch + paling	ditch + paling	paling
Total area	264 acres	62 acres	442 acres
Launds (landee) i.e. pasture	227 acres	37 acres	162 acres
Dense thorn underwood	7 acres	20 acres	{ 280 acres
Alderwood	30 acres	4½ acres	
Coppice rotation	12 years	12 years	12 years
Coppice value/acre	8s.	8s.	8s.
Coppice value/acre/annum	8d.	8d.	8d.
Pasture value/acre/annum	12d.	12d.	12d.

The total area coppiced in these three parks was 28½ acres per annum which, at 8s./year, gave an annual return of £11 8s.; the pasture, if not occupied by game animals, amounted to 426 acres at 12d./acre = £21 6s. The total annual return was therefore £32 14s. from coppice and pasture.

Though hunting was certainly sometimes practised within the confines of these medieval deer parks, as Oliver Rackham points out the real purpose of a park was the prosaic supply of venison, other meat, wood and timber. Descriptions of Welsh parks show that they contained not only deer (usually fallow deer, but sometimes red deer in addition) but also cattle. Indeed, cattle were often more important than the deer.

Among his collection of papers entitled *The Taylor's Cushion*, George Owen of Henllys, the chronicler of Pembrokeshire, gives a detailed description of a small deer park named Whytley (location uncertain, but presumably typical for the late sixteenth century).[3] It was 1 mile long, ¼ mile wide, and 3 miles in perimeter, enclosed by a dry-stone wall, with a commodious lodge for the park-keeper. There was a pen adjacent to the lodge, with a well stocked fish-pond (carp, tench, roach) fed by a spring, and some other ponds within the park. The main park consisted of 200 acres of open land, the herbage of which was worth 2 shillings per acre, and 20 acres of woodground, the herbage of which was also worth 2 shillings per acre. In addition, there were 3 acres of wood containing dense oaks 80-100 years old, and also a wooded covert of 3 acres, yielding no herbage. The wood in the park further consisted of an estimated 1,000 'rinbold' and 80 'dotters'.

Rain, rend and *rene* were all English dialect verbs for bark-stripping, and *rendlewood* was oak wood that had been barked, or branchwood from crowns of oaks. The *rinbold* in the park were trees that had been cropped, topped or polled, probably oaks but perhaps other species such as ash or elm deliberately lopped to provide winter fodder for the deer. The *dotters* (dodders or dodderels) were old pollards, in this case dead standing trees that had ceased to produce any new shoots.

The total herd of deer in this 230-acre park was 80, consisting of 30 antlered deer, 30 rascall and 20 fawns. Rascall normally means the young lean deer, as distinct from the fully-grown antlered bucks, but here it must mean the breeding does. This artificially unbalanced population, apparently of fallow deer, could theoretically be maintained at this sort of level by culling ten bucks and ten old does each year.

The records of the Court of Augmentations give a vivid picture of the pressures on some Welsh deer parks in the sixteenth century, often leading to decline, change of use and eventual destruction.

One noteworthy case involved a dispute between members of the Salysbury family, concerning damage in the King's park called Garth Snodyock in the county of Denbigh. Roger Salysbury, son of the former park keeper, was charged with: felling and selling £200 of oaks, ash and other trees; using park timber and freestone to build a limekiln and a new house; enclosing a little coppice and empaling it with timber from the park so that the King's deer could not have pasture and covert as before; diverting a common path; and grazing excessive numbers of beasts and cattle in the coppice.

Roger Salysbury's defence was as follows:

> He denies cutting down timber, its sale or the building. He has felled no timber or wood but at the order of the clerk of the King's Works for the convenient repair of the pale of the park and the convenient grousing of the King's deer and game; and has gathered and taken the wind-fallen wood and trees. As to working free stone in the quarry, there is no free stone but hard stone the which the inhabitants of Denbie have always gathered and taken at their will and pleasure as out of a common pit or quarry; so had defendant done for the building of his house, but not to a tenth part of the value mentioned. He has built a limekiln on his own ground, without any of the King's timber or stone other than he might lawfully take. The only wood he took for maintaining it were wind-fallen wood, roots, hollows, and knarry trees, as well and lawful. The enclosing and paling of the coppice was done by order of his father, forester there, with thorns and stakes and done to save the Kings 'ffannys' from being devoured by the swine of the country and safeguarding the King's game and dairy in the winter time, whereby the King's game is much saved. There is no common path altered or changed but he took away the gate which stood in the park pale, against and near the town end of Denbye, by reason whereof the swine of the town, sundry times and daily, came to the park, not only wrecking the soil, but devouring the King's 'ffannys'. He therefore hung the gate in another place further from the town in a more convenient place. As to pasturing and feeding of a great and excessive number of cattle, though park 1½ miles about there are a great number of deer there, about 400, so that a great number of beasts cannot be satisfied nor fed there.[4]

In 1595 the total area of Marsley park in the Lordship of Bromfield (Denbigh) was 625 acres, including a lodge and small messuage. Of this, 409 acres was pasture but three-quarters (301 acres) of it was 'rough land overgrown with bushes and thorns'; 175 acres was wooded land, and 8 acres was moor overgrown with alder. The timber survey stated:

> Growing in park, timber trees, trees for firewood, pales of all sorts and stubbed and cropped trees for firewood to no. of 12240, being worth to be sold as they are severally valued in certificate £296 13s. 4d., besides underwood, which are not by them valued in respect; they think they will hardly countervail the charge of the ridding and stocking up of the same. Most part of the pale is decayed, rotten and altogether insufficient to keep in the deer there.[5]

Witnesses deposed that:

> there live in the said park and about in the grounds adjoining (for in regard of the great decay of the pale many of the deer lie abroad) between 9 score and 10 score at all sorts, whereof some 30 or thereabouts are deer of antler. There is allowed to the 2 keepers their houses for their dwelling in the same park and also pasture for certain cattle in the same park and to 3 other persons for certain kine in respect they should stop breaches in the pale and keep out the neighbours cattle out of the same park.

Of the actual ritual and practice of hunting in medieval Welsh deer parks we know little, but for forest hunting we do have a general picture, derived from contemporary descriptions of hunts in Wales, England and France, in such classics as the *Mabinogion, Sir Gawain and the Green Knight,* and the French medieval treatises on hunting.

The classical hunt was of the red deer stag: the selected animal would be unharboured from its lair, and then hunted by relays of hounds and mounted huntsmen, until it finally stood at bay and was despatched. The hounds were ceremoniously rewarded at the *curée* and the venison divided according to ritual and precedence, even the raven receiving its special portion, the gristle at the spoon of the brisket. Fallow deer, roe, wild boar and even foxes were also objects of the medieval hunt.

In later days the sport degenerated, the old ritual fell away, and deer were driven by hounds and beaters to be shot at an appointed place. At Margam park in 1684, Thomas Dinely described how fallow bucks were run down by footmen and then brought alive to the assembled nobility for approval, before receiving the fatal stroke from a 'scimitar'.[6]

During the eighteenth and nineteenth century, in Sir John Aubrey's small walled park in the Vale of Glamorgan at Llantrithyd, only 77 acres in area of which nearly 20 acres were groves of trees, the fallow deer wore brass bells on leather collars. Individual animals were selected in proper season with the aid of a stone-walled funnel-shaped race leading to a pen, and then coursed with hounds within the park, the bucks in summer and the does in winter. Surplus fawns were culled by shooting in early summer.[7]

22. Old pollard oak in Llantrithyd deer park.

Chapter V

MONASTIC WOODS

> They [the monks] changed an oak wood into a wheat field
> Giraldus Cambrensis, *Opera Speculum Ecclesiae*, III, 12

The third great influence on the woodlands in medieval times, along with establishment of hunting forests and the military clearances of native woodlands, was the development and management of the monastic estates. Many orders established houses during the Middle Ages, and by early Tudor times there were still forty-seven religious houses in Wales.[1] The Cistercian abbeys (see Table 2) were the most numerous and certainly the most important with regard to the forests, and the following discussion is based mainly on these, though other religious houses, even quite small ones, often cleared woods and also owned and managed woods.

Table 2. Cistercian houses in Wales

Monasteries	Established in	Dissolved in
Basingwerk (Flint)	1131	1536
*Conwy (Caernarfon)	1190	1536
Cwm-hir (Radnor)	1176	1536
Cymer (Merioneth)	1199	1536
Grace Dieu (Monmouth)	1226	1536
Llantarnam (Monmouth)	1179	1536
Margam (Glamorgan)	1147	1536
Neath (Glamorgan)	1130	1539
Strata Florida (Cardigan)	1164	1539
Strata Marcella (Montgomery)	1170	1536
Tintern (Monmouth)	1131	1536
Valle Crucis (Denbigh)	1201	1536
Whitland (Carmarthen)	*c.*1157	1539
Nunneries		
Llanllugan (Montgomery)	before 1236	1536
Llanllŷr (Cardigan)	*c.*1180	1536

*also known as Aberconwy, Maenan or Aberllechog abbey.
Abbey Dore in Herefordshire, established in 1147 and dissolved in 1536, was sometimes included in the Welsh order.

The energy and knowledge which the Cistercians brought from their mother foundations in France strongly influenced land-use in Wales. Accounts of the economic activity of the Cistercians in Wales traditionally refer mainly to assarting, i.e. forest clearance for agriculture, but documentary evidence of the Welsh monastic establishments, though scanty, does shed some light on the management of their forests as well as on forest clearance.

The lands granted to the Cistercians in Wales lay originally in undeveloped and well wooded areas, and were extensive (see Fig. 23). The abbey of Conwy, for example, held territory totalling over 38,000 acres, in the home estate and a number of granges, nearly all of which contained substantial areas of woodlands.[3]

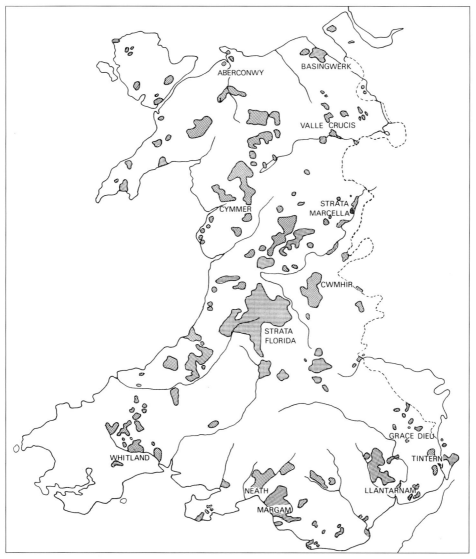

23. Map of the lands of the Cistercians (after D.H. Williams).

The original charters and grants of land to the abbeys gave the monks freedom to assart and the Cistercians became noted for their activity in forest clearance, especially in the early years of the religious houses. The charters normally use the general terms *silva* or *nemus* for wood or woods, without reference to species or condition.

The main reasons for assarting were to develop the estate for agriculture, and as a condition of land-holding for reasons of security. The result in each case was, of course, the same – the permanent clearance of woodland.

The commonest form of assarting was for conversion to arable land. As Giraldus Cambrensis said of the monks of Abbey Dore: 'they changed an oak wood into a wheat field', and if Giraldus is to be believed, this was one of the finest areas of natural oak high forest in the country, with tall straight branch-free stems and small compact crowns.[4] Such descriptions of a Welsh medieval forest are rare but the assarting he describes is typical of countless other acts, large and small, by monks throughout Wales.

The second form of assarting became frequent especially towards the end of the thirteenth century when, for example, the abbots were ordered to fell and bring into cultivation without delay the thick woods where robberies and murders and other offences against the king's peace had been committed.

The land assarted by Cistercians from the woods was often protected by a ditch and a wall, hedge or fence. The actual details of the procedure employed by the Cistercians are not known, but it presumably involved felling all the trees and undergrowth by axe, removal of all the useful assortments (especially timber, bark and fuelwood), burning of residual debris on the site, and eradication of roots and stumps by mattock and burning. Ploughing would then follow. Essentially, assarting was similar to slash-and-burn cultivation but was obviously more thorough, as the land cleared was intended for permanent cultivation. The place-name Cwrt Sart, a grange of Neath abbey, is derived from the practice of monastic assarting.

The other major activity of the Cistercians that affected the woodlands on the monastic estates was livestock husbandry, especially large-scale sheep-ranching. Flocks on some estates were large, even if fluctuating sharply as a result of outbreaks of disease. The *Taxatio Ecclesiastica* (1291) gives the following numbers of sheep:

| Margam | 5,285 | Tintern | 3,264 | Strata Florida | 1,327 |
| Neath | 4,897 | Basingwerk | 2,000 | Whitland | 1,100 |

Large-scale ranching would have required or resulted in the formation of extensive open pastures. Grazing in woodland pasture would, unless very carefully regulated, have degraded and eventually eliminated the woodland.

Timber was felled on the estates of the monasteries for building houses and ships, and also for fuel and charcoal for iron-smelting, though of course this utilization does not necessarily imply permanent forest clearance. Indeed, selective felling of large oak for constructional timber and regular cutting of coppice for smaller material would have been the normal practice expected. For example, the monks of Grace Dieu received grants of timber from local woodlands to help in rebuilding the house after its burning in 1233, and these trees were presumably carefully selected individual oaks: twenty from the Forest of Dean (1235), four from Grosmont Forest (1240) and two from Skenfrith (1253).[5]

In fact, although the Cistercians were noted for their forest clearances, they were also leading exponents of forest management, as they were on the continent. In Bavaria, for example, the forest ordinance of Ebersberg monastery dating from the second half of the thirteenth century gives details of the forester, the subordinate staff, their duties, forest products and regulations against abuses; it also indicates an appreciation of the importance of suitable forest floor conditions for natural regeneration. Special officials such as foresters, bailiffs or woodwards were appointed to take care of the woods on monastic estates in Wales too, though their quality may have sometimes been suspect. For example, Howel Melior was said to have been inefficient in his stewardship of the Abbot of Tintern's wood at Monmouth when he was bailiff there in 1340.[6]

No foresters' accounts from Welsh monasteries are known, but it is reasonable to infer a sound system of regular management and also a range of products similar to those given in the unique surviving account book of Beaulieu abbey.[7] This includes the Forester's Account for the forest year Michaelmas 1269 to Michaelmas 1270, and also the *Tabula Forestarii*, a guidebook or set of rules governing forest yield, wood measurement, and specifications and prices of forest products. This is the earliest forester's *vademecum* known in Britain. The main products were large timber, bundles of small fuelwood, bundles of vine stakes or hedge rods, faggots, billets for charcoal-burning, charcoal, tanbark and pannage payments. An acre of average wood twenty years old yielded: 400 dozen bundles of small fuelwood, each bundle containing five pieces of round or cleft wood 3ft long and not thicker than a spear; 500 bundles of vine stakes or hedge rods, each bundle containing forty stakes at least 6ft long; and 4,000 faggots. Woods younger than the normal twenty years yielded correspondingly less, and woods where access for wheeled transport was difficult were felled, cut into billets and converted into charcoal *in situ*. The prices of the various forest products were:

> Charcoal .... 3d. per quarter (1 quarter = 8 bushels)
> Bark .... 2s. or 2s. 7d. per cart-load.
> Fuelwood .... 1d. per dozen bundles
> Vine stakes .... 2s. per 100 bundles
> Faggots .... 4d. per 100
> Timber .... by size and quality, e.g. £8 per acre.

The accounts show that very large quantities of forest products were harvested and sold, and substantial stocks were also kept in reserve, all this implying a carefully planned and orderly exploitation of the resources of the abbey. One particularly interesting item of equipment used by the forester was the *modulus,* a special iron frame for preparing standard measures of timber. The *modulus* was 2ft wide, 2ft long, and 6ft around, and was filled with wood, cleft or in the round, of the size of a man's leg and 2½ft long. Eight of these standard measures made up a normal cart-load for two horses.

The Cistercian estates went through fluctuating periods of prosperity and decline, being affected by wars, pestilences and the increasing encroachment of secular authority into all their spheres of activity. In the fourteenth century the tendency grew to lease out lands to laymen and to live on the rents. Long before the time of their dissolution the monasteries 'were not, and had not for centuries been, the pioneers of estate management, stock-breeding, wool production, mining, and metallurgy that once they had been'.[8] There is reason to believe that forest management would have been a relatively stable feature of the monastic economy, though the temptation for excessive felling in the period preceding the dissolution would have been strong.[9]

Surveys of some Cistercian monastery woods at about the time of the dissolution (1536-39) reveal age-structures that betoken careful silvicultural management for at least a century. The surveys indicate that all three major silvicultural systems were in existence – high forest, coppice-with-standards, and simple coppice.

Gilbert's Hill, a monastic wood east of Abbey Dore, was an example of high forest; it contained '120 acres, whereof 13 acres be of 50 years growing, and the residue of an hundred years growing and above'. It was enclosed with a hedge and valued at £80 in 1535.[10] The age structure suggests past management by clear felling or possibly shelterwood felling to produce an even-aged stand. Again, land that had belonged to the monastery of Talley near Llandeilo was described in 1554 as carrying 'great oakes att a place called a quarrel, above the number of 120, being of the growth of 80 years or thereabouts, and upon the demean belonging to the late disolved monastery, 60 oakes of the age of 50 years'.[11]

A very detailed account of the age-structure and valuation of a 60-acre block of coppice and coppice-with-standards in the Forest of Coyd Kyrye ap heren formerly belonging to the abbey of Cwm-hir (*c*.1545) can be summarized as follows. There was an almost perfect classical coppice with fifteen blocks, each

24. A floor tile from Neath abbey, showing a hunting scene.

of two acres, carrying simple coppice 1, 2, 3, 4, 5, 6, 7, 8, 9, 10, 12, 14, 16, 18 and 20 years old; in addition there were ten acres of coppice ten years old with short shrubbed oak standards sixty years old, and a further twenty acres of coppice twenty years old with a few oak standards sixty years old. The shrubbed oak standards had probably been subjected to lopping. The whole wood was valued at £7 15s. 10d.[12]

Shrubbing or lopping off of branches, often to a considerable height on the stem, was frequently practised as a means of providing winter fodder for livestock. This practice was also called shredding or shrouding. Complete pollarding of trees was also deliberately practised in some places; at Abbey Dore, for instance, a lease in 1529 specified that 'the great oak, or the elm, or the poll wood' were not to be cut.[13]

In summary, though the evidence available is fragmentary, it is certain that there was vigorous forest clearance over considerable areas of the estates of the Welsh Cistercians during the early period, probably coupled later with relatively efficient management of selected woodlands on a sustained-yield basis.

Chapter VI

FOREST DECLINE AND ESTATE-BUILDING

> The lord hath a greate woodde there called the forest of Penkelly . . .
> aboute 500 acres of woodde . . . all growne with greate okes of 200
> yeres growth and more and some younge woodde . . .
>
> George Owen, *Extent of Cemais*, 1594

It is clear that although the principles of forest management were known and practised in some places, especially on the monastic estates, the remaining woodlands of Wales were subject to great pressures from a growing population, expanding arable and livestock husbandry, and a developing wood-based industry. Protection of woods after felling from browsing by livestock was of vital importance to secure adequate regeneration, whether by seedlings or by coppice. Though awareness of the value and importance of forests had been evident at an individual or local level for centuries, the consequences of negligence, abuse and deliberate clearance for military reasons or personal profit had reduced the woodlands to such a level by the fifteenth century that for the first time the conservation of the remaining resources became a matter of concern by government, as evidenced by the enactment of the *Statute of Enclosure* in 1482. This was an *Act for Enclosing of Woods in Forests, Chases and Purlieus,* the purlieus being lands that had been afforested (in the legal sense) and subsequently disafforested. It applied only to the royal forests, chases and purlieus, and it enabled landowners to enclose their lands against deer and cattle for seven years after each coppice felling. This purely permissive act indicates that the short periods of enclosure previously employed had often been inadequate to ensure satisfactory coppice regeneration.

The decline of individual forests and of the total forest area is difficult to quantify precisely. Machen Forest is probably fairly typical of many forests, especially in south Wales, and may serve as an example, because something of its decline can be traced from the surviving records, though these are fragmentary and the accountancy is sometimes difficult to follow.[1] This forest had been worked intensively for charcoal and other products certainly since the early fourteenth century and presumably before that. The main sources of income shown in the detailed surviving account for 1447/48 were 'Wodekevyll' (wodegavell, i.e. rents paid in commutation of wood-carrying services), pannage of pigs, and 324 loads of sawn boards and small boards; no income was obtained from swarms of forest bees that year. The summary statement of the account is as follows:

Machen Forest

The office of receiver of this forest is worth this year from the fixed rent 16s. 6d.
Item, casual profits are worth £17 11s. 4d., viz. from swarms of bees (nothing) and
from sawn and small boards sold this year (54s.) and from pannage this same year
(£14 17s. 4d.).
Total value, £18 7s. 10d.
Deductions 8s. 6d., viz. in rent allowance (2s. 6d.) and repayments (6s.).
And finally it is worth £17 19s. 4d.

Income from pannage of pigs in Machen Forest showed considerable
fluctuations, reflecting the irregularity of acorn mast production and also the
progressive deterioration of the forest during the fifteenth century:

Year	Income
1401/02	£30 17s. 11d.
1444/45	nothing
1445/46	nothing
1446/47	nothing
1447/48	£14 17s. 4d.
1497/98	nothing
1503/04	£1 0s. 0d.

Pannaging herds of swine represented the progressive consumption of a capital
asset, and the deterioration of the forest may also be gauged from the decline in
revenue paid to the Receiver of Newport over the period 1401-1522 (Table 3).

Table 3. Payments to the receiver of Newport for Machen Forest, 1401-1522

Year	Payments made			Arrears owed			Total		
	£	s.	d.	£	s.	d.	£	s.	d.
1401-02	19	11	4	8	16	10	28	8	2
1434-35	10	0	0	11	18	10	21	18	10
1446-47	2	8	8		14	0	3	2	8
1447-48	12	0	0	5	19	4	17	19	4
1451-52		nil		1	2	4	1	2	4
1456-57		nil			14	0		14	0
1465-66	3	2	0		nil		3	2	0
1497-98		9	0		nil			9	0
1503-04	1	4	7		nil		1	4	7
1521-22		14	0		–			14	0

The survey of his estates ordered by the Duke of Buckingham in 1500
included the forests of Machen and Coed Meredydd, and clearly showed the
poor condition of the woods:

yt appereth that yn all the seid woodes ys nother underwode, nor but littell faire
tymbre, but the moste substance therof stondeth in gret olde okes wherof no
wodesale ys to be made, not lytell other profite therof will growe, but pannage of

swyne onely, when mast falleth. Gret and yn maner extreme wast and distruccion
hath be doon yn the seid woodes in yeres passed . . .

In other words, the forest consisted mainly of overmature oaks worthless as
timber; few timber trees were present, no underwood, and little or no
regeneration. Similar 'gret defaultes' were also found in Brecon Forest.

The records for Radnor Forest also show evidence of deterioration. An
Elizabethan Inquisition (3 October 1564) described the 3,000-acre forest as
consisting of 2,000 acres of 'wast heath and wild, foggy and marish ground',
800 acres of 'lowe shrubbes and bushe of smalle hazill and thornes utterly
destroied by reason the same have been hewen and cutt down by th' inhabitants
dwelling there about all waies owt of season, and at the spring tyme eaten and
consumed wth wild bests and goats', and 200 acres 'somewhat more batefull
than the rest, or whereon shepe and other cattell most comenly doo pasture'.[2]

Although the forests were in decay, the administration of forest law continued
to cause problems, and this resulted in 1535 in the passing of an *Act for the
Abuses in the Forests of Wales* (27 Henry VIII, c.7). The act did not directly
affect the vegetation or management, but it did give relief from 'certain
unreasonable Customs and Exactions' in the forest, namely (1) imposition of
fines on persons passing through without official tokens, i.e. passes, or without
payment of an annual fee; (2) confiscation of money plus mutilation or a fine on
anyone found off the highway; and (3) confiscation of stray or stolen cattle. This
Statute enacted

> that it shall be lawful from thenceforth to all and every the king's true subjects . . .
> freely and quietly and in Peace to pass and repass travel and go into and through
> the said Forests, and every of them, both on Horseback and on Foot, as well
> following and driving of Cattle, as with carrying of Wares; or otherwise about their
> lawful Business and Affairs, without any Fine Forfeiture Toll Custom Exaction or
> other Imposition to be taken exacted or demanded of them, by the said Foresters
> Rulers Walkers Farmers or their Assigns . . . And further . . . that if any Manner of
> Beast or quick Cattle . . . do come into any of the said Forests by Strays, Thief
> stolen or otherwise and there be marked and seized by any of the said Foresters
> Rulers Walkers Farmers or their Assigns . . . the Owner and Owners of the same
> Cattle, within one Year and a Day next ensuing, chance to find the said Cattle so
> taken, and lawfully prove the same to be his or their own proper Cattle, that then
> the same Cattle to be redelivered to the Owner or Owners thereof . . .[3]

In this period, because much legislation governing land use in Wales was
introduced (the *Act for the Abuses in the Forests of Wales* [1535], the *Acts of
Union* [1536, 1542] and the *Act Establishing the Court of Augmentations* [1536]
for the dissolution of the monasteries), it is fortunate that a general picture of the
land-use of much of the country, including the extent and condition of the
forests, can be deduced from Leland's account (1536-39).

In the coastal areas of south Wales the woods were mainly restricted to the
valleys, the upper reaches of all the valleys being well wooded, and much of the

hill-land still carried wood, for example the forest of Llwyd Coed near Hirwaun. All the lower lands of eastern Wales, from Flint to Monmouth, were still generally well-wooded, with 'great plenty of mervelus good woodde, and thorough reasonable wood' in the Chirk area, and mention of the forests of Clun, Ceri and Cedewain. In north Wales there was good wood in the valleys of Caernarfonshire, Denbighshire and in parts of Merioneth. However, extensive areas in the west were largely denuded of wood, for example the Llŷn peninsula, Eifionydd, Anglesey, western Carmarthenshire, Pembrokeshire, Cardiganshire and much of the uplands of mid-Wales. In Anglesey peat was dug, and in the peat were found 'great roots of trees that serve men for wood'; in Llŷn the fuel was, 'turffes, ferne, and gorsses'; Pembrokeshire was 'sumwhat baren of wood' except for a few parks and the forests of Narberth and Lloydarth. In the uplands of mid-Wales, on the lands of Strata Florida abbey, Leland identified the major causes of deforestation as uncontrolled felling, browse damage, and deliberate clearance, further contributory factors being large-scale livestock grazing, peat-bog formation, and felling for lead-smelting:

> Many hilles therabout [i.e. at Strata Florida] hath bene well woddid, as evidently by old rotes apperith, but now in them is almost no woode. The causses be these; first the wood cut doun was never copisid, and this hath beene a great cause of destruction of wood thorough Wales. Secondly after cutting doun of woodys the gottys [goats] hath so bytten the young spring [coppice regeneration] that it never grew but lyke shrubbes. Thirddely men for the nonys destroyed the great woddis that thei shuld not harborow theves . . . Al the montaine ground bytwixt Alen [Elan] and Strateflure longgeth to Strateflure, and is almoste for wilde pastures and breding grounds, in so much that everi man there about puttith on bestes as many as they wylle without paiying of mony . . . The pastures of the montaynes of Cairdiganshire be so great that the hunderith part of hit rottith on the ground, and maketh sogges and quikke more by long continuance for lak of eting of hit . . . a hille side Clothmoyne, wher hath bene great digging for leade, the melting whereof hath destroid the wooddes that sumtime grew plentifulli therabout.[4]

Following the Acts of Union (1536, 1542), all legislation become applicable to Wales as well as to England, English methods of law and administration were extended to all parts of Wales, and the English system of shires and hundreds became the basis of local government. One immediate effect was to make the new Reformation legislation applicable, thus making possible the reform of the Church and the confiscation of the properties of the monastic houses in Wales. Another important effect was the introduction of primogeniture in place of gavelkind, the Welsh system of inheritance. The gradual effect of this was to prevent further fragmentation of holdings and create conditions more favourable for the building up of estates, though some large estates with important areas of woodland were already in existence. William Vaughan's estate of Corsygedol in Merioneth, for example, contained 1,000 acres of wood and 1,000 acres of underwood in 1525.[5]

The forty-seven religious houses in Wales were surveyed in 1535 and their values recorded in the *Valor Ecclesiasticus*. All the houses were dissolved between 1536 and 1539. The leasing and sale of the properties were handled by the specially formed Court of Augmentations, with officers in each county including Masters of the Woods, Surveyors of the Woods and a Woodward. The monasteries were often noted for their woods, and Leland specifically referred to several instances in Wales. Grace Dieu and Llantarnam are both described as 'stonding in a wood', Whitland as 'in a vast wood', and both Llanegwhist (Valle Crucis) and Conwy as having 'meately good woode'. However, besides the woods, the buildings themselves contained timber of great value. These timbers were dismantled and sold, or used in the repair and maintenance of royal castles. For example, the beams and 'sparres' from the roof of Conwy abbey were dismantled and shipped to Caernarfon for re-use in buildings such as the castle, King's Hall and Shire Court.[6] This indicates the high value placed on worked timber, especially in large structural sizes, and perhaps also the increasing difficulty in finding suitable material in the remaining forests in Wales.

At first, leasing was the preferred means of obtaining income from the monastic estates. Crown leases were usually for 21 years, and woods were nearly always carefully reserved. However, increasing financial pressure soon caused the Crown to start selling its interests in the former monastic lands. Surveyors of woods were appointed: for example, William Cowper and David Clayton (*alias* Cleyton or Clutton) in 1545; in 1546 Geoffrey Gate was appointed surveyor general of woods in south Wales as Clayton had died and Cowper had resigned.[7] The work was not easy, and valuations were doubtless hasty and arbitrary.

Sales of land were on such a scale that by the accession of Elizabeth I in 1558 less than a quarter of the former monastic land remained in Crown hands.[8] The biggest buyers of monastic land in Wales were local gentry who applied direct to the Court of Augmentations. They had to be men with ready cash, or men able to raise cash quickly. Examples include: Thomas Herbert and William Breton who acquired in 1545 woods called Mylnewood (20 acres), New Parke (10 acres), Priors Wood (4 acres) and Grange Than (12 acres), but not those woods called Peresgraunge Wood and Monches Wood (40 acres) from the lands of Grace Dieu;[9] Thomas Irelonde of Shrewsbury who acquired, also in 1545, two woods formerly belonging to Conwy abbey called Coyde Imynoghe (Coed y Mynach, Monk's wood) and Coyde Varleygh More (10 acres);[10] Sir Rice Mansell who in 1543 bought for £642 9s. 8d. lands formerly part of Margam abbey, including 26 acres of woods and coppices (Cryke Woode, Little Crykewodde, Kelley Gredyke Coppes, Myddecrofte Coppes, Bollys Coppe and Lytle Bolys Coppe);[11] Sir Edward Carne who in 1546 paid £727 6s. 4d. for former monastic properties in Glamorgan, including '200 oaks being timber of 100 years growth';[12] and Sir John Williams who acquired a parcel of the possessions of the monastery of Cwm-hir, including the sixty acres of coppice and coppice-with-standards already described (see p. 62-3).[13]

Men able to buy monastic land could, if they so wished and subject to the local market, make an immediate profit from the sale of wood and underwood, or could continue to manage the woods they had legally acquired. With the creation and development of small and medium estates there was increasing difficulty in distinguishing between legitimate appropriation and illegal encroachment, especially on *cytir* (joint-land) where hereditary proprietors had a share in the pasture, wood and waste which the community controlled. The records of the Court of Augmentations give many examples of complaints over alleged spoil of woods and illegal felling and utilization of woods on former monastic lands. These include at Basingwerk cutting down great woods, underwoods and young springs; at Conwy felling oaks and woods, selling bark, cutting off tops of trees a little above mid height; at Cymer spoil of woods, felling and carrying away 400 oaks; at Llantarnam cutting down 20 great oaks; at Margam taking frith stakes and wood; and at Strata Marcella wrongful entry and felling of woods.[14]

The practice of cropping or pollarding of oak was widespread. In north Wales three defendants were charged with cutting down 'timber tops a little above the myddell, and so continually do they spoil that within a mile or two you shall not find one whole tree top, to the King's loss';[15] in 'Bennye Woode' near Brecon there were 120 oaks 'called cropped trees';[16] in the park of Marseley (Denbighshire) there were 'stubbed and cropped trees for firewood to no. of 12240';[17] oaks were 'topped' in the area around Brilley and Clyro;[18] and in 1602 Norden surveyed the forest of Coed y Gaer, in the Lordship of Oswestry, and described it as being 'full of olde Pollarde oakes which have been shrowded out topt and dye all for the most part'.[19]

The growing concern for the wood resources of the country was expressed in the *Statute of Woods or Act for the Preservation of Woods* (1543), the preamble to which pointed out the great decay of timber and woods and the manifest

25. Diagram of coppice-with-standards, with twelve standard trees to the acre, by Baron Bryn-fanigl, *c*.1600 (based on BM MS Roy. 18C XX, f. 25b).

likelihood of scarcity and lack of timber and fuelwood. The *Statute of Woods* was a prohibitive act applying to all woods throughout the kingdom and designed to prevent further wastage of woods. Its main provisions were that:

   (i)   12 standils or storers (i.e. standard trees) of oak were to be left standing on every acre of coppice wood or underwood felled at 24 years old or under,

  (ii)   if 12 standils or storers of oak were not present, other species (elm, ash, aspen or beech) were to be left to make up the number of 12 to the acre;

 (iii)   any standils or storers of oak (or failing these the other hardwood species) left at earlier fellings were to be retained at the next felling, and kept to form timber trees;

 (iv)   the standils or storers were to be kept until each of them was 10 inches square within 3 foot of the ground;

  (v)   any owner not ensuring that the standils and storers were left was to be fined 3s. 4d. for each standil or storer not left;

 (vi)   any owner causing the standils and storers to be felled contrary to the act was to be fined 3s. 4d. for each standil or storer so felled;

 (vii)   coppices worked on a rotation of 14 years or less were to be enclosed and fenced for 4 years, with a fine of 3s. 4d. per acre per month for non-enclosure;

(viii)   coppices worked on a rotation of 14-24 years were to be enclosed and fenced for 6 years, with a fine of 3s. 4d. per acre per month for non-enclosure;

 (ix)   when woods or coppices having standards over 24 years were felled or weeded (i.e. thinned), then 12 trees of oak (or failing these, of elm, ash, aspen or beech) were to be left standing for the next 20 years and the felled areas were to be enclosed and fenced for 7 years, under a penalty of 6s. 8d. per tree felled in excess of the prescribed figure and 3s. 4d. per acre per month for non-enclosure;

  (x)   no coppice woods of 2 acres or larger were to be converted into pasture or arable if more than 2 furlongs from the house of the owner or tenant, under penalty of 40s. per acre.

However, the Act did make provision for woodland owners to make fellings to meet any genuine domestic and agricultural requirements. It is not easy to determine how effective the *Statute of Woods* was in practice. In 1570 it was amended by increasing the period of enclosure by two years in each case, for it had been found by experience that the original periods prescribed were insufficient to provide adequate regeneration. Certainly, the Crown made efforts to ensure that the provisions of the Act were obeyed. In 1584, the farm of the 100-acre Benny Wood (Venny Wood), a few miles west of Brecon, was granted by letters patent to Richard Price to hold for 21 years.[20] All great timber trees, all sapling oaks fit for timber, and sufficient 'Stadells' (i.e. standards) in each acre of the premises were reserved to the Crown. Price was required to cut the said wood twice only, at fit and suitable times, to enclose it with hedges and ditches, to keep it free from damage by not putting any horses or other animals into it, and to deliver up yearly sufficient standards in each acre of the wood.

Detailed technical descriptions of Welsh woods or forests are extremely rare until modern times, and therefore a full account of an individual wood in the sixteenth century is of particular interest and value.

The wood of Penkelly (modern form Pengelli) was first mentioned in the accounts for the castle of Newport (Pembrokeshire) in 1398, when two carpenters were paid 2s. 6d. for three days' work felling timber, presumably oak, in the wood to make a bridge for the castle. Then in 1594 George Owen gave his detailed description of the wood in the *Extent of Cemais*, as follows:

Forest of Penkelly
The lorde hath a greate woodde there called the forest of Penkelly which lyethe betweene bothe the lordes demeynes called Henllys in the manor of Bayvill and Coort Hall in the manor of Egloserow, and the same contyneth of the usual measure of that contrey aboute 500 acres of woodde and is enclosed with quicksett and pale rownde about and under lock, and doth conteyne in compasse nyne hundred perches, each perche being 24 foote in length, which maketh about 4 myles and thre quarters. And the lorde kepeth the same with all profittes thereof arising in his owne handes. Yt is all growne with greate okes of 200 yeres growth and more and some younge woodde of 60 yeres growth, and most of it well growen with underwoodde as orle, hazell, thornes, willowse and other sorts of underwoddes, the herbage whereof, yt beinge nowe enclosed, will somer 30 breedinge mares and winter 300 sheepe and 200 cattell well and sufficiently, beside swyne which may be kepte there. Allso there is in the said woodde 14 cockshottes wherein is great store of woodcockes taken yearly which cockshottes is the lordes owne to do therewith what he pleaseth. Allso there breedeth in the said woodde sparrhawkes which is the lordes also. Allso the panage of hogges, bees and hony, the herbage and all other profittes thereof is the lordes owne without any maner of parte or comon to be demannded by any tenannte or other. The herbage of the said woode is very good for cattell, horses, mares, sheepe and swyne and there is store of faire fresh ryvers and springes in the same woodde fitte and holsome for all kinde of cattell.[20a]

The annual issues, i.e. revenues, from the Forest of Pengelli came to the respectable sum of £20.

It is difficult to reconcile some of the dimensions and to trace the actual boundaries of the old forest precisely on the modern map. However, its general location and the extent are clear, and the main features of the woodland and its uses are unambiguous and merit careful analysis.

The wood was obviously an important and clearly defined area, securely enclosed with a quickset hedge and pale fencing, with its entrance gate under lock and key. The actual woodland was evidently being managed as coppice with standards, the latter being oak timber trees aged 200 years and 60 years indicating orderly long-term management. The underwood consisted of the usual broadleaved species – alder, hazel, thorn, willow, etc. – presumably coppiced at regular intervals. Apart from the timber and underwood, the grazing was of great importance, as shown by the large numbers of livestock (horses, sheep, cattle) that could be kept there, as well as the general rooting and pannage for pigs.

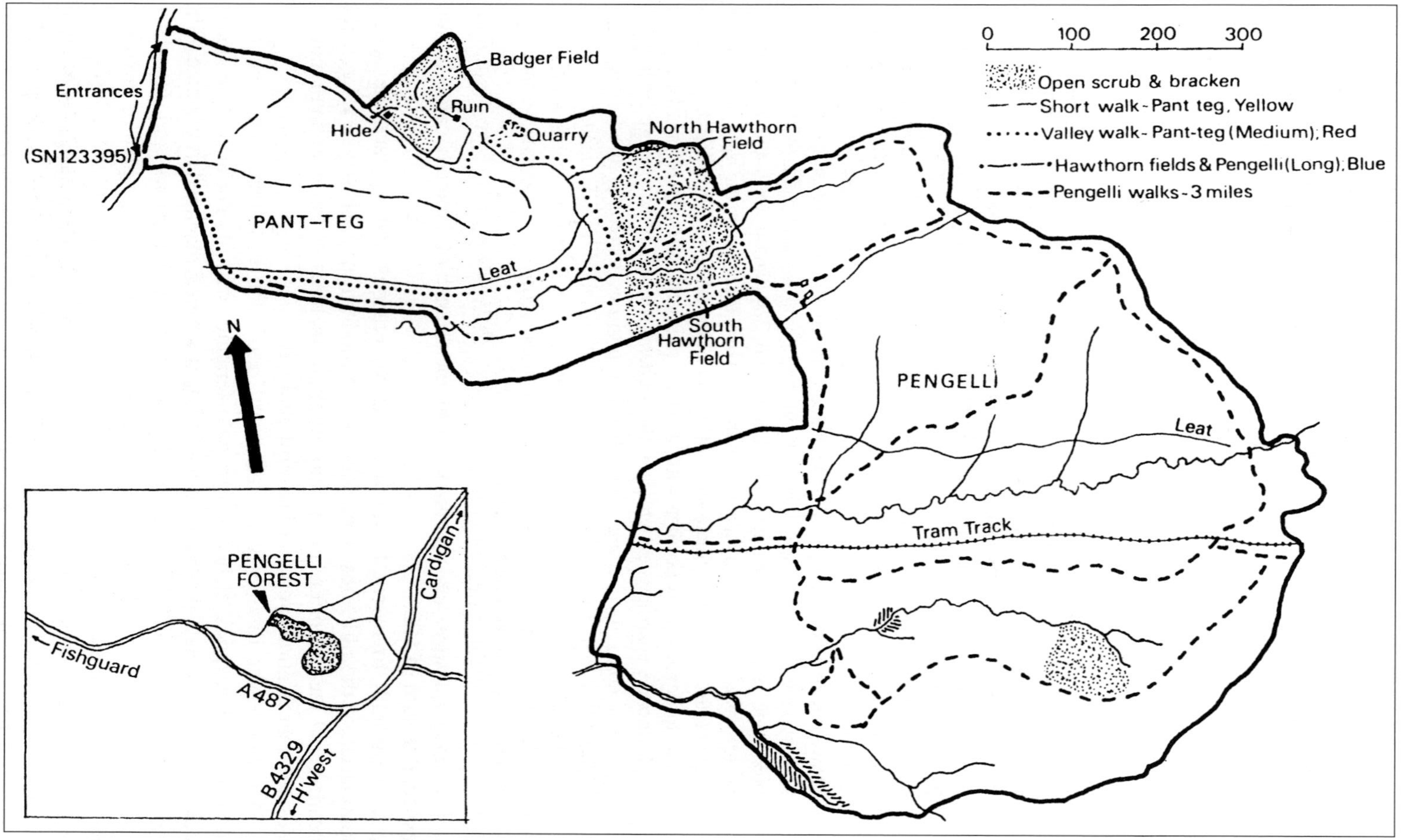
0 100 200 300
Open scrub & bracken
Short walk - Pant teg, Yellow
Valley walk - Pant-teg (Medium); Red
Hawthorn fields & Pengelli (Long); Blue
Pengelli walks - 3 miles
Entrances
(SN123395)
Badger Field
Ruin
Hide
Quarry
North Hawthorn Field
PANT–TEG
Leat
N
South Hawthorn Field
PENGELLI
Leat
Tram Track
PENGELLI FOREST
Cardigan
Fishguard
A487
B4329
H'west

26. Pengelli, a forest for many centuries and an SSSI since 1978.

Besides the herbage, the other important products of the wood were: young sparrowhawks (the nests were guarded until the birds were old enough to be taken and trained for hawking); the honey from wild bees' nests; supplies of fresh water from springs and streams; and woodcock which were taken in season in specially installed 'cockshoots'.

Catching woodcock at cockshoots was a popular and profitable woodland pastime, and George Owen described the technique in his *Description of Pembrokeshire* (p. 128):

> The chief plenty [of woodcocks] is between Michaelmas and Christmas . . . Their chief taking is in cockroads in woods, with nets erected up between two trees, where in cock-shoot time, as it is termed, which is the twilight a little after the breaking of the day and before the closing of the night, they are taken, sometimes two, three or four at a fall. I have myself oftentimes taken six at one fall, and in one road at an evening taken eighteen, and it is no strange thing to take a hundred or six score in one wood in twenty four hours if the haunt be good . . .

Like pannage or grazing, cockshoots could be rented out by the woodland owner to provide cash revenues called 'glade rents'. For example, Griffith William Powell held one glade called a cockshoot in the southern part of Pengelli wood, for which he paid the lord an annual rent of 5s., and William ap Owen paid the same rent for another cockshoot in the eastern part of the wood.

Old place-names associated with woods attest the presence of cockshoots in many parts of Wales, for example: Gwerne y Kocksuite, Cockshut Wood and Pen y Cockshute in the township of Hope (Flintshire); Coed y Cockshoot on Castle Farm, near Usk (Monmouthshire); The Cockshed and Cock Shott Wood in the hundred of Dinas Powys in the Vale of Glamorgan; Cockshead Wood (Coed Cockshead) near Silian (Cardiganshire); and the Cockshutt, the Cockshoot Wood, Cockyeat Farm and various other forms in Narbeth hundred (Pembrokeshire).

It seems safe to infer that this description of Pengelli is typical of many other woods in Wales at this period, showing the high value placed upon the woodland and its multiple-use management. It also illustrates sustainability of management for the forest of Pengelli still flourishes, now safeguarded and carefully managed as an SSSI. Its biological and ecological features have been comprehensively studied and described, and its early and more recent history and its current management plan have been published – see, for example, the two-volume report *Pengelli Forest: Nature Reserve Description and Management Plan*, by John Comont for the West Wales Trust for Nature Conservation (1986).

In addition to growing concern for preservation of natural regeneration and enclosure to protect coppice regrowth, the sixteenth century saw the start of recorded planting of timber trees for commercial purposes in Wales, though planting for shelter and for ornament had been practised for centuries. Following a survey of the Lordship of Denbigh in 1563 which revealed a shortage of timber, the tenurial structure was reformed and standard leases for 21 years were issued. These leases obliged the tenant to plant specified numbers of timber trees in an attempt to remedy this shortage. For example, a lease of 1564 required the tenant to plant 180 trees, either oak, ash, elm, poplar or walnut.[21] The leases issued by the Crown later in the century also included the obligation to plant timber trees, for example in 1592/93 a tenant was to plant 400 trees of oak, elm, beech or poplar within three years. Seven other similar leases issued in the lordship in 1593 required the tenants to plant a total of 4,180 trees within periods of three or seven years.[22] Planting for river-bank protection was also practised, for in 1561 a jury empanelled in the Lordship of Glasbury (Radnorshire) recommended the planting of three rows of osiers on the bank of the Wye, the osiers to be 3 inches compass (i.e. circumference), 1½ yards long and ¾ yard apart.[23]

With the growth of private estates, planting to embellish the country houses had already been in vogue for some time. George Owen's description of Pembrokeshire in 1603 refers to 'prettie groves of woodde, as oake, ashe, mapple, Elme, and such like, and diuerse rare tymber, as the pyne aple tree [presumably Scots pine], the spruse, and fyrre trees, the Mulbery tree & others' planted around 'houses of accompte'. Towards the end of the sixteenth century Sir Thomas Perrot established pheasants 'in a pleasante grove of his owne plantinge' at Haroldston in Pembrokeshire.[24] The voyages of discovery resulted in new trees being introduced to Wales from North America, including the 'Firre tree': 'Master Thomas Bowen of Trefloine in the County of Pembroke . . . had about fifteene or sixteene yeares past [i.e. c. 1596] manie young and small plants of this kind brought him home by saylers from the Newfound land, with some of the earth wherein they did formerly grow, and planted them together with the said earth in convenient places about his house, where they have since so well prospered that many of them at this present [i.e. 1612] are about foure foot in circuit, and also very high and tapering. And they will grow upon mountaines, gravellie soyles, or in good earth, either by planting the young tree, or sowing of the seed'.[25]

This is the first recorded introduction of exotics to Wales from North America, and also the first record of planting and direct sowing of conifers in Wales. Moreover, the fact that the trees were planted in soil brought from North America meant that mycorrhizae would have been unwittingly introduced. It is not certain whether one or more species of conifer was involved in this introduction, and the precise identity of the 'firre' is also uncertain, but in view of the place of origin and the reported rapid growth rate, *Pinus strobus* appears to be the probable species.

It is possible, from the recorded 'statistics' of the sixteenth and seventeenth centuries (acreage figures given in various surveys, fines, inquisitions and recoveries), for the first time to estimate with some degree of reliability the percentage forest cover in Wales. However, accurate surveys were not possible at that period, and the acreages given to each major category of land-use in the lordships, manors, commotes, estates and smaller holdings are approximate only. The major land-use categories distinguished were generally arable land, pasture, meadow, moor, wood and underwood, marsh, furze/heath, mountain land, and turbary. Analysis of a randomly selected number of such 'statistics' for large and small areas in various parts of Wales between the fifteenth and seventeenth centuries in fact reveals a surprisingly consistent picture with woodland generally covering under 10% of the land and only exceptionally exceeding 15%.[26]

The most accessible published data are those for Montgomeryshire, generally recognized in later centuries as the best wooded county in Wales, next to Monmouthshire. Those for the Barony and Lordship of Powys (Table 4), despite the large difference in total area between the two surveys, show fairly consistent but surprisingly low percentages of woodland.

Table 4. Land-use and % woodland in the Barony and Lordship of Powys, 1582 and 1622-23[27]

Categories of land-use	Acreages in	
	1582	1622-23
Arable land	20,000	40,000
Meadow	6,000	12,000
Pasture	10,000	40,000
Wood	3,000	6,000
Mountain land	10,000	——
Heath & gorse	6,000	40,000
Moor	3,000	10,000
Total area	58,000 acres	148,000 acres
Woodland as % of total area	5.2	4

When data for individual manors and large estates in Montgomeryshire are analysed, a somewhat different picture emerges (Table 5), with woodland covering an average of some 10% of the land.

Table 5. Areas and % woodland in individual manors and large estates in Montgomeryshire in the late 16th and early 17th century[28]

Manor & Date	Total area (acres)	Woodland area	Woodland %
Carno, 1571	1,780	340	19.1
Carno, 1599-1600	3,380	340	10.0
Carno, 1612-13	4,300	500	11.6
Deuder, 1601-02	9,100	500	5.4
Llanbrynmair etc., 1613-14	11,700	500	4.2
Llanidloes etc., 1613-14	10,000	1,000	10.0
Llanwythelan etc., 1612-13	6,300	1,000	15.8
Llanllygan, 1595-96	2,840	100	3.5
Mivod etc., 1603-04	3,700	300	8.1
Montgomery etc., 1606-07	5,500	100	1.8
Montgomery etc., 1613-14	13,392	1,500	11.2
Nethergorther, 1612-13	6,300	500	7.9
Strata Marcella, 1617-18	3,050	200	6.5
Teirtreff, 1621-22	790	100	12.6
Uchcoied etc., 1608-09	4,600	1,000	21.7
		Average % of woodland	9.9%

These analyses, despite their imperfections, show that by the sixteenth century woodland area over much of Wales was generally of the order of 10% or less, and only in certain areas such as remote valleys was it substantially higher. For example, the 1590 survey of the commote of Cyfeiliog (Powys) showed that the Dyfi valley was one of the most wooded areas in Wales, with woodland forming 21.2% of the total area of 19,490 acres.[29]

The rate of forest destruction is partly reflected in the times of final disappearance of native species of woodland fauna. The brown bear disappeared long before the Norman Conquest, the wolf and wild boar probably in the sixteenth century, the red deer at the end of the eighteenth century, and the roe deer apparently much earlier than the red deer.[30]

The overall reduction in woodland area in the sixteenth and seventeenth centuries appears to have been due mainly to continued widespread assarting, and many hundred of cases illustrating this are documented, with repeated references to the fact that corn was now growing where good timber once stood. Many place-names also provide evidence. There is, for example, the direct testimony of names such as Cwrt Sart at Neath, and the indirect evidence of names containing the element *poeth* or *poethion* (= hot), which is usually taken to imply 'burnt' or 'cleared by fire'. Thus Coed-poeth would denote 'wood cleared by fire', for example at Mitchel Troy (Monmouthshire), Mochdre (Montgomeryshire) and Bersham (Denbighshire).

The clearance of forest and the growing shortage, especially of the better grades of oak timber, was described in general terms for England and Wales by Holinshed in 1586,[31] and specifically for Wales by the poet Thomas Churchyard (1520-1604), who gave a poetic account of the border counties from Monmouthshire to Flintshire in 1587:

> They have begun, of late to lime their land,
> And plowes the ground, where sturdie okes did stand . . .
> They teare up trees, and takes the rootes away.[32]

Land-grabbing was practised on a large scale by the gentry and by industrial entrepreneurs, but countless small encroachments probably had a greater effect overall in reducing the woodland area. Encroached land was enclosed by ditches, hedges and walls, and this frequently gave rise to bloody intervention by commoners who saw their ancient rights being usurped. In Radnorshire, a crowd armed with 'long bills, picks, staves, swords, daggers, long pickforks, axes, hatchets, and bills', forced entry into Radnor wood, destroying hedges and felling trees, and threatening to burn down the remaining trees.[33] Numerous cases of encroachment occurred in west Wales in Elizabethan times, especially in the royal forests, but encroachment went on in every county in Wales. Brief details of one example from each of the former Welsh counties will illustrate the type and scope of offences.

Anglesey: felling 100 great willow trees to the loss of the Crown.[34]
Brecon: carrying away of 40 acres of woods.[35]

Caernarfon: destroying timber and woods on a waste called Gwerne Veignagh.[36]

Cardigan: spoil of hedges and trees.[37]

Carmarthen: enclosing parcels of crown lands, viz. woodlands called Coed Yssa, and felling 200 oaks.[38]

Denbigh: spoil and waste of great timber trees, and young saplings and oaks and fair ashes.[39]

Flint: felling and taking away of timber and enclosing farms out of Ewlowe Wood.[40]

Glamorgan: felling and carrying away trees to make weirs in the river Rhymney.[41]

Merioneth: cutting and carrying away Crown timber (10,000 oaks, the waste being valued at £1,500) at Llanfachreth, alleged to be within the Forest of Snowdon.[42]

Monmouth: wrongful entry into waste; cutting, spoiling, carrying away and selling of timber; refusal to allow servants of the crown to cut timber.[43]

Montgomery: cutting down and carrying away trees, underwood, hazel, birch, oak, and oak saplings.[44]

Pembroke: felling of 1,400 oak trees, value £700, in the Forest of Narberth and 600 oak trees, value £200, in Caniston Wood (complaint lodged by John Taverner, Surveyor of Crown woods south of the Trent).[45]

Radnor: forceful armed entry into a wood and woodground called Radnor Wood with divers coppices . . . overthrowing hedges and felling trees; threat to burn down the remaining trees.[46]

In 1601 an *Act to Avoid and Prevent Divers Misdemeanours* was passed, providing for punishment for illicit cutting and mischievous spoiling of woods, trees or poles. Thereafter, throughout the seventeenth century, concern over timber supplies in general and naval oak in particular manifested itself in three main ways: first by repeated surveys of resources; secondly by further legislation aimed at preserving existing forests and promoting the establishment of plantations; and thirdly by the publication of pamphlets and books devoted to timber growing.

James I took a keen interest in timber growing, and supported the publication of a pamphlet by Arthur Standish containing instructions 'for the increasing of timber and firewood' in 1615. This was one of the first of many practical treatises on forestry published in England during the seventeenth century. Such publications were either manuals of husbandry, concentrating on detailed techniques of silviculture and arboriculture, or political tracts arguing the need for stringent government action. Their general effect in Wales appears to have been slight, and no Welshman wrote on forestry matters until well into the eighteenth century.

During the reign of James I, a breviat or survey was made of the woods in the royal forests, parks and chases in 1608. The terms of the survey were as follows:

> to cause the sound trees being tymber, and other great trees which are not tymber, and dead and decaied trees. And also the said coppices . . . to be thoroughly viewed survayed and valued by skilfull and expert persons . . . you shall cause the same trees, being tymber, severally and by themselves to be nombered, valued,

appraised and marked with theis l'res J and R. And the said great trees, not being tymber, and the dead and decaied trees you shall likewise cause to be nombered and valued severally and by themselves. And all and singular, our coppices to be estimated and valued att the yearly value of the same [being such as] may be felled and cutt downe [at their] reasonable growth and according to a reasonable rate and porcon.[47]

Data for only four counties were compiled and published (Table 6), and it is probable that the full survey was never completed.

Table 6.   Survey of Royal Forests and Parks in Wales, 1608[48]

County	No. of timber trees	No. of decaying trees	No. of saplings	Coppices out of lease (acres)
Carmarthen				
Forests (Penrin,				
Pennyhearth & Cardiffe)	6,542	17,296	—	—
Riffigg Park	727	3,054	—	197
Denbigh				
Parks	50	1,595	9,500	—
Montgomery				
Parks	640	3,290	—	—
Pembroke				
Forests	2,666	22,884	21,032	786

The coppices were valued in total at £86 per annum, the timber trees at £1,352 10s., and the decaying ones at £3,127 7s. 4d.; the saplings were not valued. The ratio of decaying to timber trees indicates that the condition of the woods was highly unsatisfactory. Marking the timber trees with the king's initials (JR) did not make them safe from depredations, however, for in the Forest of Cilgerran even selected trees 'marked with the prince's name as special timber' were alleged to be illegally felled.[49]

Another survey in the Forest of Narberth in 1609 shows how sapling oaks were valued, and also how the land value was regarded.[50] One parcel called Castle Lake Wood contained sixty acres 'well set with saplinge oakes . . . amongst which . . . are some dotard oakes of bigger proportion servinge to noe other use but fireinge'. The total number of trees was about 21,000, and they were valued at 2d. each 'the greater with the lesse', giving a sum of £173 12s. Because the local inhabitants claimed common of estovers, the surveyor, Gilbert Thacker, reported, 'I can value the soyle at no higher rate, more than the value of the wood that groweth thereon'. The surveys of the Duchy of Lancaster lordships at Monmouth, Grosmont, Skenfrith, White Castle, Caldicot and Kidwelly show the names and areas of woods, rents and services, the traditional customs and rights of common, and also numerous cases of encroachment and spoil of woods.[51] In general, all great trees were reserved to the king; the lessees had underwoods, dead trees, lop and top of oaks, and honey and wax; the tenants had the herbage and pannage of the wood, wind-fallen wood and customarily one oak at a time for repairing, rebuilding or new building on their tenements, on notice to the woodward or keeper of the wood.

In 1640 an *Act of Limitation of Forests* finally defined the true boundaries of the royal forests, and led to the virtual abolition of the forest courts. The Civil War (1640-50) and its aftermath resulted in a certain amount of destruction of woods. Landowners who had supported the king had their lands confiscated or were heavily fined, and large-scale felling took place to defray the costs of land purchase or to pay fines. Detailed Parliamentary Surveys were made of crown lands following the *Act for the Sale of Crown Lands* (16 July 1649). These surveys covered 26 items in six main sections: The Nature and Extent of the Forests; The Parks, Officers, and Profits; The Divisions; The Woods and Timber; Commoners and Encroachment; and Waste and Spoil of Woods. Timber fit for the use of the navy and standing within fifteen miles of a navigable river was not to be sold. However, an analysis of the Parliamentary Surveys indicates that only one Crown woodland property was surveyed for sale in Wales, out of a total of 168 woodlands so surveyed in England and Wales.[52]

The military owners certainly felled much timber on estates during their period of ownership under the Commonwealth. Cromwell's expansionist foreign policy meant that the 1650s was a good period for selling timber and for conversion to arable or pasture; 207 new vessels were added to the navy in eleven years, and agricultural prices were higher than they had ever been. On the Restoration of the monarchy, the estates of the Parliamentary purchasers, including the woodlands, underwent further disruption and damage.

In 1663, soon after the Restoration, an *Act for the Punishment of Unlawful Cutting or Stealing, or Spoiling of Wood and Underwood, and Destroyers of Young Timber Trees* was passed. It applied to woodland generally, and amplified and extended Elizabeth's Act of 1601. In 1664 John Evelyn published his *Sylva, or a Discourse of Forest Trees and the Propagation of Timber in His Majestie's Dominions.* Evelyn's work went through several editions before the end of the seventeenth century and had considerable influence on arboriculture and the development of commercial plantation forestry in England, but its effect in Wales was slower and less obvious. In Wales, the terms of leases had often specified small-scale planting of timber trees on farms. For example, in the sixteenth century in Denbighshire tenants were required to plant hundreds of timber trees, and in Caernarfonshire a lease of 1624 required a tenant to plant four trees of oak, elm or ash each year.[53] Major landowners like Sir Thomas Myddleton of Chirk bought Evelyn's book as soon as it appeared, and under Evelyn's influence, a few landowners in Wales began to experiment with exotics for ornament and to undertake new plantations by planting and by direct sowing of oak.

Exotic conifers, though not entirely unknown in Wales, were extremely rare in the early seventeenth century, but a manuscript by Sir Thomas Hanmer, a close friend of Evelyn, shows that by about the middle of the century Scots pine, spruce fir (i.e. Norway spruce), European larch and also cypress and cedar were being grown, though only for ornamental planting in avenues, walks and groves.[54] Besides Sir Thomas Hanmer's estate at Bettisfield (Flintshire), planting was also carried out during the seventeenth century on large estates such as Chirk, Gwydyr and Margam, and also on smaller estates. For example, at Tre Wydryn in Anglesey, Justice Prydderch planted beech, pine, chestnut, ash and sycamore in rows for use and ornament,[55] and avenues of Scots pine and sweet chestnut at Llanvihangel Crucorney (Monmouthshire) were believed to have been planted in about 1670.[56] More exotics were also introduced from North America, for Edward Lhuyd sent plants to a friend in Merioneth around 1685, saying 'The Virginia Cedar is a plant lately come from yt Country & I am confident was never in Wales before'.[57] The accounts of Chirk Castle reveal both ornamental and commercial planting: fir (i.e. Scots pine) plants were acquired in the early 1660s, and several lots of Scots pine seed and plants were acquired subsequently; quite large amounts of acorns were gathered for direct sowing, for example in 1708 and 1718, and oak, walnut and elm were planted in the early years of the eighteenth century.[58]

At the very end of the seventeenth century, Edward Lhuyd attempted to produce a 'geographical dictionary and natural history' of Wales by means of questionnaire surveys of parishes.[59] The replies to these *Parochial Queries* give a general idea of the condition of the woods in about 1700, because they included information on 'the names of the most remarkable . . . woods', general land-use, and the main fuels. There are, however, serious limitations to the replies to the *Parochial Queries*. The response was very patchy, and the 143 parishes described for Lhuyd constitute only just over 15% of the number of civil parishes in Wales,[60] though further replies still occasionally come to light; moreover, the quality and detail of the replies varied considerably.

Geographical coverage of the replies was most complete for the counties of Merioneth, Denbigh and Flint. An analysis of the use of fuel in north-east Wales based on these replies shows a very mixed picture, with coal being recorded most frequently as the major fuel, followed by peat and then by wood. Wood was usually mentioned as a secondary fuel in north-east Wales. In contrast, in some places in south Wales, such as at Llyswen in Breconshire, wood was the sole or the main fuel.

Over eighty individual woods are named in the replies to the *Parochial Queries,* but rarely with any detail of area, condition, species or management. Most replies, when they mentioned woodland resources at all, referred to it in the most general terms, for example 'but little wood' (Baglan, Glamorgan) or 'nid oes agos i dhim koed' (virtually no wood; Tir Ifan, Denbigh). A few individual woods are described as small, as insignificant brushwood, as containing little or no wood, or as recently felled. Wood was abundant in a few places, such as Llanwynno (Glamorgan) and Trelech (Monmouth). The only species mentioned are oak (at Llanwynno/Llantrisant, Glamorgan), oak and ash (Llantilio Pertholey, Monmouth) and birch (Llangollen, Denbigh), and the only indication of management is at Tir y Prenniae (Bangor, Flint), described as a small coppice. (See Appendix 5, p. 243)

Chapter VII

FOREST-BASED INDUSTRIES

Over much of Wales the woods and forests had for centuries been worked at a level of subsistence utilization, to satisfy the needs of a rural peasant economy for fuel, agricultural implements and vehicles, domestic utensils, tanstuffs, furniture, and timber for dwellings and larger buildings such as castles and mills. The woodlands were also important for grazing and pannage. In general, this widespread dependence on the native woodlands persisted until the Industrial Revolution.

Welsh poets traditionally requested gifts from their noble patrons, the formal request being couched in verse (*cywyddau gofyn*). The gifts asked for were many and various, examples noted including a horse, a bull, a hound, some swans, a peacock, a fishing net, a coracle, a millstone, a sword, a knife, and a harp. In many cases, however, poets asked specifically for wood; for example, Tudur Aled (*fl.* 1480-1526) requested a chunk of good oak to make a kiln, and on another occasion an oak tree for a cooper to make the bottoms of hogsheads and barrels. Gruffudd Hiraethog (*d.* 1564) requested a good yew bow, and on another occasion a large oak table.

This Welsh custom of formally requesting wood was quite widespread and certainly persisted well into the nineteenth if not the twentieth century. For example, in 1822, on the occasion of a marriage at Mynydd Bach, Cwm-twrch (Tawe valley) the local squire was asked for permission, according to custom, to select an oak tree in the wood to make furniture for the young couple 'to have a start in life'.

In addition to this general subsistence utilization, which applied throughout Wales, forest-based industries developed which may conveniently be considered under the four main forest products: charcoal, shiptimber, tanbark and pitwood.

Charcoal

Inspir'd by me, thy hardy sons shall pour
From these long pregnant hills the pond'rous ore,
While sooty bands from tents of turf shall aid
(With jetty charcoal) the important trade
Thomas Thomas, *The Pontypool Ode* (1799)

Wood and charcoal had been used locally and sporadically for smelting since pre-Roman times. After the Norman Conquest, there was increasing development of mining and smelting, especially of iron and lead, and the need for regular and often large supplies of charcoal for these operations has already been described. Indeed, although wood was still plentiful, shortages of charcoal were often the limiting factor in smelting and refining operations. The development of a metallurgical industry before the Industrial Revolution[1] shows that charcoal-burning was associated with smelting operations from the thirteenth to the fifteenth century in eastern Monmouthshire (iron), around the rim of the South Wales coalfield (iron, lead), at Neath (copper), in a few places in north Carmarthenshire and western Breconshire (iron, lead), in Cardiganshire (lead), Caernarfonshire (iron), and in north-east Wales from the coast to Minera and Bersham (iron, lead). These same areas, and others in Merioneth, Montgomery and Pembroke, continued to form the main locations of the lead and iron industry in later centuries, and in fact charcoal continued to be used in the iron industry in some places until well into the nineteenth century. The demand for charcoal for the metallurgical industries at one period or another affected the woods over practically the whole of Wales.

Medieval miners had been given privileged status in obtaining wood, and later too the industry was given wide powers to acquire raw materials. For example, in 1486 the King's commissioners of mines were allowed to take any wood, brushwood and charcoal needed for separation, proving and purifying of the metals (land and water carriage of the materials at reasonable price to be agreed upon with the owners) and could arrest the necessary labourers for the mines and put them to work at reasonable wages.[2]

Until the sixteenth century there was, in general, no shortage of raw material for the manufacture of charcoal. In Atlantic times the forest covered 90% of Wales, but with gradual reduction due to a combination of climatic and anthropogenic factors, this figure had fallen to between 20 and 10% or even less by the sixteenth century. During this century the iron industry was transformed

27. Making charcoal in the seventeenth century, based on John Evelyn, *Sylva* (1664).

by the introduction of the blast furnace and the power forge, and this resulted in an unprecedented increase in the demand for charcoal. It was also of national importance to safeguard sufficient large timber of structural sizes, especially for shipbuilding. The conflict of interests between these two major users persisted for some centuries and the legislation enacted in the sixteenth century reflected this, with statutes for the preservation of woods, preventing the burning of timber for iron, and also licences permitting limited felling for charcoal burning.

In 1558, the first year of Elizabeth's reign, was passed *An Act that Timber shall not be felled to make Coals for Burning of Iron.*[3] This act applied to any timber tree of oak, beech or ash, one foot wide at the stub and growing within fourteen miles of the sea or of any river navigable from the sea, specifying several rivers by name, including the Severn, Wye and Dee. Strictly applied, this would have afforded considerable protection to the remaining forests of much of Wales. Local exceptions were, however, made to this rule and the tree species protected were altered according to local conditions. For example, in 1568 a licence for life was granted to Henry Sidney and certain others, to convert to fuel for the making of iron any trees of aspen, hazel, hawthorn, blackthorn, willow, sallow, beech, birch or any other kind of wood except oak, elm and ash, within fourteen miles of the sea or of the river Severn in the County of Glamorgan only.[4]

At the King's lead and iron mines at Llantrisant the accounts for 1531 show that charcoal-burners outnumbered the actual miners.[5] Initially, the smelting operations were small and relatively mobile, with simple hearths. Accordingly, there was little incentive to manage woodlands for sustained production as it was easy to move on. However, as the enterprises grew larger and more static, it became more important to ensure sustained supplies of charcoal from a reasonable catchment area, the radius of which was governed by the economics of horse or mule transport. Steps were taken to secure long-term agreements. For example, in 1589 a 14-year agreement was made for the sale of wood on the manor of Coity Anglia (Glamorgan) for making charcoal for the ironworks; the wood was to be supplied at a rate of up to 3,000 cords per year at 14d. per cord.[6] Leland's testimony shows that early in the sixteenth century the lead mines in Cwmystwyth had largely denuded the valley of wood, and in 1613 two tenements there were acquired for their wood so that the mine-owners 'would be secure from the more uncivilized sort of inhabitants'.[7]

The ironmasters obviously had a vital interest in maintaining their charcoal supplies, and therefore heedless destruction of the raw material is unlikely to have taken place. However, complaints against the iron-workers for their impact on the environment were doubtless sometimes justified. Three Welsh poems of the sixteenth century all lament the felling of local woods – Coed Marchan in Denbighshire and Coed Glyn Cynon and Coed Mwstwr in Glamorgan – to make charcoal for ironworks. In his *cwndid* on the death of Mr John Gamage of Coity, Thomas ap Ieuan ap Rhys (*c*.1510-60) castigates the charcoal-burners:

ny chair klydwr, ynghoed mwstwr	(there is no shelter in Coed Mwstwr
na phrenn ar dan, gan waith haearn	nor firewood because of the ironworks)

All thirteen verses by the unknown author of 'Coed Glyn Cynon' protest against the fellings, the first verse setting the scene:

Aber da llan wna i gid	(Aberdare, Llanwynno through,
Plwy merthyr hyd llan vabon	all Merthyr to Llanfabon;
mwia adfyd a fy erioed	there was never a more disastrous thing
pen dored koed glyn kynon	than the cutting of Glyn Cynon)

The more humorous *cywydd* 'Coed Marchan' by Robin Clidro (*fl.* 1580) describes the effects of 'anrheithio holl goed Rhuthyn' (the ravaging of all Rhuthyn's woods).

These poems accurately list the numerous traditional products and services lost to the local communities as a result of the felling and charcoal-burning operations: timber for bridges, houses and churches; firewood and twigs for fuel; game and wildlife in the form of red deer, roe deer, squirrel, wild cat, fox, hedgehog and badger; shelter for wild birds; lovers' trysting places; hazel nuts; acorns for pannage of pigs; browse for goats; and clean spring water. These complaints can be regarded as early protests by local environmentalists, and were certainly exacerbated by the fact that these Welsh forests were being acquired and felled by outsiders, ironmasters from England. In later years, the romantic English travellers who toured Wales thought that the frequent columns of smoke from charcoal-burning were an aesthetic enhancement of the landscape. For example, in 1770 Gilpin wrote: 'Many of the furnaces on the banks of the river [Wye] consume charcoal, which is manufactured on the spot; and the smoke, issuing from the sides of the hills, and spreading its thin veil over a part of them, beautifully breaks their lines, and unites them with the sky'.[9]

A large-scale clear-felling and coaling operation would have appeared a desecration for a while, but it was in everyone's interest to secure regeneration, especially by coppice, and the silvicultural knowledge and legislation were available to achieve this. If large-scale felling of valuable timber and wholesale permanent deforestation did take place, it would have been attributable more to negligence and lack of supervision than to a deliberate policy. Yarranton made this clear when he stated in 1677 that ironworks 'are so far from the destroying of Woods and Timber, that they are the occasion of the increase thereof'.[10] His arguments were that without the demand the woods would have been cleared for agriculture, and that owners would never sell valuable timber for charcoal because it could command higher prices for other purposes. Small wood was the most convenient material for charcoal-burning, and therefore when timber trees were felled, the large timber assortments would probably be sold off as such, and only the branchwood converted to charcoal. This would ensure maximum financial return, as well as avoiding the laborious cross-cutting and cleaving of large timber to make charcoal billets.

A large charcoal-burning industry developed in many areas based on smelting operations. This involved selection and purchase, felling, cording and coaling, and then the bagging and transport to the works. Oak and beech formed the best charcoal, but other broadleaved species were also used. The prime hardwood species (oak, elm and ash) were certainly used in many operations. As mentioned above, a licence in Glamorgan allowed the use of aspen, beech, birch, blackthorn, hawthorn, hazel, sallow, willow or any other species except timber trees of oak, elm and ash. Analysis of charcoal found at Coed Ithel, a seventeenth-century blast furnace at Llandogo, shows that alder, ash, beech, birch, crabapple, elm, oak, and willow or poplar were used, with oak and willow or poplar forming the main constituents.[11]

The organization of the early woods operations in Wales can be inferred from surviving ironworks accounts and by analogy with the more detailed accounts of the Sussex ironworks before the Sussex ironmasters transferred their operations to south Wales.[12] Employment in woodcutting and charcoal-burning fluctuated seasonally. The felling and cording work was concentrated in the winter and especially in early spring. Little felling was done in the summer, when the woodcutters were probably engaged in harvest work on the farms. In general, the bulk of the work was done by men regularly employed through most of the winter, working one piece of woodland until its supplies were used up. More men were engaged in woodcutting than in the actual charcoal-burning.

Wood was felled, cross-cut and corded close to stump. In general, the wood was cross-cut into one of two standard billet lengths, either 'long' (4ft, or 4ft 4in., or 4ft 6in.) or 'short' (2ft, or 2ft 2in.), but sometimes into an intermediate length of 3ft, as at Cefnmabli (Glamorgan) in 1658. Cord size varied in south Wales, both between regions and in time. Table 7 lists the sizes recorded.

Table 7. Cord sizes in use in south Wales for mixed hardwoods for charcoal burning

	Cord dimensions				
Name of cord	Length ft ins.	Width ft ins.	Height ft ins.	Stacked vol. cu. ft	Approx. solid vol. cu. ft
Statute cord	8 0	4 0	4 0	128	75
Short cord	9 0	2 2	4 6	88	51
Long cord	9 0	4 4	4 6	175	102
New Weir cord	8 4	2 2	4 4	78	45
Cefnmabli	9 0	4 0	4 6	162	94
Cefnmabli	9 0	3 0	4 6	121	70
Cefnmabli	9 0	2 0	4 6	81	47
Welsh standard	9 0	4 6	4 6	182	106
Long cord	18 0	2 2	4 6	175	102
Monmouth	16 8	2 2	2 2	78	45

These widely divergent cord sizes present a serious problem in trying to assess the amount of wood or charcoal required to produce a ton of iron, or the improvement in smelting efficiency over a period of time, unless the cord sizes are clearly specified. In the eighteenth and nineteenth centuries, wood for charcoal was often sold by the ton instead of by the cord, 2½ tons being the weight of a statute cord of 128 cu. ft.

The amounts of wood and of charcoal needed to produce a ton of iron decreased during the sixteenth and seventeenth centuries, as technical efficiency in smelting improved. The accounts and estimates of the Sidney ironworks in Glamorgan in the 1560s indicate that a load of charcoal represented 4 or 4½ cords of wood, and 5 loads of charcoal were needed to make one ton of iron; accordingly, 20-22 cords of wood were required to make one ton of clean iron, but unfortunately the cord size is not specified. The wood was valued at 2d. per cord, and the cutting at 4d. per cord; coaling was put at 2s. per load; a load of charcoal was valued at 6s. 7d. In 1567-68, the annual cut for one furnace apparently amounted to 9,611 cords.[13] In Monmouthshire in the late seventeenth century, four 'short' cords, equivalent to 12 loads of charcoal, were required for the production of 1 ton of pig iron; the costs were 14s. for 4 short cords, 6s. for cutting, 1s. for cording, and 5s. for coaling, which, with carriage, came to about 8s. 6d. per cord.[14] On the Cefnmabli estate which supplied wood for charcoal for Machen forge, standard cords of 9 x 4 x 4½ft were sold at 6s. per cord in 1658, or equivalent numbers of cords 9 x 3 x 4½ft or 9 x 2 x 4½ft; later on, at Cefnmabli an agreement of 1687 specified the felling season (from 1 September to 31 March) and completion of all operations and clearance of the site by Bartholomytide (24 August), before the start of the next felling season. Prices per long cord (18ft x 2ft 2in. x 4½ft) were 6s. 8d. if within 4 miles of the forge, and 4s. 6d. if between 4 and 10 miles.[15]

28. An old charcoal platform on Garth Maelwg, Llantrisant forest. This ancient forest was felled by the ironmasters in the sixteenth century. The spruce now occupying the site were planted by the Forestry Commission in the 1930s.

In 1704, John Hanbury's estimate for making 400 tons of cast iron and 300 tons of bar iron per annum at Pontypool was 2,400 long cords of wood (= 1,200 loads of charcoal), and for making 300 tons of cast iron and 110 tons of bar iron per annum at Llanelly (Clydach, Brecon) his estimate was 1,400 long cords of wood (= 700 loads of charcoal).[16] This estimate was based on 3 cords of wood (= 1½ loads of charcoal) to make one ton of cast iron, and 4 or 4½ cords of wood (= 2 or 2¼ loads of charcoal) to make one ton of bar iron. Each long cord (9ft long x 4ft 4in. wide x 4ft 6in. high = 175 cu. ft) was worth 7s., and cutting and cording cost 3s. or 3s. 6d. per cord; two long cords of wood made one load of charcoal, the charge for the coaling operation being 3s. or 3s. 4d. per load. Carriage of the charcoal cost between 5s. 6d. and 8s. per load, depending on distance. Well-grown coppice wood, cut every 16 years, yielded 12 long cords (approx. 1,200 cu. ft solid volume) per acre. Accordingly, the requirement for the Pontypool and Llanelly forges and furnaces was an annual cut of some 320 acres, implying a total coppice working area of some 5,120 acres.

In 1705 Hanbury noted that the old woods (semi-natural high forest) had almost all been cut, but that coppice woods were in general carefully managed because of the very good returns from cordwood for charcoal manufacture. Coppice was cut on a rotation of 16 or 17 years, but in the mountains and with beech coppice the rotation was 20 years or longer. Hanbury also proposed the afforestation of poor-quality enclosed land with birch at 2,000 plants per acre in order to produce fast-growing coppice for charcoal production, but there is no evidence that such plantations were actually ever established.

Production in the charcoal iron industry was typically intermittent. For example, at Llanelly in 1704 the furnace was worked from September to January, the rest of the year being used to lay in stocks of raw material, particularly charcoal. At Merthyr, where the first furnace was built in 1765, work at the furnace was limited to three days a week, the other three being devoted to woodcutting 'which the men enjoyed immensely, especially as . . . they combined it with snaring game, shooting blackcock . . . '[17] The Cwmdwyfran forge in Carmarthenshire closed down during slack periods and skilled men were put on to other jobs which, early in the nineteenth century, included tree-planting, felling and fencing of woodlands.[18]

Charcoal was produced close to where the wood was felled, because it was always cheaper and easier to transport than wood. The charcoal-burners were known as colliers or wood-colliers *(colier coed)*, and they lived rough in the woods during the summer coaling season. The charcoal-burners were usually men, but sometimes a whole family would be involved, like the group described by the Rev. John Skinner among the oakwoods at Baglan in 1800: 'We here discovered a large family inhabiting a mud cabin in the form of a sugar loaf. In the midst of this retirement they seem perfectly happy, tho' almost all the children were in the state of their first parents, without covering, and seemed not ashamed. These people continue here all the summer for the purpose of making charcoal'.[19]

The normal charcoal-burner's hut or cabin was a structure shaped like a wigwam, constructed of poles and covered with brushwood and/or turves; in later years, canvas or tarpaulin was used like a tent to cover the conical framework of poles.

The charcoal was made by stacking the mixed hardwood billets closely to form a regular conical or domed mound, with a central vent for firing. The following description written from Penrhyn Castle in the 1880s differs little from the classical account given by John Evelyn over two hundred years earlier:

> The pits are usually made of a conical shape, 21ft. in diameter, and about 9ft. in height . . . A strong stake is driven into the ground, and left protruding about 12in., around this are placed small pieces of dry ash of a similar length and standing as close to the upright stake as possible, around this being placed another layer in the same manner, and so on until a circle 4ft. in diameter is obtained. A circle 1ft. in diameter, and having the top of the stake formerly driven into the ground as centre, is next made, by placing the wood horizontally on the upright pieces and side by side, repeating the same by laying others on these in a similar manner, until the pit is of the required height . . . This forms a sort of chimney by means of which the pits are fired. Outside this the wood is placed on end and reclining inwards, this being continued until the pits are the required size.[20]

The mound was covered with turves, or earth laid on straw, furze or bracken. The cordwood and charcoal agreements often included the purchase of sufficient rods and poles to make hurdles to serve as windbreak screens, as well as the cabins where the men lived. The sites were called hearths *(aelwyd cols)*, and on steep slopes a platform would be made by cut and fill to form a level surface for the charcoal-burning operations. The size of the mound varied, but was usually between 20 and 40ft in diameter. Sometimes, rectangular heaps were made, as

29. Cross-section of a charcoal pile at Penrhyn Castle in the 1880s (from A.D. Webster, *Practical Forestry*).

30. Charcoal-burning site, Forest of Dean, 1920s; note cordwood, basket, rake, riddle and charcoal bagged for removal.

much as 15 x 7 yards in size. Charcoal was also made in holes or pits (*holo cols*), dug out 5-6 yards in diameter and 6-8ft deep. Such pits and platforms can still be traced at many places in south Wales, the soil at the bottom of the pits and on the platforms being black and impregnated with charcoal dust and fragments to a depth of about a foot. Good examples are to be seen at Garth Maelwg, where the woods were sold to the ironworks near Llantrisant in the sixteenth century and the forest was reduced to 'a faire and lardge sheepe leaze'.[21]

The burning or charring of the wood usually took two to six days. The piles first 'sweated' and then 'breathed', the piles gradually shrinking and the smoke thinning. The burning could be regulated by manipulating vent-holes, and the heaps were protected from wind by screens of hurdles backed with straw, bracken or heather. If the fire burned through, the hole would be plugged immediately and re-covered with earth. Finally, the soil cover was removed and the charcoal raked out. After cooling, it was bagged in sacks usually made up locally from canvas or sacking stitched with twine and tied with cord (Fig. 30). At Monmouth a standard charcoal sack held 1½ cwt. Small or broken charcoal, called braise, was of inferior value and bagged separately.

As demand grew, a class of middle-men arose to negotiate the purchase of woods and the delivery of charcoal, contracts being based on the costs of transport and the quality of the material supplied. Transport was generally by trains of packhorses or pack mules, carrying sacks or panniers for distances of up to 12-15 miles, but occasionally for as far as 25 miles, as at Dolobran forge in Montgomeryshire in the 1720s.[22] Cordwood prices depended on distance to the ironworks. For example, in Glamorgan the standard price for a short cord in 1831 was 7s. if within 5 miles of the Pentyrch works, 6s. if 5-10 miles, and 5s. if over 10 miles.[23] At Margam in the mid eighteenth century, indentures stipulated that horses carrying charcoal should be muzzled in such a manner that they could not browse the young growth in the woods.[24] The muzzling of draught animals was also specified in a large timber sale at Golden Grove in Carmarthenshire in 1757.[25]

The agreements and contracts drawn up for felling and charcoal-burning gradually became tighter, in order to protect the property. For example, at Dolgyn Ucha (Merioneth) in 1733 the purchaser agreed to buy all trees, underwoods, bushes, etc. 'excepting such Oak, Ash and Elms as are already marked and appointed . . . to stand and be preserved'.[26] Bark was included in the sale, and also rights of ingress, egress and regress for agents and workmen; liberty to dig pits and turf necessary for making charcoal (doing in all this as little damage as possible on the premises). All trees, cordwood, bark and charcoal was to be cleared by a specified date.

In the smelting of lead, the charcoal, often called 'black coal', was used in mixture with 'white coal', i.e. wood chopped or slit into small pieces and dried in a kiln; the 'white coal' was sometimes called 'gads' or faggot-wood. 'Black' and 'white coal' were usually mixed because charcoal alone made too violent a fire, and wood alone was too gentle. This mixture was quite generally used in lead-smelting operations in Wales.

31. Smoke from charcoal-iron operations by the Wye in summer 1770 (aquatint, W. Gilpin, *Observations on the River Wye*).

32. Charcoal-burner by his hut, Drymma (near Neath), nineteenth century.

33. Detail of aquatint by J. Hassell, *c.*1801, of a charcoal kiln by the river Teifi; note the large hurdles giving shelter from the wind.

The demand for charcoal in the iron industry led to several celebrated legal cases that illustrate the scale of the felling and coaling operations.

In the Penrhos Common case, for example, English speculators built an ironworks in the Ganllwyd valley in Merioneth and bought their wood supply from Hugh Nanney, a local landowner. However, the oak sold by Nanney came from Penrhos Common which was Crown land lying within the Forest of Snowdon. Nanney was accused in the Court of the Star Chamber of felling and converting to his own use 30,000 oak trees, valued at 3s. each, between 1588 and 1603. He was fined £1,500, later reduced to £800. The felling was done by local labourers, one of whom stated that he was hired for a day's felling at the piece-work rate of ½d. per tree, and that in the day he felled 28 oaks 'not choosing the lesser oaks to be Cutt but taking them as they happened to be next to hym'.[27]

In the osmond iron controversy, large areas of woods in Monmouthshire were engrossed, forestalled and bought by entrepreneurs to ensure continuity of charcoal supplies for the manufacture of 'merchant' iron (i.e. bar iron). This adversely affected the Crown interests in the manufacture of osmond iron for wire-making, and Richard Hanbury was charged with having wrongfully converted to his own use 38,000 cords of wood and 500 loads of charcoal to make merchant iron. Glascoed Wood (660 acres) was acquired from the Earl of Pembroke, and over 6,000 beech timber-trees '1ft square at stub' were felled in Glascoed Wood and the woods of Glyntrosnant, Wentwood, Wernhir, etc. for charcoal.[28]

The Wentwood case involved the enclosure of 3,000 acres of Wentwood Forest by the Earl of Worcester around 1630, and the felling, cording, coaling and removal in 1678 of wood alleged to be worth £60,000. The tenants who held rights in the forest resisted the encroachment and were accordingly prosecuted in a case that finally went to the House of Lords.[29]

During the eighteenth century, the increasing use of coke from coal resulted in the decline and eventual collapse of the charcoal iron industry, though in Wales the transition from charcoal to coal was slow. For instance, a list of the principal ironworks in Monmouthshire compiled in 1809 shows ten wireworks, furnaces and forges where charcoal was used, and six where pit-coal was used.[30]

Parallel with the replacement of charcoal by coke for iron-smelting, and following technical advances on the continent of Europe, trials began in Britain at the end of the eighteenth century on the distillation of wood in metal kilns or retorts, to produce charcoal and by-products such as pyroligneous acid (crude

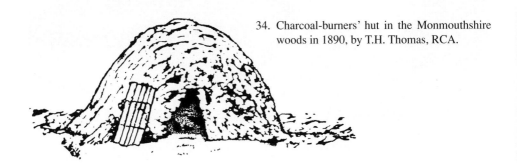

34. Charcoal-burners' hut in the Monmouthshire woods in 1890, by T.H. Thomas, RCA.

35. Llanelly Furnace in the Clydach gorge, showing the charcoal storehouse in the background.
    Drawing by M. Blackmore (1979), based on J. Aran's plan, c.1795.

wood vinegar) and wood-tar. The wood distillation industry or 'steweries'
developed vigorously in the Forest of Dean, and this method of manufacturing
charcoal spread rapidly in Wales during the nineteenth century, especially in the
industrial regions of the south and north-east. Wood chemical works or wood
distilleries accounted for an increasing proportion of charcoal production and the
traditional method of burning in pits or mounds correspondingly declined.

A wood chemical works at Hope was in operation before 1810, supplying
pyroligneous acid for the use of local cotton-dyers,[31] and the Melincryddan
Chemical Works at Neath started in 1797 and supplied charcoal and acid to local
iron and tinplate works.[32] The Melincryddan Chemical Co. was the most
important regular purchaser of cordwood, mainly oak, from the local Gnoll
estate during the nineteenth century; in the 1850s, cordwood prices for these
works were in the region of l3s. 6d. pcr ton, depending on species and quality.[33]
The Stradey estate sold cordwood to the chemical works at Llanelli, for example
elm cordwood sold at about 10s. per ton in 1878-83.[34] Even estates in remote
areas found outlets for low-grade hardwood cordwood in the chemical works,
the Hafod estate in north Cardiganshire selling third-quality beech, birch and
sycamore to chemical works at prices of 4-6s. per ton in 1869.[35] The Brechfa
wood-chemical works in Carmarthenshire operated on local woodland produce
to manufacture charcoal and other products from about 1840 until 1923.[36]

The cordwood was carried out in pack-loads by mules and horses, and the
economics of transport dictated that only a small 'catchment' area around each

works could be used for cordwood supply. In Glamorgan alone, thirteen separate chemical works were in operation in 1874.[37] However, the traditional method of charcoal-burning persisted in places in Wales until about the end of the nineteenth century. For example, at Penrhyn Castle the head-forester, Angus Webster, preferred and used the traditional method in the 1880s, believing that it produced charcoal of better quality, though acknowledging that it could be manufactured more cheaply in retorts.[38]

Though no charcoal is made by traditional methods in Welsh woodlands today, the earlier burning operations gave rise to many place-names throughout Wales. There are public houses called 'The Wood Colliers', and place-names containing the elements *golosg* (= charcoal), *gloddaith* (= charcoal pit), *cols* (= charcoal or coal), and *glo* (= charcoal or coal). Examples are the names Cefn Golosg (two places in Cardiganshire), Golosged Du (Carmarthenshire), and Gloddaith (Caernarfonshire). The word *glo* was used for coal and for charcoal, and therefore in areas where coal does not occur, *glo* can be taken to indicate charcoal, as for example Cwm-y-glo near Llanrug.

36. Brechfa 'oil-works' produced charcoal and by-products from *c*.1840 until 1923.

Shiptimber

> So effectually is this country stript of navy timber that we are not able
> to purchase so much as a futtock to put in her
> R. Fisher, *Heart of Oak, the British Bulwark*, 1763, p. 33

Another major industrial forest product was wood for shipbuilding, both for merchant ships and especially for the navy. The importance of home-grown timber, especially oak, for the navy has been assessed by Albion,[1] who described supply and demand from 1652 to 1862 with particular reference to the great Crown forests of England. Detailed studies have been made of the role of the Forest of Dean in the supply of navy timber.[2] Demand for timber for building and repairing ships was always steady, but in crisis periods it increased greatly, as for example during the Commonwealth, in the Seven Years' War (1756-63) and in the Napoleonic Wars (*c*.1798-1810). Oak was the main species required – in straight pieces and in special naturally curved and angled assortments. Straight timber was obtained from forest-grown trees, whereas more of the curved or compass timber was obtained from open-grown hedgerow and park trees (see Fig. 37). Oak forest trees, if not cut on a short coppice rotation, were normally felled at 80-120 years when 15 to 18 inches in diameter, which was too early to produce the large special curved pieces required by the navy. The navy also bought home-grown elm and ash and, in later years, timber of a variety of species from the Baltic, North America and the Far East.

Albion's assessment of the scale of fellings and the critical supply position in the sixteenth and seventeenth centuries is somewhat exaggerated, and it has been cogently argued that there is no real evidence that the shipbuilding industry was ever seriously in difficulty over timber supplies.[3] Because of incompetence and corruption, the Crown forests were incapable of supplying the amounts required, and most naval timber was bought from private estates. The navy was prepared to pay good prices for selected material but its price policy was inflexible. It was not economically very attractive to grow oak on long enough to produce the large and special assortments required for shipbuilding, and the temptations to fell earlier were considerable. The Navy Board operated a contract system for the supply of wood, and purveyors inspected the trees felled. Standard contracts specified prices for straight and compass oak timbers, oak knees (curved or angled pieces), thickstuff (planking over four inches thick), oak planks (various thicknesses up to four inches), as well as elm and ash timber. Extra prices were offered for winter-felled material, but winter-felling was against the interests of the tanbark industry.

A typical example of a naval timber contract is that between the Navy Commissioners and Trevor Nicholas, timber merchant of Chepstow, signed on 9 April 1789.[4] Nicholas contracted to supply by a specified date 437 loads of wood totalling 21,850 cu. ft, consisting of 41 loads of straight oak timber, 344 loads of compass oak timber, 4 loads of thickstuff (5½-inch plank), 15 loads of square and raking knees, 23 loads of elm timber, and 10 loads of 3- and 4-inch oak planking, all of specified cubic contents, lengths and square top-end dimensions,

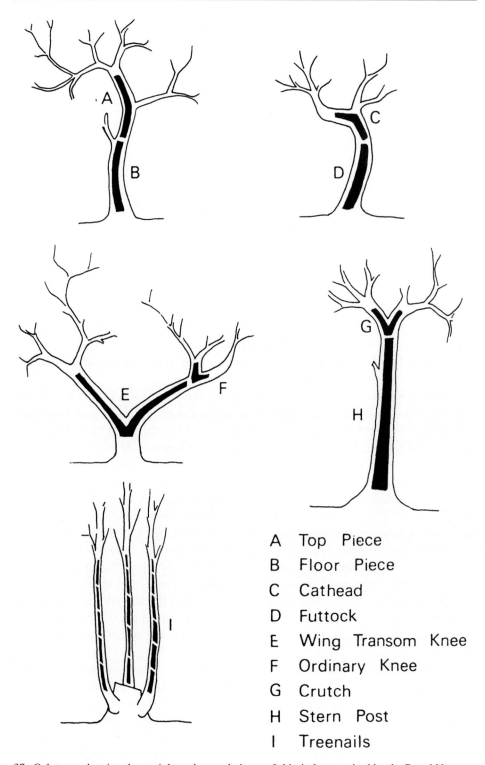

A Top Piece
B Floor Piece
C Cathead
D Futtock
E Wing Transom Knee
F Ordinary Knee
G Crutch
H Stern Post
I   Treenails

37. Oak trees, showing the straight and curved pieces of shiptimber required by the Royal Navy.

grown in Monmouthshire and Herefordshire. In addition, Nicholas contracted to supply 14,000 dry seasoned oak treenails (wooden pegs) of various lengths from one foot to three feet, cut out of 'young, clung, tough coppice timber'. The contract contained an additional clause allowing for extra payment per load above a certain figure for the expense of carriage to Plymouth. An extra payment of £7 5s. was made per £100 of material for any winter-felled timber, that had been certified and marked by the purveyor as being felled with the bark on between 1 December and 15 February.

The transport of large timber assortments overland always presented considerable difficulties, and rivers were used to float, raft or transport by ship wherever possible (Fig. 38). Large logs were moved to the water by rolling or on wagons drawn by teams of horses or oxen, but in mountainous country the timber had to be pit-sawn at stump to boards or planks which were transported on horseback. River transport of timber has been recorded on the Severn, Wye, Neath, Tywi, Teifi, Dyfi and Conwy, and was doubtless practised on all the major rivers in Wales.

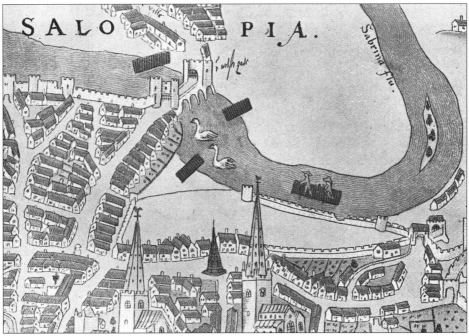

38. Part of Lord Burleigh's map of Shrewsbury, c.1575, showing a raft of Welsh timber being poled downstream on the river Severn, and three other log rafts on the banks.

There is little evidence to show that Welsh woodlands supplied much timber for the navy in the sixteenth century, and Albion dismissed the Welsh contribution as: 'Wales grew good oak of small dimensions; but much of it was inaccessible, and the Navy did not utilize it to any extent until after the Seven Years' War'.[5] However, not all the Welsh oak was small, and well before the

Seven Years' War the growing demand and the contracting resource had resulted in increased utilization of Welsh oak for shipbuilding, despite the long transport distances to the major dockyards.

The accounts for the Gwydyr estate woods in the 1680s indicate that a systematic programme of felling and conversion was in force to produce sawn timber and stock of specified dimensions to meet regular orders. The wood was converted on the estate by pit-sawing, and was sold usually one or more years after felling. Some timber was floated down the river Conwy to coastal vessels. Large and regular sales of assortments such as 1½- and 2-inch oak planks were made to Liverpool shipwrights, and small local shipbuilders were also supplied. In addition to the regular felling programme, the Gwydyr estate also made casual sales of standing trees and salvage sales of windthrown trees.[6]

Ships were sometimes built in the woods themselves, the wood being pit-sawn and shaped at stump. In his autobiography, Twm o'r Nant gives an example of a vessel of 30-40 tons burden that was built in the woods over a mile from the river Tywi near Abermarlais in the 1780s. This vessel was winched out to the river on rollers.[7]

Local enterprises building small merchant vessels operated all around the coast of Wales, using at first exclusively home-grown oak but later, and especially in the nineteenth century, buying timber from North America. Notable among the examples in Cardigan Bay were the ships built of Maentwrog oak at Porthmadog for the slate trade (Fig. 39). Some naval shipbuilding was also attempted in Wales. For example, a 74-gun ship was being built at Neyland in 1763, but the local woods could not supply sufficient suitable material for it because in the words of a shipwright 'so effectually is this county stript of navy timber that we are not able to purchase so much as a futtock to put in her'.[8] Futtocks are the slightly curved middle timbers of a ship (see Fig. 37). In the eighteenth century, Welsh woods became increasingly important as sources of supply of naval oak. For example, in 1746 Lord Mansel of Margam concluded a standard contract with the Navy Commissioners for 506 loads of straight oak timber, 1,056 loads of compass timber, 63 loads of square and raking knees, 63 loads of oak plank 3 and 4 inches thick, 79 loads of elm timber, and 50 loads of ash timber, this representing a total of 90,850 cu. ft.[9] Even in Montgomeryshire, distant from the naval dockyards, fellings of navy oak took place as early as the 1660s at Lymore Wood, and throughout the next century at various places including Abertanat Wood (c.1730), Leighton (1742), and Powys Castle Park, Abernant and Trefedryd (c.1750).[10] Intense competition between buyers occurred around 1770, forcing oak prices even above those of Monmouthshire oak.

Other important fellings of navy oak in Montgomeryshire occurred at Vaenor Park (1793, 1796), and the dimensions of some of these trees are known: one measured 68 inches in girth at a height of 73 feet; 26 of the largest trees totalled 37,772 cu. ft (average 1,452.5 cu. ft per tree); the largest tree was measured at 2,501 cu. ft.[11] The existence of very large oaks is attested from other parts of Wales. The famous oak which grew at Cefnmabli in the seventeenth and eighteenth centuries had a clean straight stem 70ft high before branching, its

39. Shipbuilding at Porthmadog in the nineteenth century.

girth at the base being some 21ft, its diameter at a height of 60ft being 3ft, and the weight of the stem alone being over 20 tons.[12] Another oak felled on the border of Montgomeryshire in 1757 contained over 17 tons of timber, over 14 cords of wood, 3 tons 6 cwt. of bark, and 160 faggots.[13]

The felling and conversion of large oaks was a laborious business, as illustrated by the example of the Golynos oak near Bassaleg.[14] It was 9ft 6in. in diameter and contained 2,426 cu. ft of timber, and when sold in 1810, five men were employed for twenty days stripping off the small branches to form a cushion, cutting down the valuable main branches from specially erected staging, and finally felling the stem with two cross-cut saws brazed together. Two sawyers were then employed for 138 days in conversion, the main stem being cut into quarter boards and cooper's staves, and the branches making naval timber assortments – three upper piece stems, six futtocks, one floor timber and about twenty knees, all suitable for ships of the line.

The Seven Years' War was a period of particularly high demand, and in the period from 1754 to 1760 over £50,000 worth of forest oak was cut on the Gwydir estate and floated down the Conwy.[15] The war caused a general shortage of naval oak timber throughout England and Wales. The extent of the problem can be gauged from a survey of people knowledgeable in the trade in Wales, made by a Liverpool shipwright named Fisher, in the early 1760s:

> If from Liverpool we trace the coast of Wales through Flintshire, Denbighshire and Caernarvonshire, counties which have been extremely well stocked with timber, and are at present part of the magazine for Liverpool, and the North . . . we shall find

them much exhausted. If we proceed to Merionethshire, this county has been much
drained of her timber . . . In Cardiganshire and Pembroke we find very little timber
. . . From hence we proceed to Caermarthenshire and Glamorganshire, where very
little timber is remaining . . . We come now to the great rivers, Severn and Wye, by
whose streams the flourishing city of Bristol, and his Majesty's Yard of Plymouth
have been long supplied. These are the grand magazines for almost half the nation,
and take in the counties of Monmouth, Hereford, Shropshire, Montgomery, Radnor
and Brecknock . . . And I am not only particularly acquainted with most of these
counties; but likewise with the universal complaint of the timber merchants residing
in them, of the scarcity of full grown timber, and the neglect of planting.[16]

Accordingly, every county was specifically named as suffering from a shortage
of naval oak timber, except for Anglesey which was ignored completely as it had
not for centuries been important as a source. The main reason for the shortage
was stated to be the felling of wood to supply the furnaces and forges of the ironworks, coupled with lack of care in protecting coppices or neglect of planting:

it is become a custom for the iron-masters to purchase all large quantities of timber
in North and South Wales; and the shipwrights and other artificers are laid under
the obligation to purchase from this set of men whatever they shall think proper
not to appropriate to the use of their furnaces.[17]

Fisher's account is merely one of the recurring forebodings of a crisis in
supply by private interests and by government over a period of at least two
centuries. In May 1771 Fisher gave evidence to a committee of the House of
Commons appointed to consider how the navy might be better supplied with
timber. He stated that the Navy Board had recently bought some large parcels of

40. Boat building at Cardigan, c.1869.

timber in Denbighshire, and that timber was available in Montgomeryshire, though he doubted, from personal experience, whether it was worth removing because of the expense of carriage to the Plymouth yard.[18]

Again in 1791 an official inquiry was instituted by the government into the resources of naval timber by means of a detailed 17-point questionnaire organized on a county basis.[19] The answers from the Welsh counties may be summarized as follows: in recent years the quantity of large oak timber fit for the navy had diminished, often considerably; the growth of oak trees in hedges was not encouraged; overcutting was general ('there are Ten Fellers for One Planter, and Ten Planters for One Preserver, of Oak Timber' – Radnor); oak prices had risen; more land had been cleared than had been planted with oak; and few plantations of oak or other trees fit for the navy had been made.

Though proximity to navigable water was important in determining the accessibility and merchantability of naval oak, in the eighteenth and nineteenth centuries improvements in roads and the building of canals made more oak accessible. For example, in 1804 a total of 1,157 oak trees in the parishes of Llantrisant and Llanwynno were advertised for sale in London and Swansea papers in the following terms:

The above timber is of the best quality, and fit for the Naval Engineer and other purposes that require timber of the largest dimensions, is situated within from one quarter or three miles of the turnpike road and canal to Merthir and a part of Cardiff.[20]

Similar wording stressing proximity to an excellent turnpike road, the Montgomeryshire canal and the river Severn was used to advertise the sale of 183 large oaks 'calculated for the Navy' in Montgomeryshire in 1808; these oaks sold for £1,402 10s.[21] Again, when a total of 7,347 scribe-marked or paint-marked oak trees in the parishes of Llanfair-ar-y-bryn, Cil-y-cwm, St Mary's Kidwelly and Cenarth (Carmarthenshire) were auctioned in March 1821, most of the timber was advertised as 'fit for ship building' and being situated within a short distance of the river or contiguous to the turnpike road.[22]

41. Typical auction poster of oak timber, 1826.

Accordingly, it is clear that from the seventeenth to the mid nineteenth century, naval oak represented a welcome and reliable market for Welsh owners. Demand for precisely specified assortments was fairly steady, with recurring peaks of particularly high demand, and in the traditionally better wooded counties of Monmouth, Montgomery, Glamorgan and Carmarthen, considerable supplies of suitable oak continued to be available throughout the period until the market received its death-blow in 1862 when, at the battle of Hampton Roads, iron ships proved decisively superior to wooden men-of-war.

Tanbark

> It is a busy scene, this oak-barking . . . it is astonishing to see with what rapidity a gnarled and rugged tree can be converted into a sleek and shining specimen.
>
> Cuthbert Bede, *Illustrated London News*, 16 April 1859

Vegetable tanning, using the natural tannins present in various plant materials, has been the commonest process of turning skins and rawhides into leather, at least since medieval times. The bark of the two native species of oak, the pedunculate (*Quercus robur*) and the sessile oak (*Q. petraea*), contains a relatively high percentage of tannin, and has been the obvious natural resource for the tannin used in the making of leather in Wales. The sessile oak tends to predominate in the west in the uplands, in areas with siliceous parent rocks and high rainfall, while the pedunculate oak occurs more in the lowlands and in the east. The latter oak in particular was widely planted, and there is considerable overlap and intermingling of the two species, with numerous hybrid forms occurring. Botanical status, however, is unimportant for the supply of tanbark. In the nineteenth century, small amounts of larch, spruce, birch and beech bark were also harvested, but their quality was greatly inferior to that of oak, and the contribution of species other than oak to the tanbark industry was so insignificant that it can be ignored.

The bark harvest is governed by the phenology of the oak and this, in turn, depends on its genetic constitution and on the climate. The bark can be detached with relative ease only when the sap is rising in the spring and the trees are starting to flush. The actual date of the start of sap-flow varies from year to year, depending on the weather, but in general the bark-peeling or bark-stripping season in Wales runs from April to June. From June onward the bark becomes progressively more difficult to strip.

Most of the tannin lies in the inner layers, and comparatively little in the coarse outer bark. Accordingly, the best tanbark comes from younger trees, though these smaller stems are more costly to peel. Oak coppice worked on a rotation of 25-30 years is ideal in giving a recurring regular yield of bark of the desired quality, but in practice tanbark was harvested from trees of all ages and sizes. For example, one giant oak felled near Chepstow early in the nineteenth century yielded 3 tons 17 cwt. 2 qrs. of bark,[1] and the stem bark of the Golynos oak, felled at Bassaleg in 1810, was three inches thick.[2] The tanners required clean, dry, healthy tanbark, and paid the best prices for this quality of material. Broken, wet, dirty, green, and old mossy bark and scraps were of inferior quality, and accordingly lower prices were paid for these categories of produce.

The recorded history of oak-bark tanning in Wales goes back at least to Norman times. The Cistercian monks regularly harvested bark for tanning. For example, in the thirteenth century the monks of Tintern abbey were allowed to buy oak bark in Wentwood Forest for 2d. per load.[3]

Yields of oak bark vary according to the age and density of the stand, but are generally of the order of one ton of bark for every 3 to 5 tons of wood. It takes 4 or 5 lb. of bark to make 1 lb. of leather, and tanners needed to secure their bark supplies for at least a year's working. Because bark could be harvested easily and economically in the spring only, there was an obvious temptation to forestall, buying up supplies and cornering the market, thereby securing a monopoly in a key commodity. Middlemen who succeeded in gaining a local monopoly were then in a position to sell at inflated prices. An Act of Parliament was passed in 1603 making it illegal to buy up bark before the stripping season (1 April to 30 June), though this seems to have been only partially successful in stopping the practice.

The bark harvest could be organized in two main ways. An estate could harvest the bark, using its own or contract labour, and then sell it direct. Alternatively, it could sell the bark 'on the tree', leaving the buyer responsible for stripping. Both methods were used concurrently on the Gwydyr estate: the estate's timber accounts for 1685 show that Robert Jones, tanner of Llanrwst, paid £28 10s. for several large stacks of bark in March, including 'ye great stacke in ye barne', but in June of the same year he also bought the bark of 117 trees at 14d. per tree 'he takeing it off at his owne chardge'.[4] Other local tanners also bought bark 'on the tree' from the estate at the same price. Bulk sales of bark were the general rule, and the account books of many Welsh estates frequently record sales in amounts of 20-25 tons at a time. As late as the 1870s, Kilvert recorded in his diary that a Scotsman had amassed an enormous stack of bark at Hay-on-Wye station, reputed to be worth £6,000.[5]

There were three basic methods of carrying out the operation of stripping the bark:

felling before barking: the trees were felled by axe or hand-saw and the stems and large branches were then peeled by people standing on the ground, sitting on the stem, or clambering about among the branches; windthrown trees were dealt with in the same way. This method had the disadvantage that the tree needed to be rolled to remove all the bark.

barking before felling: the standing trees were peeled by people working from short ladders and climbing up in the crowns; these trees could then be left standing to dry out for perhaps a year before felling, this being the method described by Evelyn: 'Bark your Trees in a fit season and so let them stand naked a full year before felling'.[6] This was also the method employed with trees in hedgerows or in the middle of a field, so that the tree could be felled after harvest without damaging the crop.

a combination of both methods: the stem was 'butted' as high as possible from the ground by peeling to a height of 6 or 7ft, and then the tree was felled and the rest of the peeling completed.

There is a picturesque eye-witness account of the first method from Cwm Ceri near Newcastle Emlyn:

> At the end of spring three women and two men would be seen going to the oak wood to bark the oak trees. The trees had been cut a week before. They carried a sharp iron, with a head at one end, a hammer and a sack. Each one sits neatly on a tree, as if riding a horse side-saddle. They start at the stump end, hitting the sharp iron in to lift the bark. They [the pieces of bark] fitted together like troughs in a sack, and great was the care not to break them. They [the barking party] would spend three weeks or a month in a wood before finishing, and the only sound they would hear was the cart that came there twice a week to take the bark to the tannery.[7]

Oral testimony is available for the second method, working from ladders and climbing up in the crowns, as it was practised near Llandovery.[8] There young women would work from the ladders, and then the active and daring young men would climb the trees to complete the barking. The third or combined method was also widely used, in Montgomeryshire, the Forest of Dean and elsewhere.

42. A gang of men, women and children barking an old oak tree (Cuthbert Bede, *Illustrated London News*, 16 April 1859).

43. A barking party on the Caerynwch estate, near Dolgellau, in the 1890s.

The tools used for barking were few and simple, namely axes, billhooks, barking irons, wooden mallets and short rough ladders. The purpose-made barking iron or *pilbren* had a small, sharp, spoon-like blade. The irons varied in size from a small crowbar weighing several pounds to a dainty little tool only slightly larger than a teaspoon. They were usually manufactured by the local blacksmith, and a simple wooden handle could be made subsequently and fitted into the socket of the iron blade. In the Forest of Dean, the irons had a handle like a spade, but in Wales most of the handles were little more than a smooth piece of wood perhaps with a knob at the end. The larger barking irons were

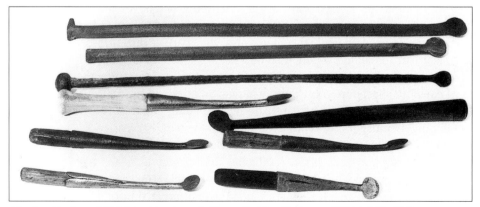

44. A collection of Welsh barking irons (*pilbrenni*) at the Museum of Welsh Life, St Fagans.

45. A bark stack on the bank of the river Wye at Llandogo, for loading on to trows.

sometimes made entirely of metal, but most were of iron with a wooden handle. Some barking tools are obviously home-made, fashioned out of an ordinary domestic poker, or from bone. The larger irons were used on the thick heavy stem bark, and the smaller ones on the branches. When bark prices were high, branches down to an inch in diameter would be peeled.

The barking process was generally as follows. The axe or billhook was used to cut through the bark right round the stem or branch at two separate places. Then the barking iron was used to make a longitudinal slit joining the two axe-cuts. The iron was then forced into the slit and used to lever off the cylindrical piece of bark between the cuts. Often, two people, each with an iron, would work together to prize off a large piece of bark without breaking it. If the bark was difficult to peel, especially at the beginning or end of the season, it was necessary to loosen it by hammering it with a wooden mallet, but this was time-consuming and damaged the bark. As the bark came loose, it made a characteristic creaking sound that has been likened to a duck's quack. Even within a single stand, trees differed in their 'peelability'; on some the bark would peel easily in sheets up to 6ft long, whereas on others only small pieces or strips could be prized off. The characteristic all-pervading smell of the fresh sap was an abiding memory for all who participated in the bark harvest.

The subsequent treatment of the bark varied according to local conditions and practice. In some places it was collected in sacks or in heaps on a canvas or tarpaulin and removed from the wood without delay to sheltered store-places such as barns. In other places the practice was to erect simple drying ranges or racks in the rides or at the edge of the wood. These ranges or racks, sometimes called horses or stages, were made of forked branches and poles, and the bark was put on or against the racks to dry. Again, in others, the bark was carefully built up into an oblong stack, with large pieces outermost to keep out the rain. These stacks would be made 'with as much neatness as farmers make a hayrick'. If the bark was left in the open, on racks or in stacks, it was essential to keep the inner surfaces dry, because of the solubility of the tannin. Where the industry was on a large scale, especially in the lower Wye valley, special stone bark-houses were built to keep the bark safe and dry. A bark-house was recorded in Conwy during Owain Glyndŵr's rebellion.[9]

The oak-bark harvest had to be completed quickly, during the sap-flow period in the spring. All accounts of the harvest emphasize this sense of urgency, and to the forester it represented the major work peak in his year. Lewis Bayne, forester at Kinmel Park, in his monthly accounts of forest work in the 1870s and 1880s stressed the need to get the tools ready in good time, and underlined the priority of bark-stripping over all other estate jobs in late April and May.[10] The same urgency is also brought out by Kilvert in his vivid account of bark stripping at Cwm Clyro (24 April 1872): 'the country is filled with the ringing of strokes of the chopping axes . . . we heard the sturdy strokes of the axes from the Castle Clump after it had grown dark. The men were working late felling oak as the sap is running fast and the bark strips well'.[11]

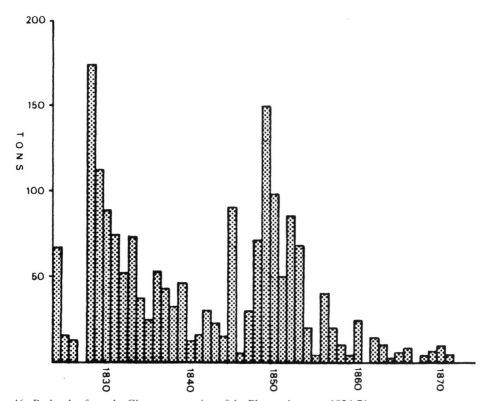

46. Bark sales from the Glamorgan portion of the Plymouth estate, 1824-71.

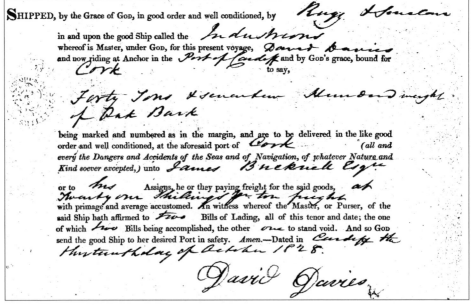

SHIPPED, by the Grace of GOD, in good order and well conditioned, by *Rugg & Sinclair*

in and upon the good Ship called the *Industrious*
whereof is Master, under GOD, for this present voyage, *David Davies*
and now riding at Anchor in the *Port of Cardiff* and by GOD's grace, bound for
Cork   to say,

*Forty Tons & seventeen Hundred weight
of Oak Bark*

being marked and numbered as in the margin, and are to be delivered in the like good
order and well conditioned, at the aforesaid port of *Cork*   *(all and
every the Dangers and Accidents of the Seas and of Navigation, of whatever Nature and
Kind soever excepted,)* unto *James Bucknell Esqr*

or to *his*   Assigns, he or they paying freight for the said goods,   *at
Twenty one Shillings pr ton freight*
with primage and average accustomed. In witness whereof the Master, or Purser, of the
said Ship hath affirmed to *two*   Bills of Lading, all of this tenor and date; the one
of which *two* Bills being accomplished, the other   *one* to stand void. And so GOD
send the good Ship to her desired Port in safety. Amen.—Dated in *Cardiff the
Thirteenth day of October 1828.*

David Davies

47. Details of a bark shipment from Cardiff to Cork, 1828.

Because of the urgency it was almost always necessary to rely on extra labour.
Casual or seasonal labour was therefore employed, whether the estate was
undertaking the barking itself or contracting the work, or whether the purchaser
was stripping the bark himself. As a result men, women and children, young and
old, were recruited from the surrounding area. Just as with the harvesting of
agricultural crops, the oak bark harvest represented a welcome break in routine
and an opportunity for earning extra income. Furthermore, it was an outdoor
activity involving most sections of the local community, often with a certain
gaiety of its own, and it generated a 'party' or 'picnic' atmosphere among the
workforce. Some lads and young men obviously went along '*er mwyn sbort*' (for
sport) and various pranks were played. At one barking party near Llandovery
around 1880, described by an actual participant, Rees Price of Merthyr Cynog,[12]
there were about fifty or sixty people – men, women and children, some of
whom had travelled many miles. Such people would stay with friends or
relatives locally during the week, returning home only at weekend. The women
and older men worked on the ground, peeling the stems as high as they could
reach; the girls and young women peeled higher, using short ladders with six or
seven rungs, the top rung made of wire to provide a better hold; and the young
men would climb the trees to complete the peeling, competing with each other in
agility, and in seeking out the straight stems without branches, as these were
easier to strip. Old women would collect the fallen pieces of bark on a canvas.
Food would be taken to the wood each day and eaten *al fresco*. On some estates,
however, the barking parties were all male, as at Caerynwch near Dolgellau in
1890s, which consisted of some forty men and boys.[13] Doubtless the atmosphere
would have reflected the composition of the company.

Day-labourers were able to command higher wages during the oak barking season. On the Hafod estate in 1857, for example, day labour was generally 2s. 3d. for men and 1s. 6d. for boys, but in the barking season it went as high as 3s. 6d. for men, 2s. for boys and 1s. 6d. for women.[14] Elsewhere in Wales, the rate for women was about half to two-thirds that of men. At Cwm Ceri, a man earned 9d. a day and a woman 6d. *'am waith diwyd a gonest'* (for industrious and honest work).[15]

Although oak bark was always in demand, it was mainly a by-product, albeit a valuable one, and as such dependent on other industries involving utilization of the wood. Supply was therefore relatively inelastic and the market was also local and fragmented. Fellings were often deliberately timed to take advantage of the spring sap-flow from April to June, when the bark was easiest to strip. However, buyers of construction timber traditionally demanded winter-felled oak. The navy offered higher prices for winter-felled material, and this naturally conflicted with the interest of the tanbark industry.

Bark was sold by the bundle, by the load, by the yard, by the tree, and by the acre, but more generally by the ton, especially in later years. On the Glamorgan portion of the Plymouth estate the traditional bark-sale agreements used in the nineteenth century specified that the bark was to be 'delivered in good order and well conditioned', i.e. clean and dry. The price per ton was fixed in the sale agreement 'the ton to be weighed as 21 cwt.' though on some estates the bark was weighed at 22 cwt. to the ton. Bark was sold 'in the wood' or at a central delivery point in Cardiff or Merthyr.[16]

Prices are difficult to compare because of the problems in determining the precise dimensions of the units of sale, but the overall picture for Wales is that bark prices were fairly stable from about 1660 to 1780 at £2 per ton. They

48. A bark rick being prepared for eventual removal by rail in the Welsh marches, *c*.1908.

49. The bark mill in the bark-store of the Rhayader tannery, now in the Museum of Welsh Life,
    St Fagans.

increased to between £4 and £6 per ton by 1790, and then quite dramatically in the next twenty years, reaching peak figures of £14 per ton in 1809 and 1810.[17] After the Napoleonic Wars, however, prices declined and by 1850 had fallen to the levels of sixty years earlier.

Welsh oakwoods were able not only to satisfy the needs of the numerous small local tanneries throughout Wales, but also to support a substantial bark export trade to Bristol, Liverpool and especially to Ireland. Bark was exported from many Welsh ports in the eighteenth century, including Neath, Milford, Aberdyfi, Aberystwyth and Cardiff. In the forty years from 1727 to 1767, some 2,000 tons of bark was exported from Cardiff to various parts of Ireland, mainly Dublin and Waterford.[18] The main centre for bark export, however, was Chepstow, and here the trade grew from a few hundred tons per annum in the early years of the century to some 4,000 tons or more per annum in the 1790s. The industry was organized in several distinct stages. Bark was stripped in the woods on both sides of the Wye, carted down to the riverside, where it was cleaned by gangs of women wielding long knives and singing as they worked, and then taken into the stone bark-house, where men cut it into pieces about four inches long. The labourers were paid by weight, the bark being weighed in long twig baskets specially made for the purpose. The chopped bark, held in the bark-house to await transport, was then loaded into Wye trows or barges, each capable of carrying up to 20 or 25 tons, and moved down-river to Chepstow. At Chepstow the unloading was performed by bark-carriers who wore a head-pad which resembled 'a cross between a life-buoy and a horse-collar', and stored in stone warehouses for eventual export.[19]

Competition from superior imported vegetable tanstuffs caused the demand for oak bark to decline during the nineteenth century. The Chepstow bark export trade came to an end in the 1880s. Prices paid by local tanneries in Wales remained at about £4 or £5 per ton to the end of the nineteenth century, and many oak-bark tanneries closed. The decline in the industry is mirrored in the records of bark sales from the Glamorgan portion of the Plymouth estate, almost complete from 1824 to 1871.[20] Figure 46 clearly illustrates the sharp fluctuations in production from year to year owing to dependence on fellings for other purposes, and the overall decline in demand for oak bark for tanning during the nineteenth century.

There was something of a short-lived revival in oak-bark harvesting during the First and Second World War in west and central Wales, but afterwards the industry declined again. The last oak-bark tannery in Wales, at Rhayader, finally closed in the early 1950s.[21] The former widespread importance of the oak-bark industry can be traced to a certain extent by place-name evidence, for many places in Wales contain the noun element *rhisg(l)* (= bark) or the adjective *rhisglog*, for example: Blaen Rhisglog, Nant Rhisglog, Cwm Rhisglog, Tŷ Rhisglog, Gwern Rhisglog, Tŷ Rhisgl, Hafod y Rhisgl, Rhisca (Rhisga), etc.

Pitwood

> *Royal National Eisteddfod pitprop competition* (*Treorci, 1928*): For a
> group of timbering by six men. Four pairs of timber set in a line 3ft.
> apart from centres. The timbers to represent a road dipping six inches
> per yard.

Besides charcoal, shiptimber and bark, the other major industrial forest product
from Welsh woods was pitwood. From the earliest times, mining operations, for
metalliferous ores and for coal, had required substantial amounts of wood for
charcoal, for roof and wall supports, and for mine buildings, ramps, sluices, etc.

Though mining for metals was locally important over many centuries, coal in
the two major coalfields was relatively unimportant until the sixteenth and
seventeenth centuries. Coal was little used in Wales for domestic heating until
the seventeenth century. Thereafter it was increasingly used in towns, but wood
and peat remained the preferred fuels in most rural areas until the nineteenth
century. For example, in Montgomeryshire 'the fuel of a great part of the county
consisted almost entirely of the best cleft timber' until towards the middle of the
eighteenth century, when the large-scale utilization of oak for navy timber
began.[1] Following the pioneering work of Abraham Darby (1666-1718), the use
of coke and coal in place of charcoal for smelting heralded the beginning of the
decline in the production of charcoal as a major forest product, but it
simultaneously launched the great expansion of coal-mining, and with it the
beginning of the increase in demand for pitwood. From the mid eighteenth
century onwards, coal increasingly replaced wood, peat and charcoal as fuel,

50. Oak coppice was managed for pitwood in the eighteenth century.

thus affecting the market for fuelwood but creating its own demand for pitwood. By 1812 in Monmouthshire the use of coke from pit-coal had caused the price of cordwood for charcoal to remain stationary or nearly so, while the price of timber had increased three- or four-fold.[2]

Before softwoods from conifer plantations or imports became generally available for pitwood at the end of the eighteenth and during the nineteenth century, all the pitwood used in the coalmines in Wales was hardwood, most of it acquired from local woods or from woods in other parts of Wales. The Welsh woodlands were mixed hardwoods with a preponderance of oak, and the composition of the pitwood used underground reflected this.

The nature of the geology in the South Wales coalfield required much greater amounts of pitwood for the support of the roofs and sides than in other coalfields. Most of the wood used underground was used in the round, and trimmed to shape as necessary by axe. The two main types of hardwood required were poles to make posts, props, arms and collars, and shorter corded material to make cogs or cogwood, i.e. short billets or blocks that were built up in a crib framework and filled in with waste material to support the roof. These two categories of material could be produced by thinnings or, more generally, by coppice fellings. With the later development of the coalmining industry, sawn or dressed timber was used for special purposes such as the lining of shafts. In this connection it should be noted that Britain as a whole and Wales in particular were very slow to adopt mechanical sawing in sawmills, even though sawmills were extensively used on the continent and in New England in the seventeenth century. In Wales, the framed pit-saw and later the open pit-saw remained in more general use until well into the nineteenth century. Continuous-action water-powered circular saws, frame saws and band saws did not become common until the nineteenth century.

It was important for mine-owners to secure adequate supplies of suitable wood, and whole woods were bought for the purpose. For example, in 1713 seven acres of 'fine wood . . . which the colliers say is the best they ever saw for that use' were bought at £40 an acre for the use of Cartmakers' Pool coalpits near Picton Castle in Pembrokeshire.[3] In the eighteenth century the main demand for pitwood was in the form of barked oak roundwood (poles), and forest management was directed to this, mainly by simple coppice rather than coppice-with-standards, on a rotation of twenty to thirty years. An account of Llanbadarn Fawr near Aberystwyth in 1755 stated that 'there are no quantities of large timber, the mine-works destroying them all, but oakwood of 20 or 30 years growth are sold at about 6d. a foot'.[4]

The typical management of coppice oak woods in Pembrokeshire in the eighteenth century is known in detail: the coppice shoots on the stools were thinned out in an operation known as 'waste weeding' at age three or four years so as to leave four to six of the most vigorous shoots per stool; five years later a heavy thinning called a 'cordwood weeding' was done, the produce being used for making charcoal; then about fifteen years later (i.e. at about 23-35 years) the 'coppice of poles' was fit to cut for the use of the mines and the final clear felling was made. The poles were sold at about 7s. 6d. per dozen, bark and

MONMOUTHSHIRE.

To be Sold by Auction,

By Mr. GEORGE BREWER,

ON THURSDAY. THE 2ND OF OCTOBER. 1823.

AT THE HANBURY ARMS INN, CAERLEON,

Between the Hours of Four and Six in the Afternoon, subject to such Conditions as will be then and there produced;

THE PRESENT FALLAGE OF ABOUT

Two Hundred & Thirty Six Acres

OF VALUABLE

Coppice Woods,

ASH AND BEECH TIMBER

TREES;

STATUTE ACRES.

LOT 1. The upper part of a Coppice Wood on the Ariel Farm, in the Parish of Aberustruth, called Graig Shinkin, containing - - - - - - - - - - - 26

2. The lower part of a Coppice Wood on the same Farm, and adjoining lot 1 called Graig Ellis, containing - - - - - - - - - - - about 26

3. A Coppice Wood on the same Farm called Coed Beeg, containing - - - 28

4. Part of the Llanarch Wood in the Parish of Monyddyslwn, standing opposite the Foundry, containing - - - - - - - - - - - 16

5. Part of a Coppice Wood called Graig Ddu in the same Parish, situate opposite the Corn Mill, containing about - - - - - - - - - - 12

6. A Coppice Wood called Gwern Y Gofmudi, in the Parish of Llanfihangel, including 106 Ash Timber Trees - - - - - - - - - - - 21

7. A Coppice Wood called Coed Ty Mawr in the same Parish, including 6 Ash and 16 Beech Timber Trees - - - - - - - - - - - 9

8. A Coppice Wood called Coed Ty Newydd, in the Parish of Glascoed, including 3 Ash and 18 Beech Timber Trees - - - - - - - - - 46

9. Coed Ty Coch, in the same Parish - - - - - - - - - - - 7

10. A Coppice Wood called Coed Carrw Powell, in the Parish of Panteg, including 10 Ash and 24 Beech Timber Trees - - - - - - - - - 6

11. A Coppice Wood called the Lodge Wood, in the Parish of Llangattoc Juxta Caerleon, including 14 Ash and 34 Beech Timber Trees - - - - - - - 42

The above Coppice Woods are of excellent Growth, very convenient for Land and Water Carriage, and are well worth the attention of Wood Dealers.

N. B. The Ash and Beech Timber Trees, included in the above Lots, are numbered with Red Lead and Oil, with a Cross over each Number. For Particulars apply to Mr. John Aram, Pontypool, or Mr. George Brewer, Coalbrook Vale; and for a View of the Different Lots to Mr. Richard Jones, Woodward, at Geytre.

JAMES HILEY MORGAN, MINERVA PRINTING OFFICE, HIGH STREET, ABERGAVENNY.

51. Auction of coppice woods, Monmouthshire, 1823.

cordwood included. The bark was stripped off and sold to local tanneries or exported, often to Ireland or Scotland. The report adds that 'whilst the collieries have occasion for such vast supplies of small wood, to support their underground ways, it is not likely that the woods will be suffered to grow to timber for husbandry and building uses'.[5] Dominated by the market for pitwood and also for cordwood for charcoal, the management of coppice oak was on similar lines throughout south Wales. Early in the nineteenth century sapling oak poles for the collieries were selling for about 8s. to 12s. per dozen, according to size.[6] Indeed, the demand for pitwood in south Wales was so great that oak woods in north Wales were managed for this special market, and the poles shipped to the south. The port records of Aberdyfi, for example, show that between 1791 and 1794 over 27,000 'British oak poles' were exported, mainly to Milford Haven.[7] The poles were sold and recorded in the port accounts in dozens.

Besides poles, the smaller material needed in pits was prepared and sold by the cord, using cordwood measures adapted from the charcoal industry (see Table 7). For example, a lease relating to a coalmine at Aberavon in 1746 specified a payment of 10s. for 'every Long Cord of Coal pitt Wood or Timber The Measure thereof to be adjusted and Ascertained according to the usual way or Method of Measuring the Long Cord of Wood for Charcoales now used in the Sd County of Glamorgan Allowing Breadth for Length'.[8]

Pitwood was generally cut to size at stump or at roadside and extracted by teams of horses or mules equipped with slings or cradles. For example, in about 1800 near Pontypool, iron frames 'like the horns of an ox' were fixed on the pack-saddles of horses, each horse carrying five or six logs 10-12ft long and 8-9 inches in diameter, lying lengthways on the animal.[9] A similar method was still being used 120 years later, for extraction of European larch pitwood near Crickhowel: poles cut to 6ft lengths and down to 2in. top diameter were loaded into slings or pannier cradles attached to the saddles of mules; each mule carried a load of about 4 cwt., the extraction being done on contract by mule-drivers each of whom had up to six mules working under his guidance.[10] As late as the 1920s mixed hardwood pitwood in the form of sprags, cogwood and poles was extracted by mule-teams with wooden cradles and leather straps from the woods above Tongwynlais to the railway at Taff's Well (Fig. 53).[11]

Welsh estates, some with their own mining interests, sold large amounts of pitwood throughout the last century. It consisted of hardwoods and softwoods, particularly larch. Various measures were used for sales – by volume, number, weight, stacked measure, and by length. On the Hafod estate in 1857, for example, larch pitprops over 4¼ inches in girth were sold by the cubic foot, at 10d. per cube; smaller props were sold by the dozen, for example larch poles

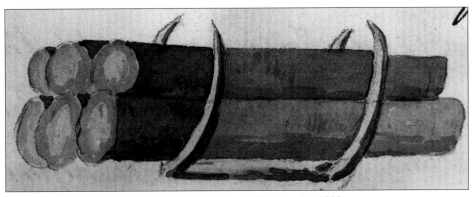

52. Frame used for transport of wood by horses near Pontypool, *c*.1800.

53. Mules carrying cogwood from the woods near Tongwynlais (Glamorgan) to the railway at
Taff's Well in the 1920s.

25ft long at 6s. 6d. per dozen; and in 1869, oak pitprops sold for 3d. each and
larch pitprops for 4-6d. each.[12] On the Stradey estate near Llanelli in 1878-83
larch, oak and elm pitwood was sold at 28s. per ton.[13] On the Glamorgan portion
of the Plymouth estate, pitwood was sold by the cord, at prices ranging from 12
to 40s. per cord.[14] At Brynllywarch, Leighton and Kerry in Montgomeryshire,
pitprops were sold by the yard, for example at 1½-3d. per lineal yard.[15]

The dominant role of the pitwood market especially in south Wales can be
seen from analysis of wood sales on estates in that region during the last century.
On the Glamorgan portion of the Plymouth estate, for instance, the Wood
Account Books (covering the periods 1825-35, 1835-52, 1852-83, and 1883-
1905) show five classes of entries: Timber Sold; Timber Used on the Estate;
Pitwood Sold; Cordwood Sold; and Bark Sold.[16] These accounts reflect the
change in operations with growing industrialization. In the 1820s and 1830s, in
addition to the timber, pitwood and cordwood, the accounts also contained many
items indicating typically rural or small-scale craft uses, such as cutting wattling,
lopping oak, stripping oak bark, and the cutting of boat knees, whereas later on
the accounts are completely dominated by sales of pitwood and cordwood.

The pitwood was sold off in cords, generally in small amounts of 1-10 cords,
but occasionally in large amounts of over 100 or even over 200 cords each. In
the period 1852 to 1876, prices ranged from 12s. to 40s. per cord, depending on
species, size and location. The species of trees used for pitwood are rarely
specified but certainly included oak and larch, and presumably mixed
hardwoods. Later in the century, cogwood appeared as a special assortment in

the accounts. The frequent cash income from Wernddu wood near Caerphilly shows the importance of the pitwood market.

Table 8. Yields from Wernddu Wood, Caerphilly (Plymouth estate)

Year	Produce sold	Area acres	Value £
1857	larch, pitwood + cordwood	30	700
1858	larch, pitwood + cordwood	45	1,205
1859	pitwood + coppice, larch	30	1,310
1860	larch etc.	c.12	c.400
1862	larch + coppice	15	135
1867	pitwood + cordwood	40	900
1869	larch, pitwood + cordwood	13	c.300
1875	unspecified	—	c.500
1892	larch, birch, alder, beech, ash	29¾	530
1892	larch, alder, birch, oak, beech & ash	22½	540

However, the home-grown contribution was inadequate in quantity and in quality to meet the demands of the rapidly expanding coal industry. Imports of coniferous pitwood into Wales started at least as early as 1775, for in that year the firm of John Howells of the Steam Saw-Mills, West Dock, Cardiff was engaged in importing 'Norway mining poles or pit-props'.[17] Norway and the Baltic states provided considerable imports, but as the business built up rapidly in the second half of the nineteenth century with the advent of Free Trade, the bulk came in from south-west France, Spain and Portugal. In 1882, imports of pitwood and sleepers into Cardiff alone were 226,175 tons, and the local supply was said to be 'insignificant'.[18] In each of the ten years before 1914, pitwood and pitprop imports into Cardiff, Newport and Swansea totalled more than 1¼ million loads, this representing some ½ million tons per annum, and in 1913 the record figure of 1,641,952 loads was reached.[19]

Wales was able to supply large amounts of home-grown pitwood during the First World War, much of it from the conifer plantations which by now formed a substantial proportion of the woods on most estates. Large amounts of immature hardwoods, especially oak, were also felled during the war, to provide pitprops and cogwood for the South Wales coalfield, and these fellings left large areas of devastated woodland. In 1919 the Monmouthshire & South Wales Coal Owners' Association awarded a gold medal to the Earl of Lisburne, of Crosswood estate, for the best contribution to pitwood supplies during the war. Out of a total woodland area of just over 2,000 acres on this estate, 1,119 acres were actually cut for pitwood, and a further 136 acres were sold but not cut; the only potential pitwood remaining on the estate at the end of the war was 25 acres of larch. The estate's total yield of pitwood had been some 50,000 tons, or approximately 1½ million cu. ft.[20]

Further details of the production of home-grown pitwood during the First and Second World War are given in the final chapters of this book.

Chapter VIII

FAMOUS TREES AND BIG TREES

brenhinbren: the largest tree in the forest, a giant spreading oak-tree;
fig. for a nobleman or noble family

Geiriadur Prifysgol Cymru

Individual trees famous in legend and history occur in many countries, and Wales is certainly no exception. Some of these Welsh trees are from the fanciful realms of magic or superstition, while others are associated with legendary or historical personages or events; some are of local importance as boundary trees, while others are famous in their own right as striking individuals, the big trees that have inspired general admiration, even awe, by their form and dimensions.

The *Red Book of Hergest*, compiled at the end of the fourteenth century, contains a list of the wonders of Britain, among which was a very strange tree:

> There is a tree in a wood in the Island of Britain, like the hazel, with rosy-coloured leaves. The tree divides into two branches. On one part of the tree in the summer time the bark and leaves and fruit grow, and when winter comes the fruits and leaves and bark on it are taken and it is left bare. And just as the leaves and fruit and bark grow in the summer on the one half of the tree, so in winter the other half of the tree grows leaves and fruit and bark, and when summer comes they disappear.[1]

This phenological oddity may have been some form of natural sport, or even two individual trees, perhaps of different species, growing close together or actually fused in such a way as to create the wondrous appearance described in the old Welsh text.

Another miraculous tree was the ash (*Fraxinus excelsior*) at St Donat's in the Vale of Glamorgan.[2] This aged tree was badly damaged by a spring gale in 1559:

> its butt, although laid open and riven to the centre, yet anchored by its roots, stood for seven feet above the ground. And lo! in the interior structure of the gaping trunk there appeared a cross rather longer than a man's foot; and, and what was more marvellous, the part which lay upon the ground presented the same figure of a cross in all its details . . . the cross did not suddenly disappear, but remained several years in the trunk of the tree.

Catholics interpreted the miracle as a symbolic representation of the triumph of Christ, as the translation on the next page of John Fenn's contemporary Latin verse shows.

Welsh peasants traditionally distinguished two forms of oak, the female oak which shed its leaves in autumn, and the male oak which retained some of its leaves through the winter. The favourite trees of the Welsh fairies were the hazel

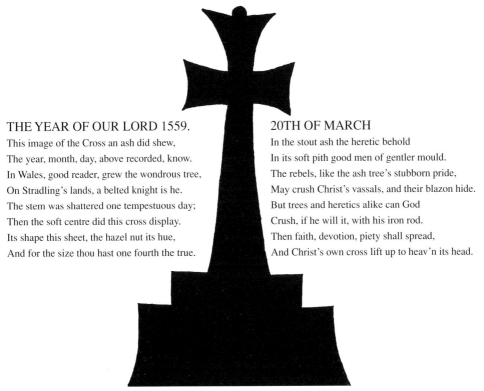

THE YEAR OF OUR LORD 1559.

This image of the Cross an ash did shew,

The year, month, day, above recorded, know.

In Wales, good reader, grew the wondrous tree,

On Stradling's lands, a belted knight is he.

The stem was shattered one tempestuous day;

Then the soft centre did this cross display.

Its shape this sheet, the hazel nut its hue,

And for the size thou hast one fourth the true.

20TH OF MARCH

In the stout ash the heretic behold

In its soft pith good men of gentler mould.

The rebels, like the ash tree's stubborn pride,

May crush Christ's vassals, and their blazon hide.

But trees and heretics alike can God

Crush, if he will it, with his iron rod.

Then faith, devotion, piety shall spread,

And Christ's own cross lift up to heav'n its head.

54. The miraculous image of the Cross in the ash tree at St Donat's, 1559 (from Nicholas Harpsfield, *Dialogi Sex,* Paris, 1566).

and the oak, especially the branching female oaks, beneath which the fairies danced.[3] According to local folklore, bad luck would certainly afflict anyone foolish enough to damage or fell a fairy oak. Edmund Jones gives examples in his history of Aberystruth (1799), and William Coxe, during his visits to Monmouthshire in the late eighteenth century, also recorded several instances of this belief persisting, while his friend and companion, Sir Richard Colt Hoare, illustrated a famous fairy oak at Newcastle near Monmouth.

Merlin's oak was an ancient tree which stood at the entrance to Carmarthen town. The fate of this tree has long been popularly linked to the fortunes of the town itself:

> When Merlin's oak shall tumble down
> Then shall fall Carmarthen town

Long after this old tree had died, its decaying remains were carefully preserved *in situ* by means of metal and concrete supports, until finally a road-widening scheme resulted in the remaining fragments of wood being removed to the safekeeping of the local museum.

In Nannau Park, on the estate of Sir Robert Williams Vaughan near Dolgellau, stood *Derwen Ceubren yr Ellyll* (the Goblin's Hollow Oak or the Haunted Oak).

55. The female oak or fairy oak at Newcastle, drawn by Sir Richard Colt Hoare *c.*1785 (from William Coxe, *An Historical Tour in Monmouthshire*, 1801).

This veteran, which girthed 27 feet, played its part in a medieval murder mystery: on a hunting trip at Nannau, Owain Glyndŵr fought with his treacherous cousin, Howel Sele, killed him, and hid the body in the hollow trunk of the old oak, where it lay for forty years before it was eventually discovered. The Nannau oak stood until 1813, when it was finally destroyed by lightning.

Yews, like the oak, certainly long-living but more difficult to date with accuracy, have also attracted superstitions and legends in Wales. The yews of Hafodunos near Abergele are reputed to have provided a sanctuary for the night for Saint Winifred, the patron saint of virgins, who was killed by a ravisher while defending her honour.

The 'bleeding' yew, which stands in the avenue of yews in the churchyard of Saint Brynach's church at Nevern, has acquired its name because it oozes a reddish liquid. This has given rise to gruesome stories of a man being hanged from the tree, or having his hand cut off for infringing forest law. These fairly modern legends must certainly be firmly debunked. The oozing 'blood' is a natural slime flux, red from pigments in the yew and probably attributable to a bacterial infection in an old wound in a crotch of the tree.

Certain prominent or otherwise distinctive trees, growing naturally or deliberately planted, were of local importance as boundary features or markers. The twelfth- and thirteenth-century land boundaries recorded in Welsh and Latin in the *Book of Llandaff* mention alder, apple, ash, broom, willow and yew.[4] For example, in the Manor of Thountur (Chepstow) the boundary ran

> To the mound of the Yew-tree, through the wood downwards to the dyke, along it to the Wye . . .

and the boundary of Lann Uvien (? Llangovan, Monmouthshire) ran from

> the spring of Laguernnuc, along it straight upwards to the Apple-tree. From the Apple-tree to the great wood. Along the wood towards the east . . .

In Villa Junuhic (Undy, Monmouthshire) the boundary was:

> Nant y Gov on one side; on the other side Nant y Golchetva as far as the Pill, to the
> ash-tree towards the east. From the ash-tree straight downwards to the Nant y
> Golchetva; along it as far as the Pill. From the ash-tree, on the other side, as far as
> the Gwver as it leads downwards to Nant y Gov, to the Pill.

Taking another example from north Wales and five centuries later, several trees –
sycamore, ash, birch, holly and rowan – are noted in the perambulation of the
boundaries of the Lordship of Rhuthun (1737):

> to Moel Eythinen and from thence down to a Siccamore tree standing in the road
> by the house of Mr Hugh Davies . . . near an ash tree standing upon the mountayn
> near a place called Tomen-rhodwy . . . a little house called y Castell and by a
> Quickberry [rowan] tree standing there . . . to a field called Cae Cay and to an ash
> tree at the upper end and from thence through the field down to an ash tree in the
> lower end . . . to a place called Tavarn y Grifiolen [*criafolen* = rowan] and so on
> along the road near an ash tree called Croes y wian . . . and from thence by a Holy
> tree or two . . . to the Commons called Gwrych Bedw [Birch Hedge] and crossing
> the said common to the hedge to a Holy tree there standing.[5]

Trees noted as landmarks in boundaries were often referred to as the Fair
Tree, without specifying the particular kind. Such trees may well have been
unmistakable, as being the only one present for a considerable distance, but
sometimes they were described in more detail, for instance Y Dderwen Deg (The
Fair Oak) or Y Ddraenen Deg (The Fair Thorn), and these have in turn given
their name to nearby houses or pubs.

The bounds of the parish of Llantrisant in Glamorgan, as described in a
survey in 1630, specified several species of trees – birch, broom, beech and
willow – as well as a Fair Oak: 'to a burchen tree in theste parte of the said
meadow . . . to the stile in Kae Banal [Broom Field] neere the oake called y
Derwen Deg [The Fair Oak], and from the said stile alongst the headge on the
right hand to a beech tree that groweth in the said headge . . . to a ffoorde called
Ryd Helyg [Willow Ford] . . .'[6]

Boundary trees and marker trees were sometimes deliberately planted, often
to replace old trees that had died. The perambulation of the bounds of the parish
of Llanfaches in Monmouthshire on 19 March 1810 listed many trees as
boundary markers – sycamore, ash, oak, yew, beech, crab and cherry, some of
them newly planted. In the same county a man recalled walking the boundaries
of Usk *c.*1816, the perambulation including planting a tree in the middle of an
island in the river.[7] These parish boundary trees were sometimes known as Coed
yr Efengyl (Gospel Trees), where the procession stopped to hear the parson read
a portion of the gospel.

Tradition asserts that some individual trees or small clumps of Scots pine
(*Pinus sylvestris*), popularly called Charley trees, are the survivors of trees
planted in Wales after 1745 by supporters of Bonny Prince Charlie to

56. Scots pine trees at Dynefwr castle, traditionally called Charlie trees and said to have been planted in 1746 to commemorate the 'Forty-five'.

commemorate the 'Forty-five'. Another tradition is that pine trees were deliberately planted at prominent places in order to mark the line of the old drove routes across Wales, along which the drovers led their cattle into England. That the trees exist is not in question, but there is no positive evidence to verify the truth of either of these Scots pine traditions. The Charley tree tradition appears inherently more probable than the drovers' trees, which would have required many years to become effective as long-distance markers. Both traditions would date from a period when conifers, and especially pine, were starting to be planted quite widely in Wales as ornamentals with commercial potential.

The dimensions of the largest trees in Wales are summarized by Hyde & Harrison in *Welsh Timber Trees* (1977), and the latest tree records are contained in the continuously updated index established by Alan Mitchell and published in *Champion Trees of the British Isles* (Forestry Authority Technical Paper 7).

Big trees have always graced the Welsh countryside, though until quite recently their actual dimensions were often obscured by exaggeration and ambiguous measurements. For example, John Evelyn referred in his *Sylva* (1664) to the inscription cut on an old beam 'somewhere in Wales': *Sexuaginta pedes fuerant in stipite nostro, excepta coma quae speciosa fuit* (Sixty feet were in our stem, beside the crown which was remarkable).

Again the poetic account of the *brenhinbren* (king tree), a giant oak which grew at Ganllwyd, near Dolgellau, was certainly true in describing it as *derwen felen-wen flaenwych gwmpassog* (a fair yellow oak, fine-topped, of great girth), but its actual height was less certain:

> *Union tw' gwych pren teg wyd*   (A splendid fine straight tree thou art
> *Tri' gain llath, twr y Ganllwyd*   Sixty yards, the tower of Ganllwyd)

In this poetic description 'sixty yards' is figurative and must not be taken literally as indicating the tree's true height.

Most of the records of big old trees in Wales refer to oaks, but fine specimens of yew, beech and elm also occur. Significantly, most of these big old trees grew, or are still growing, in the eastern and south-eastern counties, fairly close to the English border, where the combination of climatic and soil conditions appears to be most favourable for growth.

The Foresters' Oaks in Wentwood, already mentioned in Chapter III (p. 37), where the medieval forest courts were held, were the two trees of greatest historic interest in all Wales. In 1875 the dimensions of one tree were: 26ft sitting measurement (i.e. girth at ground level) and 19ft girth at 3ft; the other tree measured 23ft and 18ft 6in., respectively. However

> time seems to have gathered all his storms against them . . . The upper portion of each trunk is torn away, many branches are snapped, but the great bodies stand firmly, holding out tortuous arms covered with crisp foliage . . . Strip after strip of bark have been flayed from the larger of the two, and many a split and cranny filled with black mould shows how surely both are doomed.[8]

57. Artist's impression of the decapitated lead-capped oak, 56 ft high, standing
before the old mansion of Cefnmabli.

Cefnmabli, close to the boundary between
Glamorgan and Monmouthshire and for
centuries the seat of the Kemeys family,
boasted giant oak trees.[9] In 1684 Thomas
Dinely described one tree, standing in a field
below the house:

> it is in height seventy foot, having no bow
> in ye way to obstruct its being laudable
> timber; at above sixty foot whereof it
> carrieth about 3 foot diameter, rather more
> than less, and is in circumference about the
> butt neer seven yards.

This giant tree was probably at least three
hundred years old when Dinely described it,
and in 1739 it was recorded as measuring 66ft in clean stem height and
containing 31 tons of timber. About this time it began to decay and Sir Charles
Kemeys 'caused it to be cut at the height of 56ft and capped with sheet lead'. Sir
Charles was obviously so proud of the tree that he wanted to preserve as much of
it as possible for as long as he could. After this arboreal decapitation, probably
the first recorded operation of tree surgery in Wales, the residual standing trunk
was estimated to contain 22 tons and 38ft of timber. The decapitated top
produced over 8 tons of timber, and the branches 20 cords of firewood.

According to the testimony of Iolo Morganwg, the lead-capped stem of this
tree continued to stand erect, like some monstrous phallic symbol, until 7
October 1779. Over the years the bark and sapwood rotted away and fell off, and
the roots decayed. When the remains of the Cefnmabli giant finally fell, it was
measured as 56ft long, and its girth was 21ft near the ground, 15ft in the middle,
and 11½ft at the top. It contained over 19 tons of wood.

The old mansion of Cefnmabli was justly famous for another prime oak
specimen, the enormous shovel-board also described by Thomas Dinely on his
visit in 1684:

> The Gallery of Kevenmably hath in it of note either fitted to the length thereof, or
> the Gallery to it, an extraordinary Shovelboard of 42 foot in length, – foot in
> breadth, and – in thickness, of one intire plank of an Oak, whereof 20 foot was also
> cut off before.

This long table, used as a gigantic shove ha'penny board for the entertainment
of the guests at Cefnmabli, had evidently been cut from another giant oak, with a
straight stem 60ft long. Its full dimensions, which Dinely did not record in 1684,
are breadth about 2ft 9in. and thickness about 5 inches. With change of

ownership of the mansion, the table was moved from Cefnmabli and for many years was stored in quite inappropriate conditions and was inaccessible to the general public, but happily the magnificent table top is now on display at Tredegar House, Newport. The condition of the wood is still excellent, apart from some small patches of decay caused by the unfortunate storage period.

The giant oak and the enormous shovel-board of Cefnmabli bore eloquent testimony to the woodland wealth of the Kemeys family. The Welsh motto above the fireplace in the great parlour at Cefnmabli reads:

> *Aml ei goed*
> *Abl ei dan*

or as Dinely explained it 'He that hath plenty of wood has fire enough'.

Not far from Cefnmabli stood another famous oak tree, the Golynos oak.[10] It was purchased by Thomas Harrison, his Majesty's Purveyor of Plymouth Dockyard and Dean Forest, for one hundred guineas, and was felled and converted in 1810:

> Five men were each twenty days stripping and cutting it down; and a pair of sawyers were constantly employed one hundred and twenty eight days in its conversion . . . It was felled in separate parts, and stages were erected for workmen to stand on to cut down the valuable limbs. Previous to being felled it was divested of its brushwood, which was placed as a bed, to prevent the timber from bursting in falling. The main trunk of the tree was nine feet and a half in diameter, and

58. The giant shovelboard of Cefnmabli, a single piece of oak 42 ft long.

consequently no saw could be found long enough to cut it down; two saws were therefore brazed together ... The rings in its butt being reckoned, it was discovered that this tree had been improving upwards of four hundred years ... When standing, it overspread four hundred and forty-two square yards of ground.

Its produce was as follows:

	Feet
Main trunk, at ten feet long	450
One limb	470
One do.	355
One do.	235
One do.	156
One do.	113
One do.	106
Six small do.	413
Dead limbs of the size of timber	126
Total quantity of timber	2,426

The heavy body bark was three inches thick. When all its parts were brought to market they produced nearly £600.

A major difficulty in comparing the dimensions of big old trees is the difference in the place(s) at which the trees were girthed, especially for trees growing in the open, in a non-forest environment. Some authorities recorded the 'sitting girth', i.e. the circumference measured at grass level or round the bosses or root spurs; others measured girth at heights of 1ft, 3ft, 4ft 6in. (breast height) or even 6ft, or indeed wherever was most convenient, given the stem form and branching habit of the particular tree.

Most counties of Wales have oaks over 20ft in girth and up to 100ft in height. Notable specimens include: the sessile oak at Pontfadog, girth 42ft 9in., one of the largest oaks in Britain; the Champion oak at Powis Castle, a hybrid 110ft tall and 24ft in girth, reputedly the largest tree then standing in Britain, which contained 2,248 cu. ft of timber and fell on 13 April 1939; and the Giant oak, another hybrid at Powis Castle, 90ft tall and 33ft 9in. in girth in 1961.

A great old pollard oak, 32ft 6in. in girth (= 3.15m diameter at breast height), still stands near Llantilio Crossenny, between Penrhos Farm and Pant Wood (Fig. 61). This is not very far away from the famous Pontrilas oak, better known as Jack o' Kent's oak, in Kentchurch Deer Park, just over the English border. This latter tree, a veteran probably 1,000 years old, was measured by the Royal Forestry Society in October 1997 as having a girth of 11.35 metres at breast height, and its age has been estimated at 954 years.

In the 1870s T. H. Thomas compiled a *Silva Silurica*, a collection of water-colours and etchings of notable specimens of trees in the counties of Monmouth and Glamorgan, now preserved at the National Museum of Wales.[11] These trees include the Llantarnam oak, which girthed 27ft at 4ft 6in.; the Newbridge-on-Usk oak which girthed 25ft at 6ft; and the Caerhyder hybrid oak near Llanhennock – 'an almost perfect example of a first-class tree of the short-stemmed wide-spreading type of growth', the dimensions of which were as follows:

circumference 3ft from ground	31 ft
circumference 1ft from ground	38½ ft
circumference where roots dip	46 ft
small circumference	23½ ft
length of branch due north	63 ft
diameter of spread of branches	126 ft
height	70 ft

The pedunculate oak in the grounds of Hensol Castle, described by T.H. Thomas, was a fantastic specimen:

I cannot hope to convey in words the wonderful character of this tree. I have seen nothing at all to equal it. One ought to be an ancient Druid to appreciate it properly, and before it the spectator cannot wonder that 'tree worship' has taken such a hold upon mankind. A vast and grotesque trunk bears, in some aspects, a resemblance to some fantastic Eastern or Mexican idol. Thence protrude twisted limbs, tossed aloft and below, as if they had been those of some Briarean monster suddenly metamorphosed when in a storm of anger or agony of change. Heavy masses of foliage are reared in air, others are dashed down upon the sward, and twigs creep on and on amidst the grass far from the parent stem. The boughs are hoary with lichen and fungus; they are spotted, like a serpent's skin, with ashen colour and brown. To stand under the circuit of the branches and to look around, is to seem encircled by a writhing mass of pythons, and shows us in living form 'such stuff as dreams are made of.' I do not exaggerate; I am sure those who have seen the tree will not consider my report incorrect. In the course of some years, during which I have given attention to tree-form, I have seen no tree so remarkable for fantastic growth. Neither the most weird of the Burnham Beeches, the rent and contorted chestnuts of the Forest of Vallombrosa, the oaks of Fontainebleau, nor the aged olives of Sorrento or the Riviera, equal it in this respect. For it must be

59. The pedunculate oak at Hensol Castle, Glamorgan: smallest girth 11 ft, spread 110 ft. Drawn by T.H. Thomas *c*.1875.

remembered that at Hensol all is natural growth; none of its singularity is the effect of imprisonment by other trees, pruning, sea winds, decay, or storm. Mr. David Jones was kind enough to drive me down to sketch the Hensol Oak, and carefully measured it. The dimensions are as follows:

circumference at level of grass ....18 feet
circumference at 4 feet high ....11 feet
circumference at 6 feet level of under side of limbs ....13½ feet

The tree is enclosed by an iron fence almost circular in form, 104' diameter in one direction, 110' in the other. The longest branches creeping upon the sward have pushed twigs through this fence.

After oaks, it is the yews which have attracted most attention as big trees in Wales, but in contrast to oak almost all the large old yew specimens are planted trees in churchyards. A notable exception is the solitary old yew standing in Kentchurch Deer Park, just over the English border. This tree was measured by the Royal Forestry Society in October 1997 as having a girth of 11.32 metres. The special difficulties involved in measuring and especially in dating old yews are well known, but despite this, much valuable fieldwork has been done in Wales in recent years, notably by Allen Meredith, and also by J. Daryll Evans on the churchyard yews of Gwent.

Calculation of tree age by the extrapolation of growth rates is claimed to indicate that some individual yews are several thousand years old, though the unusual growth habit of yews, with aerial roots forming within decayed stems, means that such calculations are fraught with uncertainty. Such great ages lead on to somewhat speculative discussion of the possible pre-Christian 'meaning' or original purpose of the oldest yews now growing in churchyards, such as the great yew at Mamhilad in Gwent.

The Mamhilad yew measured 35ft 3in. in girth at a height of 3ft 3in. in 1987, having apparently increased by some 5 or 6ft since 1838. In the 1870s T.H. Thomas gave its girth as 31ft at 4ft from the ground, at about which height 'it divides into four principal branches, the largest being 9 feet around . . . Hollow and decaying, its bole is filled with mould, into which new roots are creeping . . . the tree stands full of glorious leaf, spreading its branches 60 feet wide and 50 feet in air, while at the season it is studded with queenly *parure* of ruby berries'.

Hyde & Harrison record at least 81 yew trees over 10ft in girth in Wales, some of the largest being in churchyards in the old counties of Montgomery (Llanerfel, 40ft girth), and Merioneth (Llandderfel 33ft 4in.; Llanelltyd *c*.50ft; and Mallwyd 30ft).

T.H. Thomas described three of the largest elms ever recorded in Wales:

Of Elm trees (*Ulmus campestris*, L.), Monmouthshire has lately lost a very fine specimen, which, before its fall in 1876, was probably the best known 'big tree' in the two counties – the Elm in the Plaisaunce of Raglan Castle. Mr. Cuxson, the Warden of the Castle, has kindly sent me the following particulars:- 'The trunk of the large elm is 21 feet in girth, 2 feet from the ground; the sitting circumference is

31 feet 2 inches. The huge limbs, seven in number, fell during Divine Service (fortunately when the Castle was closed to the public) on the 30th of July, 1876. The trunk still remains, and is converted into a mushroom-topped, bark-covered summer-house'.

Of the Wych Elm (*Ulmus montana*) we have two noble trees. The first fronts the old mansion of Llanaravon, near Cwmbran, Mon., and combines the qualities of grandeur and grace in an eminent degree. The sitting circumference is 29' 6", and 17' at 6' high. The trunk rises 10', when it divides into two limbs of 8' girth, or more, which support a fine canopy of pendulous foliage, which has a spread of 79'. Standing under the shade of the tree, the spectator is almost surrounded by a tent of delicate hanging tracery, the tips of the branches drooping almost to the ground.

60. The great wych elm at Cottrell Park, near Cardiff. Girth 21ft at 5ft from the ground. Drawn by T.H. Thomas *c*.1875.

The second specimen is nearer Cardiff. It stands at the gate of Cottrell Park, St. Nicholas. Dr. Vachell kindly drove me down to sketch the tree, and on our arrival we were dismayed to find that the grand branches had been wrenched away by winds, and we had only the trunk, bound by an iron girdle, to study. From a root circumference of over 30', it tapers to 21' at 5' high, and thence rises, garlanded with enormous shoots to the mangled stump of the limbs, about 15' from the grass. A gale some twenty years ago partially destroyed the canopy, and the remaining portion fell during a storm in March, 1878. A drawing of the tree in its maturity is preserved at Cottrell House.

The Dutch elm disease epidemic of the 1970s has killed all the magnificent specimen elms recorded in Wales.

Several old beech trees of imposing dimensions, with heights up to 100ft and girths approaching 20ft, have been recorded in south-east Wales, for example at Ruperra and Cefn Onn. The most notable of all these big beech trees was the tufted beech which stood prominently on a knoll near Glascoed, Usk.

T.H. Thomas sketched it and described it in 1875, not long before it was first broken and then thrown down by gales in the winter of 1878-79:

> ... it could be seen, owing to its prominent position and height, from great distances. I have descried its canopy from the old encampment above Weston-super-Mare. A grove of small oak and pine grew around it, and the outline of the whole group so reminded people of a couchant lion, that it was sometimes called the 'Lion-tree'. The old Welsh name was 'Ffawyddan-twys', or Tufted Beech, an instance of that nice discrimination of character common to Welsh local nomenclature. More than other beeches it was 'tufted'. From the capital of a smooth, columnar trunk, 21' girth at the ground, 18' 6" at 5' high and 13' 6" at its summit, 27' in air, issued, within the vertical space of 4' 6" four limbs, the girth of the two largest being 7' 6" each. These divided into many branches, and subdivided into thousands of twigs, all holding an ascending course till they formed an intricate "tuft", the terminal leaves of which waved 80' above the grass. On the fall of this giant I visited the spot, and was able to verify my measurements and obtain

61. The great oak at Llantilio Crossenny, girth 10m, April 1998.

others. The trunk was hollow, although outwardly sound; much wood remained, and I was able to estimate the number of rings in the butt. One half of the semi-diameter gave over 91 clearly, the total was at least 185. It will be understood from these figures that the tree was a magnificent specimen, and its fall a loss to the county, of which it was the central ornament.

The dimensions of most of the notable native trees of Wales are recorded by Hyde & Harrison in the successive editions of their *Welsh Timber Trees*, but they do not include the following impressive old specimens: an ash (*Fraxinus excelsior*) at Plas Newydd, Anglesey, 16ft in girth and 'straight as a javelin for 50ft'; a holly (*Ilex aquifolium*) at Clochfaen, Llanidloes, reported as girthing 29ft 8½in. at the base in 1888; two poplars at Rhuthun, girthing over 18ft at 5ft from the ground; and two lindens at Llanfair (Denbighshire) over 18½ft in girth.

Over the centuries, the owners of private estates in Wales have obviously taken great pride in their best specimen trees, native and exotic. The trees in individual Welsh parks and estates have formed the subject of numerous articles in arboricultural and horticultural journals since the nineteenth century. Special attention was paid to the performance of newly introduced exotics, mainly conifers, and some of these are described later on in this book, for example the large larches (*Larix decidua*) at Hafod and at Pen-pont (see p. 166), and Leighton redwoods (see p. 209). Perhaps the most important of the older publications on Welsh estate trees was Lord Dynevor's book *Trees at Dynevor Castle* (1934), which gives the dimensions of specimen trees of nineteen different species in the Castle Park at Llandeilo.

Chapter IX

CONIFERS, NURSERIES AND PLANTING

Master Thomas Bowen of Trefloine in the County of Pembroke . . . had manie young and small plants of this kind [the Firre tree] brought him home by saylers from the Newfoundland.

R.C. *An olde thrift newly revived*, 1612, p.8

The influence of John Evelyn and the legislation of the seventeenth century exerted comparatively little effect in promoting forestry in Wales, though some planting of ornamentals and exotics did take place, and commercial hardwoods were established by direct sowing and by planting.

During the course of the eighteenth century, a succession of acts were passed in order to stimulate the development and utilization of the forest resources of the American colonies, and also to promote planting and the protection and preservation of woods and plantations in Britain itself, the more important affecting woods in England and Wales being listed in Table 9. In addition to these general acts, a total of 179 individual Acts of Parliament were passed between 1714 and 1901 for the enclosure of individual commons in Wales, and in at least some the purpose of enclosure included planting.[1]

The legislation relating to forests as shown in Table 9 remained extremely severe during the eighteenth century. The *Black Act* of 1723, which decreed the death penalty for a number of offences in royal forests or chases, including cutting down or otherwise destroying 'any trees planted in any avenue, or growing in any garden, orchard or plantation, for ornament, shelter or profit', was enforced on many occasions throughout the eighteenth century and even as late as 1814, when an Essex labourer was hanged for cutting down an orchard.[2]

Table 9. The more important forest acts of the eighteenth century

Year	Brief outline of main features or purpose of the act
1714/15 (1 Geo. I)	encouraging the planting and preservation of timber trees, fruit trees and other trees for ornament, shelter or profit (making parishes liable to owners for malicious damage to timber trees)
1719/20 (6 Geo. I)	amended and extended the above
1722/23 (9 Geo. I)	The Black Act, decreeing the death penalty for various offences in royal forests, including cutting down or destroying trees
1754/55 (28 Geo. II)	against burning in forests

1755/56 (29 Geo. II)	for agreed enclosure of waste lands for planting
1763/64 (4 Geo. III)	for seizure of any tools and implements used in unlawful cutting
1765/66 (6 Geo. III)	encouraging the cultivation and preservation of trees (defining as timber trees oak, beech, ash, elm, fir, chestnut and aspen); with an amendment to include also walnut, lime, cedar, sycamore and birch as timber trees
1772/73 (13 Geo. III)	amending the above to include also poplar, alder, larch, maple and hornbeam as timber trees.

The legislation also clearly reflected the increasing importance of plantations, and the start of conifer plantations. The definition of timber trees had hitherto been restricted to oak, ash, elm and beech; in 1766 the range was extended to include 'fir' and 'cedar', and in 1773 further extended to embrace other species, including larch.

In this respect, legislation as usual tended to lag rather behind events. Even in Wales, commercial plantations of forest trees, including conifers, were made during the eighteenth century. Although the accounts of the Gwydyr estate in the 1680s show evidence of carefully organized forest management for commercial ends, there is no indication of plantations or of conifers. However, shortly afterwards, some estate owners in Wales began to plant conifers, one of the first being Lord Mansel at Margam. In 1738 a survey of the woods and trees on the Margam estate by a three-man team headed by the 'house carpenter' Edward Harris (who was in effect the forester, being 'solely entrusted with the care, management and inspection of the woods of the sd. Lord Mansel') recorded the weight in tons of all timber 'eight inches square and above now growing on the estate'.[3] The results of the survey are given in Table 10.

The identity of the fir (spelled 'ffirr' in the survey) is uncertain, but it was probably Scots pine. Most of the timber was classed as 'thriveing', which means young trees or trees approaching maturity. The pollards were 'trees that have been from time to time Lopp't and Headed for severall uses', and were mostly scattered in hedges and hedgerows of the estate.

Table 10. Timber survey on Lord Mansel's Margam estate, 1738

Species	Standing timber, in tons			
	Thriving	Full-grown	Decaying	Pollards
Oak	12,449¼	482½	22½	1,410¾
Ash	413¼	49½	4	106¾
Elm	140½	7	3	17¾
Sycamore	123¼	18½	–	5½
Walnut	5¼	–	–	–
Chestnut	15¼	–	–	–
Fir	7½	–	–	–
Total	13,153¼	557½	29½	1,540¾

The current prices of the various species of timber are given in Table 11, and show that the young softwood ('fir') was valued at 30 shillings per ton, the same as walnut and more than any of the other hardwoods. This is a striking indication of its rarity value.

Table 11. Prices of species and categories of timber on the Margam estate, 1738, in shillings/ton

Species	Thriving	Full-grown	Decaying	Pollards
Oak	20	16	15	12
Ash	18	18	10	10
Elm	18	18	10	10
Sycamore	18	18	–	10
Walnut	30	–	–	–
Chestnut	25	–	–	–
Fir	30	–	–	–

Another annotated list of trees on part of the Margam estate, undated but undoubtedly early in the eighteenth century, also includes fir:

lime	36	(7 very fine)
oak	872	(at least half will measure as timber and some very large)
ash	142	(generally small)
elm	95	(some 'pritty large & generally midling')
poplar	58	(for the most part well grown)
beech	117	(small, except about 20)
sycamore	14	(half large, the rest small)
fir	5	(& Do. small)
lignum vita	5	
horse chestnuts	5	
yew	1	

Pictorial evidence also attests the increasing planting of conifers on estates in this period, as ornamental plantings became semi-commercial. For example, large numbers of conifers were planted at Erddig House between 1715 and 1740 because no conifers are shown on a plan of 1715, but an engraving by Thomas Badeslade in 1740 shows many conifers, apparently pine, large and small, planted in rows and avenues; some of their stumps still remain. An engraving of Neath Castle and the Gnoll House in 1741, by Samuel and Nathaniel Buck, shows rows of large conifers, apparently spruce.

The identity of the conifers planted is not always certain. They were usually called 'fir' and this could refer to Scots pine (*Pinus sylvestris*) or Norway spruce (*Picea abies*), or possibly even silver fir (*Abies alba*). Silver fir was planted in 1722 at Newport (Pembs).[4] Sometimes the conifers were described more precisely, as Scotch or Scots fir (*Pinus sylvestris*) and spruce fir (*Picea abies*). For example, Arthur Young on a tour of the Vale of Tywi in the 1770s reported that the locally grown spruce fir was 'very good; almost as white as Norway deals', and sold for 7d. per foot.[5]

62. Conifers planted in the eighteenth century to adorn a cascade in the Gnoll demesne, Neath (engraving by Newman, *c*.1850).

On the Gogerddan estate a large conifer plantation was established in the middle of the eighteenth century. Wyndham, who saw it in the mid 1770s, referred to 'a very extensive and flourishing plantation of firs, which covered the steep declivities of hills'. He maintained that 'Such an example deserves imitation, especially, in country where the soil and climate seem averse to the production of all other kinds of forest trees. But, notwithstanding the very thriving state of this plantation, the beauty of its appearance, and the certain profit attending it, I am sorry to add, that this was the only instance of such oeconomical cultivation which we saw in this part of our tour'.[6]

It is significant that Wyndham stressed not only the vigour, beauty and profitability of this large conifer plantation, and the suitability of Wales for such plantations, but also the fact that the plantation was at that time a rare and unusual feature in the rural landscape. He was not to know how greatly things would change in the twentieth century.

The other European conifer that was planted in Wales in the eighteenth century was the larch (*Larix decidua*), the earliest known plantings of which were at Abercamlais and Pen-pont in Breconshire in about 1740.[7] However, although the conifers of northern Europe were the only ones used in commercial plantations in the eighteenth century, increasing interest was also being shown in North American species. Newfoundland 'fir' had been introduced into Pembrokeshire before 1600, and Virginian cedar to north Wales in 1685, but later on, more extensive collections became possible. For example, William Morris acquired cones, seeds and acorns from North America, and tried to grow them in his garden at Holyhead. On 16 May 1761 he wrote that he had sown about fifty different kinds of North American conifers and oaks.[8] On the Rhual estate in Flintshire, the planting in 1774 included small numbers of 'Black American Fir, Pinaster, Virginia Cedar, Newfoundland Pine and Balm of Gilead Fir', as well as larger amounts of 'Scotch Fir, Silver Fir and Larch'.[9]

Nurseries

> One- and two-year-old seedlings of all sorts of forest trees, nearly as cheap as in Scotland, reckoning carriage, and one thousand worth two of theirs.
>
> John Williams' nursery catalogue, Burgedin near Welshpool, *c*.1810

However, casual acquisitions, gifts and exchanges of seeds and planting stock were clearly inadequate to sustain the establishment of plantations on any large scale. To meet this need, commercial forest nurseries were becoming established in England, Ireland and Scotland early in the eighteenth century, but no forest nurseries were started in Wales until towards the end of the century. Accordingly, Welsh planters seeking planting stock for afforestation schemes were obliged to turn to commercial nurserymen outside Wales.

In 1722, the Chirk Castle estate bought '10 dozon of Scotch Fyr plants' at 1s. 6d. per dozen, and '2 ounces of ye seed' at 1s. 6d. per ounce from Mr Robert Beck, apparently a commercial nurseryman at Chester.[10] Welsh planters commonly acquired planting stock from nurseries in England and Ireland, and even in Scotland, such as the famous firm of Dickson's at Hassendeanburn in Teviotdale, established in 1729.

Walker's nursery at Marybone in Ireland supplied elms to Anglesey in 1735. Holbert of Gloucester sold spruce, silver fir and larch to estates in Breconshire in 1778. Malcolm of Kennington supplied Golden Grove with many conifers and hardwoods in 1781, and Watts of Piccadilly sold conifers, chestnut and oak to Pencerrig in 1794. Nurseries in Birmingham, Liverpool and Scotland supplied large amounts of planting stock to Corsygedol and Hafod in the 1790s. Mackie of Norwich shipped plants to Ffynone. Other nurseries that supplied Welsh estates with plants in the early decades of the nineteenth century were Miller & Sweet of Bristol (Golden Grove), Rogers of Chester (Llanferres), Austin & M'Aslan of Glasgow (Penrhyn), and Dixon of Chester (Stanage).[11]

The shortest journeys were Gloucester to Brecon and Chester to Denbigh. Plants were also freighted by sea from Norwich to Pembrokeshire, wrapped in matting, and from Ireland to Anglesey. Very long journeys were also made, by road or by a combination of coastal vessel and road transport, from London and Scotland to north and west Wales. These journeys caused deterioration and failure of the planting stock, as described for example by Hassall: 'Some seedlings are purchased in boxes, from the London and other nurseries; but the high price of the land and labour in those parts, occasions the plants to be so crowded in the nurseries, that when they come to be set out in more exposed situations, they do not often thrive to the satisfaction of the planter'.[12]

Walter Davies also described the problems associated with buying stock from distant nurseries: 'Proprietors planting upon a large scale, and not raising trees from seed in their own nurseries, were formerly used to procure seedlings of larch, firs, and pines, &c from Scotland; but owing to their heating in close bundles, and otherwise damaging upon the road, not above one half, and frequently not above one fourth, of the number, could be expected to grow'.[13]

This excessive mortality led many landowners in Wales either to set up their own estate nurseries or to encourage the development of local commercial nurseries in Wales.

Technical information on nursery management and plantation establishment was contained in the numerous treatises, pamphlets and books on forestry and trees that had been published during the seventeenth century, and which were available in Wales. It was not until the mid eighteenth century, however, that publications on forest trees by Welsh authors appeared. The first of these was *A Treatise on Forest-Trees,* published in 1753 by William Watkins, curate of Hay-on-Wye.[14] Watkins urged landowners to promote planting as a 'public and private Oeconomy', to ensure naval defence, the creation of a strategic reserve of timber, and as a benefit to posterity; he gave practical advice and rules on fencing, site cultivation, the nursery, the management of young plantations, etc.; and also presented directions for the propagation of eleven major tree species or species-groups. These were mainly the major native hardwoods (oak, ash, elm, beech) and also wild cherry, chestnut, sycamore, walnut and lime, but Watkins also dealt with four coniferous species: spruce, Scots pine, cedar and cypress. The other publication emanating from Wales and dealing with forest trees was *Idea Agriculturae* by the Rev. Henry Rowlands of Llanidan in Anglesey, written in 1704 but not published until 1764. It dealt *inter alia* with nursery establishment and management, planting for shelter from sea winds, and the site requirements of various species.

There seem to have been two main types of nursery on estates in Wales. The first was the normal seedling nursery from which plants were removed to their final planting site. The other type was the 'nursery wood' or 'nursery plantation', in other words an area of land marked out, direct-sown with tree seed, and then gradually thinned out to the desired final density by removing surplus plants to a nursery where they could be held as further planting stock until required, this being the equivalent of the transplants or standards section of modern nurseries.

Typical instructions for the formation of seedling nurseries are those given by Henry Rowlands:

> let every Freeholder or tenant, if he will not go to the Expence of buying Quicksets, fence to himself a little Garden or Nursery in some waste Corner of a Field, of the best and deepest Soil, near his House; and so fence his Nursery that no Cattle may be able to break in upon it, to tear and brouse it; which Garden one may make up in any Place that is convenient for it, with the Labour of two Men in two Days; then let him dig, manure and order the Soil of it, one Day more; and

then sow in it the Seeds, Berries, and Kernels of such Quicks and Plants as he will judge will best grow and prosper in the Place; and these Seeds he may in the Seasons of them procure for the Gathering.

This Nursery well dressed, weeded and husbanded, will in a few Years furnish him with Quicks for as many Hedges as he shall have Occasion to raise; and, as he spends his Seminary upon new Hedges, he may resupply it with Seeds, Berries, and Kernels again; and so continue his whole Farm or Tenement with new Fences yearly, till it be thoroughly inclosed, warm, and well sheltered.[15]

The transplant nursery is described by William Watkins. He generally advocated the establishment of plantations by direct sowing on well prepared and securely fenced sites, and then thinning out the surplus trees and removing them to the nursery and planting them at 3 x 3ft square spacing: 'Your Nursery, in which you intend to train your young Plants for removing, ought to be very well digged, and free from all Weeds; and such a Soil and Situation as is most like to that you design your Trees should be transplanted to for good. For, if your Trees are taken from a good Soil to a steril one, from a deep to a shallow, from a stiff to a light, &c. they will seldom thrive'.[16]

Watkins recommended growing rarer and more tender plants such as cedar of Lebanon in boxes for two years, and then transplanting into the nursery. A standard 3 x 3ft spacing for transplants in the nursery was recommended for oak, ash, beech, wild black cherry, walnut, cedar, pine and spruce, and wider spacing of 3 x 6ft for 1-year layered lime and elms.

These instructions, of course, follow the same general pattern as those given in greater detail in the treatises published in England, and there is no doubt that these standard instructions were followed by landowners in Wales. One typical example is John Morris of Clasemont near Morriston. In the last quarter of the eighteenth century he planted over half a million trees, principally beech, oak and ash, but also fir, larch, sycamore, birch, sweet chestnut, plane and poplar. A contemporary observer noted that Morris raised nearly all his trees from seed: 'when they are about three feet high, he plants them out about a yard distant; when the trees increase in size, so as nearly to touch each other, they are taken out to make further plantations; so that every young wood is in fact a nursery'.[17]

The seed for the establishment of private estate nurseries was obtained in various ways. Seed of exotics, especially larch and other conifers, had to be bought from commercial nurserymen outside Wales. Seed of native species, especially oak, ash and, in south-east Wales, beech, was obtained from local sources. The need to use good parent trees was well known. For example, Watkins' instruction was to gather 'a sufficient Quantity of Acorns off tall straight thriving Trees',[18] but it is certain that seed was often collected and used without any regard to the quality of the parent trees, being bought by the bushel from local people who doubtless gathered from the most convenient source (Fig. 63). For example, plantations were established at Chirk in 1718 from acorns gathered locally by children at 15d. per measure,[19] and plantations in Caernarfonshire were made in 1808 using acorns bought for 2s. per bushel.[20] In the nursery at Hafod, acorns were sown in rows about 1ft apart for ease of weeding, the tap roots were pruned with a spade to promote a well ramified root system, and the plants were lifted as two-year-old seedlings. The Hafod nursery produced nearly one million oak seedlings between 1798 and 1802.[21] Wildings of pioneer species such as birch and mountain ash were also dug up and used in some afforestation schemes, for example at Hafod.

Many Welsh estates, large and small, set up their own nurseries in order to avoid relying on commercial sources of planting stock, or at least to supplement the supplies obtained from commercial nurserymen. Thomas Johnes of Hafod and John Morris of Clasemont are examples of owners who resolved upon the establishment of a regular estate nursery for the production of planting stock of forest trees. Other Welsh owners who did the same were Sir John Glynne of Hawarden, Sir Herbert Mackworth of the Gnoll, Bell Lloyd of Bodfach, and John Maurice Jones who had several nurseries on his extensive estates in Denbighshire and Merioneth. These nurseries were often under the supervision of expatriate Scottish staff, employed as gardeners, agents or foresters proper.

Increasing demand for planting stock, coupled with the active promotion of nursery activity by agricultural societies, eventually led to the formation of many small and a few larger commercial nurseries in Wales towards the end of the eighteenth and during the nineteenth century. The role of agricultural societies was quite significant in some areas, and during the half-century following the establishment of the Society of Arts in 1754, societies for the encouragement and improvement of agriculture were set up in every county of Wales. The first was the Brecknockshire Agricultural Society, set up in 1755, and this was followed by societies in Glamorgan and Carmarthen (both in 1772), Cardigan and Pembroke

63. Gathering acorns to supply the nurseries.

(both in 1784), and Monmouth (before 1794). The Radnorshire Society (later the Radnorshire Agricultural Society) was formed in 1790, the Wrexham society in 1796, Merioneth in 1801, Caernarfonshire in 1807, Anglesey in 1808, Vale of Clwyd in 1810, and Flintshire before 1833. Attempts were made to establish a Montgomeryshire agricultural society in 1795 and again in 1821.

These societies generally modelled themselves on the Society of Arts. Some were short-lived and ineffectual, while others had a long and distinguished history. Their general aim was to improve agriculture by the award of premiums or prizes to landowners, tenants and others for various classes of crops, livestock, advanced techniques, meritorious behaviour, and so on. Most of the societies gave prizes for the production and planting of hawthorn (white-thorn quicks), holly and crabapples for hedge planting, but only a few of the societies, notably those in Brecon, Cardigan and Carmarthen, included the promotion of forestry proper in their sphere of interest in the eighteenth century. The surviving records of these societies are generally very fragmentary, but they show the typical rules and premiums relating to forestry activities, and also give details of some of the achievements that were rewarded with premiums. For example, the premiums of the Society for the Encouragement of Agriculture and Industry in the County of Cardigan in the 1790s included the following:

Class IV Premium I. Planting Forest Trees.
To the person who shall plant, during the season (viz. from September last to May) the greatest number of forest trees, in order to raise timber, not fewer than 4000 and effectually fence and secure them, three guineas. The next greatest number, not fewer than 3000, two guineas.

Premium II. Planting by a Tenant.
To the occupier, being a tenant who shall plant as in the last premium, the greatest number of forest trees, not fewer than 600, and effectually fence and secure them, three guineas. The next greatest number as before, not fewer than 500, two guineas.

Premium III. Planting Willows, &c for Hurdles.
To the person who shall plant, during the season, the greatest number of any kind of willows, in the same manner as for a twig garden, (only the plants not quite so close,) or hazel, or any other wood used for twig hurdles and watling, not less than one acre, three guineas.
The next ditto, not less than half an acre, two guineas.

Premium IV. Forest Trees for Sale.
To the person who shall have for sale, at the time of giving in his claim, the greatest number of transplanted forest trees of his own raising, in rows about one foot by six inches, from plant to plant, three guineas.
The next greatest number, two guineas.

Premium V. White Thorn for Sale.
To the person who shall have for sale, at the time of giving in his claim, the greatest quantity of white thorn plants, on an average eighteen inches high, fenced in, and kept clean of weeds, not fewer than ten thousand, two guineas.
The next greatest number, not fewer than eight thousand, one guinea.[22]

64. Advertisement by James Dickson & Sons, nurserymen in Chester and north Wales, late nineteenth century.

The premiums of the Society for the Encouragement of Agriculture and Industry in the County of Carmarthen followed closely the Cardigan premiums. The Brecknockshire Agricultural Society gave premiums from 1768 until 1810 for collecting seeds and establishing forest trees. In 1810 the premium was a gold medal worth £5 'to the person (whatever his Property) who shall prepare the greatest Quantity of Land, and sow it with Acorns, Ashkeys, Chestnut, Beechmast, and Seeds of other Timber Trees, and shall preserve the young Growth by Weeding, Hoeing and good Fence against Cattle; keep such Coppices in good Order for five years, not less than two Acres'.[23]

The premiums appear to have been popular, and certainly stimulated some planting by tenant farmers. For example, in 1796 John Bowen of Cwmbychan Farm, Troed-yr-aur, planted 16,000 trees and received a cup worth three guineas, while John Williams, tenant of Penywern Fawr, Llandygwydd, received three guineas for planting 1,100 trees. Prizes were also awarded to people for establishing osiers and for raising nursery stock. For example, Daniel Davies of Pant-yr-odyn in Troed-yr-aur parish was awarded three guineas in 1797 for having planted upwards of one acre of willows and hazel for hurdles, wattling and hoops.[24]

The following are typical examples of the awards made in 1798 for raising forest plants for sale: John Williams, Penwernfawr, Llandygwydd parish (20,000 trees), and Benjamin Williams, also of Penwernfawr (40,000 white thorn).

The rules of the societies prevented any individual landlord from taking the prize year after year, and landowners generally received honorary prizes only. Their aim was to inspire the tenants and peasantry, and the prizes in the form of cash, cups or implements were generally reserved for them. The emphasis in Breconshire was on the production and planting of native hardwoods, whereas the premiums in Cardiganshire often went to men such as Thomas Johnes, the bulk of whose commercial planting consisted of European larch. The agricultural societies promoted tree planting, nurseries and forestry in general in the three counties of Brecon, Cardigan and Carmarthen only, and even here the effect was significant only for the period 1770 to 1810. Interest in forest planting generally declined thereafter.

Besides the active promotion of nurseries by the agricultural societies, one of the main factors stimulating the development of local forest nurseries in Wales was undoubtedly the expense and delay involved in purchasing planting stock from nurserymen in England and Scotland, and also the dubious quality of many of the plants, as a result of the long transport times. The planter's fear of a high failure rate was presumably one reason why some nurserymen undertook to establish plantations and then to 'insure' them for several years, with regular inspection and making good any failures by beating up. A good example of this system is a large wasteland afforestation scheme at Llanferres in Denbighshire, for which the owner, Henry Potts, was awarded the large Silver Medal of the Royal Society of Arts in 1821. Some 194 acres were planted up with 528,240 forest trees, chiefly European larch and Scots pine, the planting being done between October 1817 and April 1818 by Messrs Archibald Dickson & Sons, nurserymen of Hassendeanburn near Hawick. Several hardwood species were also included in the planting. The numbers and types of trees, all from the Scottish nursery, were vouched for in a certificate supplied by Archibald Dickson, who also inspected the plantations in November 1820.[25]

The many small and a few larger commercial nurseries in Wales produced a wide variety of forest planting stock and hedging plants. Unfortunately, many of these enterprises were short-lived, or run on a cottage-scale only, and evidence is at best fragmentary, even for the larger nurseries. Some of the nurseries are known to have published printed catalogues, but unfortunately none of these appears to have survived. Some details of size of the nurseries and the types of plants produced at Burgedin and Felindre were recorded in the reports to the Board of Agriculture. At Burgedin, Mr John Williams managed a 'very extensive concern in the nursery line', and inserted as an appendix to his printed catalogue of forest trees the following advertisement: 'One and two-year-old seedlings of all sorts of forest trees, nearly as cheap as in Scotland, reckoning carriage, and one thousand worth two of theirs'. Walter Davies considered that this was true when the tenderness of seedlings, distance of carriage, and length of time, are considered.[26] Williams and other Welsh nurserymen followed the example of the big Scottish nursery firms and guaranteed trees of their own growth and planting for a number of years.

There were no commercial nurseries of any size raising forest trees for sale in Carmarthenshire in 1794.[27] However, the situation in Cardiganshire and Carmarthenshire improved considerably in the next twenty years, and by about 1815 there were in the area six nurserymen, some occupying nurseries from five to ten acres in size.[28] The largest of these was Hindes' nursery at Felindre near Newcastle Emlyn, which occupied some 18 acres on a site rather unwisely chosen with poor clay soil and some peat, which needed expensive draining. In 1810-15 Hindes' sales of forest trees from this nursery averaged about 400,000 plants a year. One year he sold a total of 578,596 plants, consisting of 576,365 forest trees, 1,506 fruit trees, and 725 flowering shrubs. The prices ranged from 20s. to 50s. per 1,000, according to size, species and demand. Hindes' nursery stocked seedlings, transplants and standards of over twenty species of forest trees, as the following inventory shows:

Species, age and size of plants	No. of plants
Oak seedlings	500,000
Oak seedlings, 2 and 3 years, transplanted	90,000
Ash seedlings, 2 years old	200,000
Ash seedlings, transplanted, 1½-4ft	160,000
Beech, transplanted, 1-4ft	50,000
Birch, various ages	10,000
Horse chestnuts, transplanted	5,000
Spanish chestnuts, transplanted, 2-4ft	3,000
Wych elm, transplanted, 2-4ft	13,000
English elm, transplanted, 4-7ft	5,000
Sycamore	20,000

Mountain ash	20,000
Plane trees, 6-9ft	200
Lime trees, 4-5ft	500
Black poplars	3,000
Silver & Balm of Gilead fir	5,000
Spruce firs, various sorts and sizes	50,000
Scotch pines, 1-3 years transplanted	500,000
Weymouth pines and pineasters	3,000
Larch seedlings	300,000
Larch seedlings, 2 years transplanted	200,000
	2,137,700
White thorns and crab stocks for grafting, 1-4 years	500,000
Apple trees, of choice sorts	3,000
Total	2,640,700

Like the big Scottish nurserymen, Hindes undertook planting on contract. For example, on one estate in the Teifi valley he planted a total of 395,000 trees over a period of three successive spring planting seasons (1811, 1812, 1813). The plants were 2- and 3-year-old larch, fir, pine, oak, ash, elm and beech. The plantation was established at the following charges:

Planting stock, per 1,000	£1 0s.
Carriage (15 miles), per 1,000	4s.
Planting, per 1,000	12s.
Total	£1 16s.

Hindes guaranteed the growth of 17 plants out of every 20, in other words he undertook to make good any early mortality by replacing plants in order to achieve the specified survival rate. The whole plantation cost £711.

Even in Angelsey, notoriously the most treeless of the Welsh counties, commercial nurseries were established in the first half of the nineteenth century.[29] One was established at Maesyllan, another at Henfelin was offering half a million trees for sale in 1828, and another at Llynfaes sold over 100,000 plants in 1832, and had stock of half a million plants growing.

Side by side with the larger nurseries there developed in Wales a 'cottage-scale' forest nursery industry. Its beginnings were indeed humble: 'Cottagers, who at first tried by way of experiment, to raise a few plants from the cones of firs, and pines, from acorns, or other mast, to shelter their own dwellings, have by degrees been encouraged to extend their nurseries, and accommodate the public with plants'.[30] Iolo Morganwg cites an early example: the bard Benjamin Simon (1703-93), a shoemaker or bookbinder who died a pauper, planted a wide range of conifers and hardwoods for shelter around his cottage at Porth Myrddin near Abergwili in the 1740s.[31]

The very small nurseries, producing forest planting stock and also whitethorn and blackthorn quicksets for hedging, were a feature of the countryside in the nineteenth century. They were called *gerddi coed bach* (small tree gardens), and were usually tended by local women, some of whom had obtained experience in London nurseries as migrant workers. D.J. Williams gives a delightful description of the women and the nurseries at Tŷ Mowr near Llanybydder: 'The plants were grown from seed . . . It was a pleasure to see them, with a few old women in Welsh dress and petticoat opening the drills with small spades, or squatting down weeding industriously. The rows ran as straight as linen threads, and thousands of fine green spears pierced the air like an army from Lilliput'.[32]

Some of the orders placed with English nurseries are revealing in that they show the surprising variety of trees being planted on Welsh estates before 1800. For example, in 1794 Thomas Jones of Pencerrig bought from a London nursery:

100	Balm of Gilead, bedded
50	White American Spruce, bedded
50	Black American Spruce, bedded
200	Spanish Chestnut, 3-year-old
100	Filberts, 3-year-old
100	Stone or Italian Pine, 2-year-old
100	Pine ashes, 2-year-old
100	Cluster Pine, 2-year-old
1	Quart Ilex Acorns[33]

and John Vaughan of Golden Grove bought from a Kennington nursery in 1781:

600	Weymouth Pines	24	Hemlock Spruce Firs
600	Spruce Firs	400	lime trees
200	Silver Firs	24	Alexandria Laurels
500	Common Larch	200	New White Broom
600	Portugal Laurels	400	Common Laurels
300	Common Alaternus	150	Fine Red Virginian Cedars
24	Cedars of Lebanon		

as well as Scotch Fir, Spanish Chestnut, Beech, etc.[34]

The prices of forest seed and nursery plants varied with the species, age, height, nursery source, size of order, demand and transport costs. Only rarely do records give adequate details of the type and cost of planting stock used, and therefore it is not easy to reconstruct any pattern in prices, more especially as no early catalogues of Welsh nurserymen have survived. The prices of plants bought by a number of Welsh estates from various sources during the late eighteenth and early nineteenth century conform broadly with those given by Harvey from his analysis of some thirty priced catalogues of English and a few Scottish nurseries, covering the period 1775-1845.[35] The general picture is of stability of prices before 1800 and gross variations thereafter, starting at a high level and generally dropping.

65. 'The Woodman and his Dog' by Thomas Barker of Pontypool, c.1787.

Tree Planting by 'Spirited Planters'

> Below me trees unnumbered rise
> Beautiful in various dyes:
> The gloomy pine, the poplar blue
> The yellow beech, the sable yew
> The slender fir, that taper grows
> The sturdy oak, with broad-spread boughs
>
> John Dyer, *Grongar Hill*, 1727

The list of species known to have been planted on estates in Wales in the period 1750-1825 (see Table 12) contains all the major species that were planted commercially and many that were planted for ornamental purposes, though it is probable that some other species not included in the list were also planted as ornamentals.

The main commercial species used in plantations during the eighteenth and in the first half of the nineteenth century were the European conifers (Scots pine, Norway spruce and European larch, and small amounts of silver fir), and the native or long-naturalized hardwoods, principally oak, ash, beech, elm and sycamore. Throughout the eighteenth century, many plantations, of conifers and of hardwoods, were established by direct sowing of seed in patches of prepared soil at a spacing of about 8ft x 8ft, and thinned out later as necessary. Increasingly during this century plantations were also established with seedlings or with transplanted stock, often quite large plants. Elm and lime were usually established by planting layered plants, and poplars by cuttings.[36]

Table 12. Species known to have been planted on Welsh estates, 1750-1825

Conifers
Larch (*Larix decidua*)
Scots pine (*Pinus sylvestris*)
Norway spruce (*Picea abies*)
Silver fir (*Abies alba*)
Pineaster or cluster pine (*Pinus pinaster*)
Balm of Gilead fir (*Abies balsamea*)
Weymouth pine (*Pinus strobus*)
Corsican pine (*Pinus nigra* var. *maritima*)
American larch (*Larix laricina*)
White American spruce (*Picea glauca*)
Black American spruce (*Picea mariana*)
Italian pine (*Pinus pinea*)
Newfoundland pine (*Pinus ?*)
Hemlock spruce fir (*Tsuga canadensis*)
Red Virginian Cedar (*Juniperus virginiana*)
Cedar of Lebanon (*Cedrus libani*)
Italian Cypress (*Cupressus sempervirens*)
Yew (*Taxus baccata*)

Broadleaves
Oak (*Quercus robur, Q. petraea*)
Beech (*Fagus sylvatica*)
Birch (*Betula*)
Ash (*Fraxinus excelsior*)
Mountain ash (*Sorbus aucuparia*)
Lucombe oak (*Quercus x hispanica*
   '*lucombeana*')
Portuguese laurel (*Prunus lusitanica*)
Scotch elm (*Ulmus glabra*)
English elm (*Ulmus procera*)
Spanish chestnut (*Castanea sativa*)
Horse chestnut (*Aesculus hippocastanum*)
Sycamore (*Acer pseudoplatanus*)
Alder (*Alnus* spp.)
Willow (*Salix* spp.)
Poplar (*Populus* spp.)
Black Italian poplar (*Populus x
   euramericana*)
White Italian poplar (abele) (*Populus alba*)

Athenian poplar (*Populus* sp.)
Golden willow (*Salix* sp.)
Balsam poplar (*Populus balsamifera*)
Filberts (*Corylus avellana*)
Ilex oak (*Quercus ilex*)
Limes (*Tilia* spp.)
Walnut (*Juglans regia*)

Acorns were either dibbled in, or sown in small prepared patches. For example, at Hafod the technique was to pare off a thin turf with a spade and throw it over. The exposed soil was loosened with the spade, and a spadeful lifted up, two or three acorns were thrown in by a boy and the earth replaced and gently trodden down.[37] These direct sowings of oak often gave excellent survival and growth rates, especially in the eastern parts of Wales. Sir Humphrey Howarth, MP for Radnorshire from 1722 to 1754, had set acorns himself and most of them had grown to timber of twenty inches square within his lifetime.[38]

Though native in south-east Wales, beech had not spread naturally northwards and had been planted little if at all in north Wales by 1700. Edward Lhuyd, for example, noted on 1 July 1690: 'in noe part of Northwales is found any flint or chalk, nor beech trees', and again on 24 November 1696: 'In South Wales I found several plants common, which I had never seen in North Wales, such as . . . Fagus'.[39]

A century later, Iolo Morganwg reported a few instances of beech as 'curiosities' in north Wales, at places such as Rhiwlas, Foelas, Cinmel Park, Gwydir and Conwy: 'Beech grows spontaneously in great abundance on Carreg y Gwalch (Gwydyr)' and 'very fine grove of many thousands of beech planted within the memory of living. some girt 6½ feet, many upwards of five. they are strait & very tall. a proof that beech will succeed in N.W. and once introduced will, as at Gwydir, propagate themselves. they grow here [near Conwy] on a bare schist'.[40]

Over 150,000 beech trees were planted on the Denbighshire and Merioneth estates of John Maurice Jones in the six planting seasons from 1804/05 to 1809/10.[41]

Sycamore, introduced into Britain from Europe soon after the Norman Conquest, was extensively planted for shelter, and as a producer of valuable wood particularly suitable for the manufacture of dairy utensils. Sycamore was planted early in the eighteenth century on estates such as Chirk and Margam, and later in quite considerable numbers on many other estates throughout Wales. In six years, over 50,000 sycamore trees were planted on John Maurice Jones' estates in north Wales.[42]

The interest in fast-growing plantation species extended also to poplars, which were planted widely on many estates. For example, in the period 1804/05 to 1809/10, a total of well over 75,000 poplars were planted on the estates of John Maurice Jones including black Italian, white Italian, balsam, and Athenian poplars.[43]

66. The woods at Hafod, by John 'Warwick' Smith, 1795.

The spacing and pruning of poplars were matters of interest and debate. The stem dimensions in a small block of black poplar, planted in 1774 at Tre-ffin at a square spacing on alluvium or mixed gravel and loam, were measured in 1805 and analysed by Walter Davies.[44] Stem volume growth was by far the greatest in unpruned trees having the greatest growing space.

An essential requirement for successful plantation establishment was adequate protection from trampling, barking and browsing by cattle, sheep and goats. This involved building walls, hedges, fences or banks surmounted by a wall, hedge or fence. All records of planting and recommendations on plantation establishment emphasise the vital importance of protection from livestock, especially sheep. At Hafod the plantation grounds were all properly enclosed before any of the trees were planted: 'The greatest part of the plantations is fenced with a stone wall, five feet high; the remainder with a turf-fence, the same height, with a dead hedge, and willows planted on the top . . . The stone walls which surround the plantations are all kept in proper repair by a man who has a yearly allowance for that purpose'.[45] However, even with all these expensive precautions, sheep still caused severe damage to some of the plantations.

The plantations of John Maurice Jones in Denbighshire and Merioneth were protected by walls six feet high or by quickset hedges,[46] and at Stanage a mixed plantation made in 1807/08 was enclosed by a 'park paling on one side and fleakes or cleft hurdles on the other'.[47] In some areas of north Wales, sheep were even hobbled in an effort to protect enclosed plantations, and goats, though not as numerous as sheep, were even more destructive. In Merioneth, landlords generally prohibited their tenants from keeping goats, which caused damage not only to young plantations but also to older trees because: 'where the trees are so high that they cannot easily get at the branches, they stand erect and pull them down, with their fore legs, holding them in that manner until they totally destroy the tree'.[48]

Modern experience has shown that drainage is vital to the success of plantation schemes on many of the upland sites in Wales, but for many estates draining was an expense that was avoided wherever possible in afforestation schemes. Even so, considerable drainage works were undertaken by some estates, as for example Corsygedol in the big plantings carried out there between 1795 and 1815.[49]

Site preparation within the enclosures depended on the method of plantation establishment, and on the ground cover. For direct sowing, the general rule was complete ploughing or digging, or the cultivation of prepared patches. Smaller seedlings or transplants were notch-planted, usually with no or only minimal soil cultivation. Larger plants were hole-planted.

The sites afforested were generally those judged incapable of improvement for agriculture, because they were too steep and uneven, or had very shallow and stony soils. In the period of planting at the end of the eighteenth and early in the nineteenth century, the areas planted were generally up to 1,000ft or in some cases even up to 1,200ft above sea level.

The size of planting stock varied according to the species and the preference of the planter, but for conifer plantations, two-year seedlings were generally preferred. For instance, Thomas Johnes looked upon 'the two-years-old seedling Larches as preferable to any other sizes for planting high grounds, as the winds make little or no impression upon their tops before their roots get properly fixed in the grounds'.[50]

Similar stock – namely two-year seedlings of oak, Scots pine and larch – was used for a 90-acre plantation in the parish of Beddgelert in 1814.[51] Again in a planting of 528,240 trees in 1817-18 at Llanferres the bulk of the planting stock were two-year seedlings of Scots pine and larch, and some larch transplants 9-18 inches tall.[52]

The method of planting also depended on the stock. Holes had to be dug for larger plants, but most estates found the labour requirement and expense to be excessive for large plantation schemes. Examples of the practice of hole-planting can be cited from Stanage where in 1808-09 a total of 5,000 larch 3-7ft high and 4000 oak 2-4ft high, were planted in holes fifteen inches in diameter, at a spacing of three or four feet. The holes were dug and prepared by men, and the planting was done by women and children, the children holding the tree and the women putting in the mould and firming the trees in with their feet. The Stanage estate persisted in hole-planting: in 1827, 35 acres of ground were planted with 66,500 trees including Scots pine, spruce, larch, silver fir, beech, oak and sweet chestnut. The total cost of establishing the plantation was £153 13s. 7d. of which the planting stock accounted for £99 15s., while the making of 48,400 holes cost £23 7s. 10d.[53]

For smaller plants, nicking-in or notching with a spade or mattock was the general method of planting. For example, at Hafod 'a man with a spade, holding the edge of it towards him, makes a cut about six inches deep if there is that depth of soil; he then turns the spade the right way and makes a cut across the end of the other thus ⊥; he then works his spade backwards and forwards three or four times, to loosen the mold for the roots of the plants to grow therein. A boy attends with a bundle of trees, to assist every man: the boy puts one tree in each hole, and presses with his foot the turf hard about the roots, to make the tree stand firm'.[54]

The technique was similar in other planting schemes, for example at Beddgelert: 'the labourers being each provided with a small pick or mattock, and a basket to hold the plants, and placing themselves within a yard of each other, proceed to work, striking the broad end of the mattock deep into the ground, and loosening the soil a little the plant is then placed in the hole, and the soil well closed about it with the heel ... The labourers are supplied with plants by boys, who carry them from the persons who dig them up, and shorten their roots'.[55]

67. Emblem of Thomas Johnes' press at Hafod, incorporating a tree-planting spade.

The planting rate at Hafod for a team consisting of one man and a boy was 1,000 plants per day. In the Beddgelert operation, a good workman was expected to plant at least 500 plants a day. Supervision of the work was often strict. For example, at Hafod one man's job was to give each newly planted tree a tug to see that it was properly planted and firmed in; the plants were generally put in so securely that the top would break before they could be pulled up.

The planting season was from October through to the spring, sometimes as late as April. Care was taken to protect bare-rooted planting stock from desiccation between the nursery and the planting site. The Scots staff on the Hafod estate devised a method of coating the roots with a slurry made of 'muck water and finely sifted mould', especially for plantings carried out late in the spring: 'a hole is dug about two feet in diameter and the same in depth; it is then half-filled with water, and fine mold is added, to make it like thin mud: a man then takes as many trees in both his hands as he can conveniently hold to drench in the mud: having prepared a heap of dry soil near the side of the hole, he alternately draws the roots of the plants through the above mud-hole and the dry soil, and thus the fibres of the roots are prevented from hardening or drying, as they would otherwise do'.[56]

The technique was successful, for of 80,000 larch planted on a very dry site in April 1796 and which had little or no rain for nearly two months after planting, not more than 200 died.

Plant spacing varied with the species and size of the planting stock. In the earlier plantings on the Hafod estate, two-year seedling larch were planted at

2 x 2ft, one-year transplants at 2½ x 2½ft, and larger plants at 3½ x 3½ft. With the youngest plants, this gave a planting density of about 10,000 plants per acre; in the later years, larch was planted at 4,000 plants per acre. Also at Hafod, ash 1-3ft high were planted 6-8ft apart and oak 1-2ft high at 4-5ft apart.[57]

In the wasteland afforestation scheme at Llanferres, the spacing was mainly four feet, but somewhat denser in the more exposed places. In replanting a cleared woodland site, oak was planted nine feet apart, with beech, sycamore and larch planted in between as nurses to the oak.[58] In the plantings in the Denbigh and Merioneth estates of John Maurice Jones in 1804-09, the planting densities were generally of the order of 5,000-9,000 plants per acre.[59]

Much wider spacings, reminiscent of modern agroforestry schemes, were advocated for larch by Iolo Morganwg, from his observations of the plantations at Pen-pont (Breconshire).[60] He proposed either a spacing of 5½ x 5½ yards, equivalent to 160 plants per acre on a 40-year rotation, which would ensure abundant yields of grazing forage throughout the life of the plantation, or a spacing of 8¼ x 8¼ft equivalent to 640 plants per acre, which would still produce large amounts of grazing in addition to the wood. It is important to remember that livestock grazing was an integral part of woodland management in most areas. For instance, the Glamorgan part of the Plymouth estate had nearly 3,000 acres of woodland in 1766, mostly in small blocks of less than ten acres and mainly if not exclusively oak and other broadleaves, but in nearly every case the use was recorded as 'pasture and wood' or sometimes 'herbage and wood', 'meadow and wood' or even 'arable and wood'.[61]

In the period from about 1780 onwards, planting was undertaken on most estates in Wales, often on quite a large scale, but although details are known for some estates it is not possible to get accurate statistics for the country as a whole. The Rev. Walter Davies, reporting on the state of agriculture in Wales for the Board of Agriculture, estimated that the rate of planting in south Wales from 1800 to 1815 was of the order of at least three million trees per annum.[62] The figure for north Wales was probably of a similar order. Most of this was afforestation of non-woodland sites, and represented an overall planting rate of perhaps 500-1,000 acres per annum. Some of the major planting operations during the period 1770-1830 were as follows:

John Morris of Clasemont planted half a million trees on his estate in Glamorgan in 1770-95, the Penrhyn estate 600,000 in 1780-97 and the Peterwell and Millfield estate in Cardiganshire 395,000 trees in 1811-13; Mr Vancouver planted 460,000 trees at Llangennech in 1804, Talbot perhaps a million at Margam in 1780-1814, and Potts over half a million at Llanferres in the single season 1817/18; the Stanage estate planted over 650,000 trees in the period 1805-31, Lord Newborough over 3,700,000 on his Denbighshire and Caernarfonshire estates in 1815-27, and over 1,700,000 trees were planted on the estates on John Maurice Jones in Denbighshire and Merioneth in 1804-10.[63]

Who then was the greatest of all the 'spirited planters' in Wales? Some planting was done by the Cawdor estates in Wales, but much more in Scotland, and it was this which misled two eminent Welsh historians into calling Baron

68. Thomas Johnes of Hafod, 1748-1816, the greatest of the Welsh planters.

Cawdor of Stackpole Court the greatest planter in Wales. However, this is certainly incorrect. There is no doubt that the honour rightly belongs to Thomas Johnes of Hafod. No other estate in Wales approached his achievement of planting approximately five million trees in the period 1782-1816.[64] This represents an area of some 1,000 to 1,200 acres, mostly on difficult upland sites.

Some of the major landowners in Wales not only earned premiums for tree planting from their local agricultural societies, but also were awarded gold and silver medals by the London (later the Royal) Society of Arts. Among these, the outstanding figure is Thomas Johnes of Hafod who was awarded gold medals on no fewer than five separate occasions between 1800 and 1810.[65] Other winners were Charles Rogers of Stanage (gold medal, 1835), Henry Potts of Llanferres (large silver medal, 1821) and Lord Newborough (gold medal, 1828) for planting on his estates in Denbighshire and Caernarfonshire.[66] The Society abandoned the practice of giving awards for tree-planting about the middle of the nineteenth century, but it continued to promote good forestry and to press for state action in this field.

By the early nineteenth century, conifer plantations were becoming a significant feature of the landscape. Even as early as 1791, replies to a government questionnaire on planting indicated that in most counties in Wales the plantations were not of oak but of tree species not 'fit for the navy', in other words mostly of fir or other softwoods.[67] At Hafod, for instance, the larch plantations accounted for well over half the total woodland acreage of the estate. On the Gnoll estate at Neath, in 1815 the woods and plantations formed some

173 acres (7%) of the total area, and 'fir' plantations accounted for at least 20% of all the woods and plantations on the estate.[68] Since about 1750, many landowners had obviously become enthusiastic planters of conifers. The attitudes of the common people to this development are not known, though they presumably derived some benefits from the additional employment generated by the establishment and maintenance of the conifer plantations. Like the English traveller Wyndham, Iolo Morganwg realized the value and benefits of fast-growing conifer plantations, especially of larch, which had rapidly became the most popular of the conifers planted. Its early growth rate was superior to pine and spruce. Some of the earliest plantings of larch were at Pen-pont in Breconshire in about 1750. Observations and measurements of these plantations some 40 years later were reported by Iolo Morganwg, and the larch compared favourably with spruce and pine of the same age. Some of the larch were 60ft high and girthed 8ft.[69] At Rhiwlas in Merioneth he noted: 'Larch luxuriant. I hope this will soon be the favorite tree of Wales to clothe its mountains . . . larch is a much more valuable timber of speedier growth and greater beauty [than fir]'.[70]

Larch was also looked upon with favour because it was believed to be less attractive and palatable to sheep than most of the other tree species planted.

In general, 'fir' (i.e. Scots pine or Norway spruce) was neither planted as widely nor regarded as favourably as larch. At Rhiwlas, for example, Iolo Morganwg criticized 'a tall & large grove of firs in an abominable taste of Cockneyism. Was glad to see them marked for a general fall [i.e. clear felling], their timber consigned to useful purposes, and their dirty verdure to the flames'.[71]

Some English travellers in Wales in the late eighteenth and early nineteenth century were of a similar opinion. Fenton wrote of hills 'deformed with miserable clumps of Firs' near Ceri in Montgomeryshire, and of views 'disfigured by a strait belt-planted line of grim fir trees' at Gwydyr, though he too was more favourably disposed to larch – at Drws-y-nant in Merioneth the larch had the 'most flourishing look . . . Wherever they are seen their shoots are amazing and their bark betrays health', and at Gwydyr 'the Larch seems to suit the Soil best, and outshoots every other species of tree'.[72] Byng regarded both larch and Scots pine as 'proper ornaments for a desert'.[73]

These travellers were seeking the romantic and the picturesque. Almost without exception, those who recorded accounts of their journeys complained in exaggerated terms of the universal and widespread felling of the native oak woods. For example, Bingley wrote: 'It is truly lamentable that the practice of taking away the timber should be so general . . . Depriving scenery of wood is ruinous to picturesque beauty; and if the owners of land do but go on in the manner they have done, for a few years longer, there will be scarcely a tree remaining in all North Wales'.[74] The Hon. John Byng reported: 'The sides of these hills abound with woods of oak . . . they clear the ground entirely, and then succeeds a crop of oats: destructive, idle – ignorant management! . . . they now in Wales make a sweep, and fell every oak! So that the land then becomes a brushy common, open to cattle never to produce timber again'.[75]

The great diversity of species choice and plant spacing discussed above shows that there were few generally accepted principles in plantation forestry. Personal predilections and availability of planting stock dictated the form and composition of the plantations. Though many plantations, especially of larch, were established as pure stands, mixtures were probably more popular.

There were sound reasons for the formation of mixtures:

The first was in order to eke out scarce and expensive planting stock, especially of conifers, by planting among native hardwoods. This was a favourite method of establishing larch, Norway spruce and Scots pine amongst oak early in the nineteenth century, and the method was also practised later on with other exotics, the earliest plantations of Douglas fir being established by planting amongst hardwoods and other conifers in north Wales in the second half of the nineteenth century.

The second was in order to determine which species gave the best performance on any given site; for example, at Clasemont John Morris was reported as planting 'trees of various kinds in each acre of ground, by which he observes the sort that best suits the soil, exposure &c'.[76]

The third reason was in order to insure against the failure of one species, in the belief that mixtures were healthier than pure stands. This practice became widespread during the nineteenth century in an effort to counter the 'decline' of European larch.

And the fourth was in order to create a varied landscape for aesthetic reasons, such as that described by John Dyer in his description of Grongar Hill in the Vale of Tywi in 1727:

> *Below me trees unnumbered rise*
> *Beautiful in various dyes:*
> *The gloomy pine, the poplar blue*
> *The yellow beech, the sable yew*
> *The slender fir, that taper grows*
> *The sturdy oak, with broad-spread boughs*

As silvicultural awareness increased, the need to provide nurses for oak and to thin plantations was appreciated. The special role of birch as a nurse for oak was recognized in the Welsh saying *mamaeth y dderwen yw'r fedwen* (the birch is nurse to the oak) and expressed clearly by a woodman in the Vale of Neath: 'birch, or some other upright growing underwood, should always be planted with oak, and left uncut with it, to train it up clean and straight, as well as to shelter it'.[77]

As with species choice and spacing, considerable diversity of opinion also existed concerning thinning and pruning. Contemporary observers of woods and plantations in Wales generally agreed upon the need for thinning, but most reports in the early nineteenth century indicate that thinning was frequently neglected and that plantations, which were in any case usually established at very high initial planting densities, were left excessively dense and often in a state of stagnation. In a graphic description of one plantation, the trees 'were so closely confined, that, like the unfortunate captives of Hyder Ally in the black-hole at Calcutta, they were literally dying for want of air'.[78]

The formulation of thinning prescriptions was slow to develop, and here again individual predilection governed procedure on the various private estates. Similarly, opinions differed on the advisability of pruning. In some places, trees of all species were so heavily pruned as to amount to lopping or shredding. Elsewhere pruning was practised in a more reasonable manner. For example, in 1811 the Rev. Sir Thomas Gery Cullum toured Wales, and in the Vale of Tywi he recorded that: 'trees of all descriptions seem more taken care of in Wales than in England, a Pollard being hardly ever seen, & the trees are judiciously pruned, not like the trees in many parts of England like a Cabbage stuck on a May Pole, or left with long stumps like the teeth of a rake'.[79]

Early in the nineteenth century the choice of exotics was effectively limited to European and eastern North American species, but as botanical exploration and collecting developed in new parts of the world, the acquisition and planting of exotic ornamental conifers from western America, Asia and South America became fashionable on all the great estates of Wales. Dozens of different species were planted as individual specimen trees or as small clumps, and many published lists of these plantings giving botanical names (often incorrect or now obsolete) are available for various estates, for example Penrhyn Castle, Hafodunos, Coed Coch, Stanage, Golden Grove and Stackpole Court.[80] These lists generally record the age, height, girth, crown diameter, and information on silvicultural characters such as wind resistance, frost hardiness, soil preference, etc.

These early ornamental and park plantings of a wide range of exotic conifers proved valuable as species screening trials for commercial forestry. Most of the species tried proved unsuitable for commercial planting, but the performance of some species such as Douglas fir (*Pseudotsuga menziesii*), noble fir (*Abies procera*), Japanese larch (*Larix kaempferi*), Lawson cypress (*Chamaecyparis lawsoniana*) and Sitka spruce (*Picea sitchensis*) was such as to encourage trials at commercial planting.

The introduction and spread of the green (coastal) form of Douglas fir is interesting as an example of the development of a promising conifer species from the status of individual ornamental specimens in parks into one of the most important commercial conifers in forestry in Wales. Douglas fir was first introduced into Britain in 1827, and the earliest known plantings in Wales were as specimen park trees in 1840 at Penrhyn Castle, in 1842 at Powis Castle and about 1845 at Stanage.[81] Fertile seeds were obtained quite early from the two trees in Penrhyn park, and sown in flower pots. Attempts were made to grow some of the young plants in forest conditions, but because of the scarcity and cost of the planting stock it was necessary to make the plants go as far as possible by wide spacing and by planting among hardwoods and other conifers such as larch and spruce.[82]

The young plants from the Penrhyn trees were planted out in Cochwillan wood among young oaks in a meadow alongside the river Ogwen in about 1854;

one small enclosure was cleared of oak and a pure crop of Douglas fir was raised at a spacing of about 18ft. In 1912, i.e. at age 66 years and with 119 trees per acre, the mean height was 101ft, mean quarter-girth 17½in., and quarter-girth volume over bark 11,450 cu. ft per acre. Other plantings of Douglas fir in hardwoods or other conifers were made in Caernarfonshire at Betws-y-coed, Bethesda and Tregarth soon after the Cochwillan trial, and excellent growth rates were obtained.

On the Llandinam estate, Douglas fir was planted in a number of plantations established in the 1880s. Here the practice was to plant one Douglas fir to every three or five larch, rows of pure larch alternating with rows of larch and Douglas fir. The Douglas quickly outgrew and suppressed the larch.[83]

The development from arboriculture or the growing of individual specimen trees to the establishment of trial plots of exotics in woods and forests was a feature on several private estates in Wales, such as Coed Coch, Penrhyn, Stanage, Coedarhydyglyn and Golden Grove. One outstanding proponent of silvicultural experimentation was the Earl of Plymouth who in 1908 determined upon a Park Enclosure scheme at St Fagans that would combine private recreation and his own

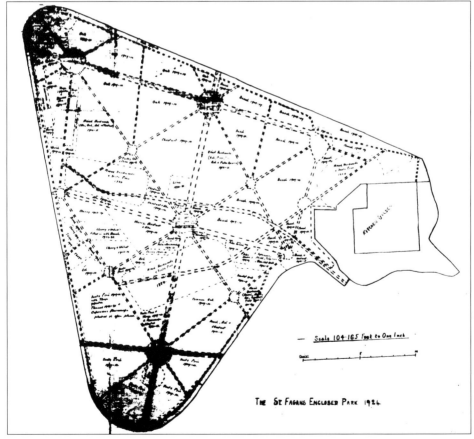

69. Layout of the silvicultural trial of exotics and mixtures, Park Enclosure, St Fagans.

70. Aerial view of the plantations in the Park Enclosure, St Fagans, c.1945.

interest in silviculture, especially in the performance of mixtures, exotics, and the effects of thinnings and stand density. In the words of H.A. Pettigrew, his Scottish woods manager, the Earl 'wished to decide by procedure on novel lines the relative merits of different methods of admixture . . . Again the density requisite in the successful rearing of timber trees, and the effect of light and air on their subsequent development had always absorbed his interest and attention . . . he realized the great importance and possibilities of discriminate thinning, a subject on which so great a diversity exists both among sylvicultural theorists and practitioners alike. Here in the Park Enclosure he hoped to glean knowledge and enlightenment by treating groups of species to thinning operations governed solely by forethought and discreet considerations, and this unfettered and uninfluenced by the preaching of experts'.[84]

The Park Enclosure was conceived as a fenced 78-acre triangle within St Fagans park. It lies partly on shale and thin limestone, and partly on red marl, at 100-140ft altitude. The enclosed land was part of open parkland, carrying only two small mixed conifer plantations of Scots pine, Corsican pine and European larch, and some much older line-plantings of oak. These were retained and an infrastructure pattern of open circles fifty yards in diameter connected by a complicated pattern of broad and narrow rides was laid out within the triangular enclosure. In all, the triangle contained 1½ miles of rides 30ft wide and 1½ miles of rides 12ft wide. The rides divided the planting area into ten compartments and these compartments were further subdivided into lettered blocks or sections. All the land was double-ploughed and scuffled, and planted up by pit-planting. Some of the planting stock was produced in the estate's own home nursery, and the rest was bought from commercial nurseries in Cardiff or further afield. The Earl of Plymouth's choice of species and mixtures was interesting. The full list of species planted is given below, in Pettigrew's original nomenclature:

Alder	*Alnus glutinosa*
Ash, American	*Fraxinus americana*
Ash, Common	*Fraxinus excelsior*
Beech	*Fagus sylvatica*
Birch	*Betula verrucosa*
Cherry, American Black	*Prunus padus serotina*
Cherry, Gean	*Prunus avium*
Chestnut, Spanish	*Castanea sativa*
—	*Cupressus macrocarpa*
Elm, English	*Ulmus campestris*
Elm, Scotch	*Ulmus montana*
Hornbeam	*Carpinus betulus*
Lime	*Tilia vulgaris*
Oak, Common	*Quercus robur* var. *pedunculata*
Oak, Ilex	*Quercus ilex*
Oak, Scarlet	*Quercus coccinea*
Pine, Scots	*Pinus sylvestris*
Pine, Corsican	*Pinus laricio*
Pine, Austrian	*Pinus laricio* var. *nigricans*
Poplar Black Italian	*Populus serotina*
Robinia	*Robinia pseudoacacia*
Sycamore	*Acer pseudoplatanus*
—	*Thuya plicata*
Tulip Tree	*Liriodendron tulipifera*
Walnut, Black	*Juglans nigra*
Willow, Cricket-bat	*Salix coerulea*

Of these species, eight are North American exotics. Most of the others are native or long-naturalized British species. None of the species planted was new to arboriculturists in Wales, but some of the species, especially the black walnut, robinia and tulip tree, had probably never been tried as forest trees in Wales before. Planting was done in pure stands, especially in the case of the major native hardwoods beech and oak, and also in various mixtures of two or more species, for example ash/robinia/oak/birch, or sycamore/ash/oak/Scots pine/ Corsican pine. The Earl had a strong personal preference for Scots pine as an ornamental species, but he considered European larch 'an incongruity and blemish on our landscape', and expressly prohibited its planting within the Park Enclosure, though he was prepared to tolerate it in the commercial plantations on outlying parts of the estate.

The remains of these trial plantations can still be seen in the grounds of the Museum of Welsh Life at St Fagans.

Chapter X

PROFESSIONAL FORESTERS AND PRIVATE ESTATE MANAGEMENT IN THE NINETEENTH CENTURY

Staffing on Welsh Estates

> It had been for something like twenty years under Scotch management, and it must be admitted that there was a ring of order about it.
> *Journal of Forestry & Estate Management* 1880, p. 614

The pattern of forestry in Wales from the late eighteenth century onward was greatly influenced by the Scots employed as foresters, gamekeepers, stewards, agents or bailiffs on the larger private estates. During the eighteenth century a generation of skilled practical foresters arose in Scotland, familiar with their native pine and with large-scale softwood plantation forestry as exemplified by the larch planting of the Dukes of Atholl. The pre-eminence of Scots foresters in experience and reputation is reflected in the way in which they were sought after for positions in Wales and elsewhere – it was both fashionable and practical to employ Scots as foresters on Welsh estates.

Amongst the earliest examples of a Scot whose duties consisted wholly or partly of the supervision of forestry on a Welsh estate was a Mr Robson, 'a Scotchman of a quick and active mind' who was in charge of the Gnoll estate near Neath in the 1780s.[1] On the Hafod estate between 1790 and 1810 the extensive plantations and forest-nursery activity were in the charge of the bailiff John Greenshields, and the gardener James Todd, formerly head gardener of the Botanic Garden at Edinburgh.[2] Later on, more and more Scots foresters were employed on estates throughout Wales, the following list being merely a representative selection of those traced and in no sense complete:

Scots foresters and agents on Welsh estates in the nineteenth century[3]

Peter G. Balden	Vaenol Park (Caerns.)
Lewis Bayne	Kinmel Park (Denbs.)
Robert Cameron	Pale (Merion.)
Robert Forrest	St Fagans (Glam.)
David Guthrie	Hafodunos (Denbs.)
Angus Macintosh (M'Intosh)	Llanerch (Carms.)
Thomas M'Kay	Crosswood Park (Cards.)
James McNair	Hafodunos (Denbs.)
Archibald Mitchell	Dunraven Castle (Glam.)
J. Muir	Margam (Glam.)

A. Pettigrew	Bute (Glam.)
H.A. Pettigrew	St Fagans (Glam.)
Walter Ritchie	Dinas Mawddwy (Merion.); Doldowlod (Radnor)
George Robson	Crosswood (Cards.)
Robert Russell	Mostyn (Flint)
Alexander Stewart	Bodnant (Denbs.)
D. Scott	Penrhyn Castle (Caerns.)
David Tait	Gwysaney (Flint)
A. Waterson	Penrhyn Castle (Caerns.)
Angus D. Webster	Penrhyn Castle (Caerns.)
Alexander Whitson	Kinmel Park (Denbs.)

A landowner, once satisfied with the performance of his Scottish forester, naturally tended to appoint another when the time came for a successor, and Scots foresters, once established in Wales, would often encourage the appointment of their fellow-countrymen as deputies and assistants. They were strong men, confident in their expertise and status, and often patronizing or even supercilious in their view of the Welsh, as emerges from a description of a typical estate in Wales employing about fifty men in 1880: 'Previous to my time it had been for something like twenty years under Scotch management, and it must be admitted that there was a ring of order about it'.[4] Some large estates such as the Bute and the Cawdor held land in Scotland and in Wales, and close links in forestry staffing and practice were natural.

Forestry in Scotland was often a family profession, in which son followed father. In the Shaw family, for example, at least five successive generations were foresters, first in Scotland and later in Wales. William Shaw, whose father and grandfather had been woodmen before him in Scotland, was woodman on private estates in Ayrshire before becoming head woodman on the Killearn estate in Stirlingshire in the 1890s. It was at Killearn that his son, James Lymburn Shaw, served his apprenticeship as forester towards the end of the last century, being reared in his turn in the old estate tradition in Scotland, and later moving to Radnorshire during the 1914-18 war to supervise a gang of Portuguese labourers preparing pit-props. Subsequently he took charge of the new Gwydyr Forest for the Forestry Commission in 1925, and was eventually followed as forester there by his own son Donald.[5]

The hierarchy of management in forestry varied on the different estates, but the typical arrangement was for the overall management to be in the hands of a Scottish or English agent or steward, resident on or near the estate, and for the lower management, often called woodwards, to be local men. In a large estate where forestry was important, a head forester, typically a Scot, would rank between the agent and the woodwards. For instance, the general management of the Plymouth estate during the nineteenth century was in the care of a succession of agents or stewards based at Barnt Green in Worcestershire, while the Glamorgan portion of the estate was administered by a local agent, Scottish or English, at St Fagans. Until 1878 the agent at Barnt Green had general oversight

71. Edward Barnes, woodman at Erddig, 1830.

over the local agent at St Fagans, but in 1878 the local agent assumed complete control over the Glamorgan properties.

The woodwards in day-to-day charge of the Glamorgan woods of the Plymouth estate were Welsh and were responsible to the local (Glamorgan) agent, and until 1878 through him to the Barnt Green agent.[6] On this estate there was a general trend towards concentration of authority over the woods during the nineteenth century. In the 1820s, separate local woodwards were employed at St Fagans, Radyr, Rudry and Eglwysilan, for example, but from the middle of the century, the estate employed fewer woodwards but on a more professional basis and responsible for larger areas; for example, in 1850 Daniel Williams received £42 as a salary as woodward of the Merthyr District and William Morgan £50 for the Caerphilly District. The estate concentrated the supervision of the woods in the hands of a single woodward at the end of 1865, when William Williams formally accepted the post for the Merthyr, Aberdare and Caerphilly Districts at a salary of £100 per annum. In his letter of acceptance he wrote: 'my Utmost Effort will be to Give full Satisfaction in my Agency by Adhering to the Golden Rule, of Watching and Superintending the interest of the Right Hon[able] the Baroness Windsor as if the Estate had been my Own'.[7]

Small sums such as £1 per year were also regularly paid to people for 'looking after the woods' or 'looking after the young plantations' at various places on the Glamorgan portion of the Plymouth estate. These payments were in the nature of a 'retainer' to a local resident for keeping a general eye on the woods and plantations near his home, and reporting any trouble to the official estate staff.

72. Robert Forrest, 1845-1910, the Scottish agent of the Plymouth estate, St Fagans (Glamorgan).

73. Angus D. Webster, forester at Penrhyn Castle (Caernarfonshire) in the 1880s and 1890s.

The labour force on Welsh estates varied both seasonally and from year to year, depending mainly on the amount of work involved in plantation establishment, fellings and bark stripping. Many estates had a permanent woods gang, supplemented by casual or seasonal labour as required, and on some estates female or juvenile labour would often be employed for planting, weeding and bark-stripping. On other estates the woods labour force was not permanent but consisted of general labourers, these being 'a class of handy men, who can do all kinds of farm work, and when not required on the farm they are employed at felling, barking and rounding of timber, and also at hedging, ditching and fencing, and when the season comes round, at the planting of forest trees'.[8]

During the nineteenth century, training in forestry was generally acquired as an informal or formal apprenticeship, as in the case of James L. Shaw, in which an able youth picked up his knowledge in service from an older experienced man. There was no shortage of published literature to aid his studies, for many practical manuals of silviculture and arboriculture were written by English and Scottish authors during the eighteenth and nineteenth centuries. In contrast, publications on forestry by Welshmen, whether in Welsh or in English, were conspicuous by their absence, and after the appearance of William Watkins' short work *A treatise on forest trees* in 1753, no Welshman appears to have written on technical forestry matters until the twentieth century. Surprisingly, even Thomas Johnes, the champion planter in Wales, who published his book *A Cardiganshire landlord's advice to his tenants* in 1800 and brought out a Welsh translation of it, included no original information on forestry in the work.

Measurement and Valuation

> Owing, however, to the wastage incurred when cutting timber it is usual
> for calculations to be made on the basis of quarter-girt figures.
>
> *Hoppus's Measurer*

Although in most parts of Wales the estate labour was predominantly local and Welsh-speaking, in general all the management instructions would be given in English, and this undoubtedly helped to prevent the formation and establishment of a standard technical vocabulary in Welsh. English-language books formed the exclusive basis of information available on silviculture in Wales, but at the practical level of timber measurement and sale there was also a demonstrable need for manuals in Welsh. English editions of Hoppus tables were available for calculating the cubic volume of roundwood and were widely used, but during the eighteenth century several Welsh-language versions of Hoppus, or ready-reckoners and manuals based on it, were published.[9] These mensurational booklets are the only technical instructions on forestry that have ever been published in Welsh (see Fig. 74). They contain standard Hoppus tables or extracts of tables, for measuring square and round wood appropriate to the sizes of trees found in Wales; some also contain instructions for measuring wood with

WYNEBLUN.

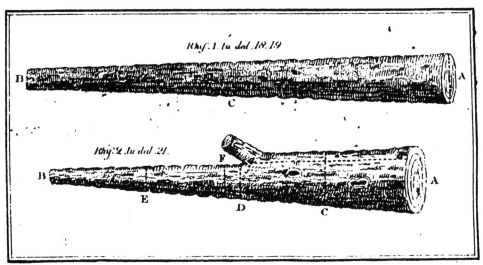

74. Frontispiece to *Y Mesurydd Tir a Choed* (Denbigh, 1858), containing Hoppus tables for measuring the solid content of square and round wood.

the 'sliding rule', and for measuring the height of standing trees, for example with Gunther's Quadrant.

From the time of Hywel Dda onwards, trees in Wales were valued at fairly arbitrary fixed prices, and this pattern persisted until at least the end of the seventeenth century, though increasing attention was, of course, paid to differentiation of trees by size. On the Gwydir estate in the 1680s, sales were generally by arbitrary prices for standing trees or parts thereof, though the converted timber was sold by the piece in specified dimensions or by superficial measure. In the early and mid eighteenth century, the trend was for standing trees to be individually numbered and measured, and their weight estimated, the timber generally being valued and sold by the ton or by the load. For example, the Margam estate valued timber by the ton in 1738, and at Golden Grove in 1757 the articles of agreement between the owner John Vaughan and Richard Chitty, timber-merchant from Sussex, specified the sale of 6,620 trees, mainly oak, for £10,300, the price being 40s. per load or ton.[10] Oak shiptimber was generally sold by the load, the standard load being 50 cu. ft.

However, the increasing professionalism of foresters and the importance of fast-growing plantations helped to promote an awareness of the need for accurate mensuration of volume and evaluation by measured volume instead of estimated weight. Measurement of cubic foot volume of timber became increasingly common towards the end of the eighteenth century, though cords of various sizes continued to be used as the measure for smaller material.

Not until the end of the nineteenth century was tree girth or diameter measured at a standard height. Previously, estates had measured their trees at 2ft, 3ft, breast-height (approximately 4ft 3in.), 5ft, or even 6ft above ground. Large old specimen trees, especially oaks, were girthed at ground level and at about 5ft and often also at heights further up the stem. For example, a very large oak at Cefnmabli had a girth of 21ft near the ground, 15ft at about 30ft, and 11½ft at 56ft.[11]

Though the importance of rapid growth was becoming realized in the eighteenth century, the measurement of volume increment was not well developed, and even recorded height measurements are often suspect.

In the early plantings at Hafod, the height increment of young European larch averaged some 2ft per annum, the maximum annual shoot increment being 3ft 8in., and radial growth rates were approximately 7-9 rings per inch; at 70 years some specimens contained 120 cu. ft, having produced about 1½ cu. ft (solid) per annum. A larch stand at Hafod, planted about the year 1800 at an altitude of 1,150ft, was measured at age 115 years; its mean height was 73ft, and the quarter-girth volume under bark was 4,970 cu. ft per acre. In 1865, one individual larch tree at Hafod was reported as being 160ft in height, and if correct this would be a record for European larch in Britain, but the figure is not accepted by modern authorities.[12] In 1880, a park specimen of larch at Pen-pont in Breconshire, reputedly the largest in Wales, was girthed at 19ft 7in. at the ground, and 13ft 10in. at a height of 3ft; the maximum crown diameter was 106ft, and the estimated crown projection was 980 square yards.[13]

Some examples from the late eighteenth and early nineteenth century on the Cawdor, Golden Grove, Taliaris, Corsygedol and Plymouth estates illustrate the development of forest mensuration and valuation in Wales.

On the Cawdor estate, strips of coppice (called slangs) were valued in 1790 by measuring the surface area in acres, rods and perches, and estimating the expected yield in cords in the next coppice felling, for example 10, 12 or 18 long cords per acre. The cord was valued at 12s., the bark at £4 per ton, and the seven standard trees left per acre at the previous cutting were valued at 1s. each.[14]

In 1812, fifty-nine trees at Llandybïe on the Golden Grove estate were described as '66 feet each at 3s. 6d. per foot being 77 tons at £8 15s. per ton'. This shows the dual form of measurement with values in cubic feet and in tons (50 cu. ft to the ton).[15]

In a valuation of the timber growing on Corsygedol demesne and adjoining tenements early in the nineteenth century, detailed measurements and estimates were made for each individual (numbered) standing tree, namely the length (in feet), girth (in inches), content (volume in cubic feet), value per foot (in pence), total value (£. s. d.), amount of bark (tons, hundredweights, quarters) and amount of cordwood (in cords and feet). The timber value ranged from 12d. to 20d. per foot (generally 15d. or 18d.); the bark was valued at £9 per ton and the cordwood at 10s. per cord. The timber was almost entirely ash and oak, and the total valuation was £4,045 18s. 10d.[16]

On the Taliaris estate a valuation in 1838 made a very careful distinction between species, and of tree-classes within a given species:

Species of tree	Value per foot[17]	Species of tree	Value per foot
	s. d.		s. d.
Ash	1 9	Larch	1 3
Aspen	8	Lime	8
Beech	9(or 1s.)	Maple	1 0
Birch	8	Oak	1 9
Cedar	3 0	Service	8
Chestnut	1 0	Spruce fir	1 3
Elm	2 0	Sycamore	8
Fir	1 0	Walnut	2 6

In addition to the oak timber, the amount of bark was estimated at 39 tons and valued at £2 15s. per ton. 'Tellers', i.e. the young trees that had not reached the size of timber (8 inches girth and upwards), were divided into one of six classes and valued per stem, by class, as follows:

Species	Class 1	Class 3	Class 6
Oak	5s.	–	2s. 6d.
Ash	5s.	4s.	2s. 6d.
Beech	4s.	–	2s. 6d.

The hardwoods such as oak, ash and elm were valued higher than the softwoods (spruce, fir, larch), in contrast to the situation obtaining just a century earlier at Margam, when the rarity of softwoods had made them more valuable than oak.

On the Plymouth estate in Glamorgan, the woods were valued before sales. An example of a typical valuation at Coed y Bowdra Wood, Rudry in 1833 shows that measurement of cubic volume of standing timber was now standard practice along with estimates of the amount of bark and cordwood.[18]

638 oak timber trees = 12,603ft. at 3/6. per foot, including lop, top & bark	£ 2,205	10s.	–
57 beech trees = 890ft. at 1/- per foot, including lop & top	£ 44	10s.	–
Total	£ 2,250	–	–
300 oak cyphers* = 15 short cords of pitwood at 9/- per cord	£ 6	15s.	–
Bark of ditto, say 3 tons	£ 15	–	–
Say 20 cords of White wood cyphers* at 10/-	£ 10	–	–
Cordwood exclusive of timber & cyphers, 150 cords at 4/-	£ 30	–	–
Total	£ 61	15s.	–
Deduct tithe of Cordwood	£ 5	–	–
	£ 56	15s.	–
Grand total valuation	£ 2,306	15s.	–

*Cyphers are inferior stems, i.e. non-timber trees; white wood cyphers are inferior stems of species other than oak.

Llanvihangel Crucorney

MONMOUTHSHIRE.

TIMBER FOR SALE

MR. J. MICHAEL

WILL OFFER BY AUCTION,

AT THE ANGEL HOTEL, ABERGAVENNY,

On Tuesday, the 30th day of January, 1866,

At 3 o'CLOCK in the Afternoon, (under Conditions of Sale,) the following

TIMBER

AND COPPICE WOOD, STANDING & BEING IN THE PARISH OF LLANVIHANGEL CRUCORNEY, IN THE COUNTY OF MONMOUTH

LOT 1.

The FALLAGE of Llwygy Wood, containing by admeasurement about 6 Acres. Also 24 Oak Timber Trees, numbered with white paint from 1 to 24 inclusive, and 14 Ash Timber Trees, numbered with white paint from 1 to 14 inclusive, standing in the said Wood.

LOT 2.

51 Oak Timber Trees numbered with white paint from 1 to 51 inclusive. Also 107 Ash & 3 Wych Timber Trees numbered with white paint from 1 to 110 inclusive. Also 7 Sycamore Timber Trees numbered with white paint from 1 to 7 inclusive, standing on the *Llwygy, Bridge, and Mill Farms.*

LOT 3.

69 Oak Timber Trees numbered with white paint from 1 to 69 inclusive. Also 154 Ash Timber Trees numbered with white paint from 1 to 154 inclusive, standing on the *Berry Farm on the west side of Campstone Hill Road.*

The Timber and Wood will be shown by THOMAS THOMAS of the Village, Llanvihangel Crucorney.

ᶠᵘᵣther particulars apply to Mr. J. SAYCE, SOLICITOR, Abergavenny ; or Mr. J. LLOYD, Hill Grove.

PRINTED BY J. HILEY MORGAN, BOOKSELLER AND STATIONER, HIGH STREET, ABERGAVENNY.

75. Auction of timber in Monmouthshire, 1866.

From about 1850 onwards, this estate tended to organize its woods operations so as to have fewer but larger sales. The whole or part of a wood was measured, valued and sold at auction. Some agreements specified price 'per foot cubic string measure', with measurement jointly by representatives of the buyer and vendor. The sales were generally held in November, and the conditions of sale were specified in standard printed forms (Fig. 76). At times, however, the demand for wood was so great that the prices reached at sales were very much above those expected. After one sale in 1853, which realized a total of £2,005, the agent Thomas Goddard wrote, philosophically: 'In this time it is impossible to value anything. The sale price has far exceeded my views, so much so that I fear it has been sold almost too dear; however, the purchasers are the best judges'.[19]

Before 1800, instances of good management were exceptions rather than the rule, and there are few cases where the actual economics of forestry in Wales are given in any detail. One example is a 29-acre coppice oak wood with some ash in the Vale of Aeron, which was bought in 1792 for £400. It was fenced, and the bark and wood from the thinnings 'paid periodically the interest on the purchase money, or nearly so'. The coppice oak was 1-10 years old in 1792. In 1809 one lot was sold for £750 and another in 1813 for £375; the remainder was valued at £500, i.e. a total of £1,625 in 21 years from a piece of woodland bought for

---

CONDITIONS OF SALE.

— • • —

1...... The highest bidder to be the purchaser; and if any dispute arise between two or more bidders the lot shall be put up again.

2.;....No person to advance less than   at each bidding under   ; and at each bidding above

3......   in part of the purchase money, shall be paid to the seller's agent, imme-diately after the sale; and the purchaser of each lot shall, within ten days afterwards, give such security as shall be approved of by the seller, for the payment of the remainder, viz. half on the   next, and the other half on the
                                                                              and the expenses of such security, as well as of the agreement of sale, shall be paid by the purchaser.

4......The trees in the woods and coppices shall be axe fallen or sawn down, and taken out of the same on or before the
                          and whatever timber, pit wood, cord wood, or other part of the pur-chase, may be left in the said woods and coppices after that time, shall be deemed and taken as the property of the seller.

5.....,The trees on the farms shall be fallen and removed to some convenient place, on or before the
                          which place shall be appointed by the seller's agent; and whatever timber, pit wood, cord wood, or other part of the purchase may be elsewhere found upon the farms after that time, shall be absolutely forfeited to the seller. And from the place appointed by the agent, the whole shall be taken away before the   day of

6......The purchaser to be permitted to use all accustomed roads, to and from the above-mentioned woods, coppices, and farms; and if any trees are felled across any road, the purchaser of them shall remove them out of the way, so as not to obstruct or hinder the purchaser of any other lot, in removing his timber, &c.

7......Any unnecessary damage, whether proceeding from accident or carelessness, shall be fully com-pensated for, to the parties sustaining it.

?......In case any purchaser shall neglect, or refuse, to comply with the foregoing conditions, the depo-sit money shall be forfeited, and the timber resold; and if any loss shall happen to the seller, from such second sale, then the same shall be made good by the purchaser at this sale, so neglecting or refusing.

76. 'Conditions of Sale' form used on the Plymouth estate in the nineteenth century.

£400.[20] This, of course, was during the boom period of the Napoleonic Wars, when prices for wood and bark showed a dramatic increase.

The woods accounts of several estates are available, but usually for short periods only during the nineteenth century. The method of bookkeeping varied, but a good general idea of the system is provided by the accounts of the Glamorgan portion of the Plymouth estate, an estate where the woods were important and were relatively well managed.[21] In 1766 the woods, mainly in the upper part of the Taff valley and in the area of Caerphilly, amounted to nearly 3,000 acres which represented almost 16% of the total area of the estate. Of the 54 years for which accounts are available between 1821 and 1881, the woods showed a healthy book profit in 45 years, and a book deficit, generally small, in nine years only. The income from the woods fluctuated considerably, but annual expenditure on them was much more constant, generally amounting to between £400 and £800 per annum. The main sources of estate income were rents from tenants, and royalties from collieries, quarries, etc., and the woods contributed some 10% of the total. The main expenditures of the estate were repairs to property and 'incidentals', and though in the early part of the century the expenditure on the woods and plantations formed over 20% of the total outgoings, it declined thereafter to values generally below 10%.

The main expenditure on woods and plantations was for salaries and wages of supervisory staff and labourers; other expenses included sums spent on advertising wood for sale, auctioneers' charges, purchase of planting stock, payment of tithe rents, payments to mole-catchers, expenses on beer for workmen, etc. The labourers were employed on the whole range of forestry activities typical of a large private estate: walling, ditching, draining, site clearance for planting, fencing, planting, looking after young plantations, weeding, cutting gorse, marking and painting trees, measuring wood, felling, cross-cutting and cording wood, barking, hauling, and so on. Expenditures associated with barking such as stripping, drying, weighing, loading and hauling, and with the preparation of pitwood, cordwood, etc. were greater in the first half of the century than later; during the second half of the century the bark trade slumped, and the sales of wood were often arranged so that the buyers and not the estate woods staff were responsible for the felling, cording, etc. The accounts also clearly reflect the change in the operations with growing industrialization: in the 1820s and 1830s, for example, the accounts also contained, besides the timber, pitwood and cordwood, many items indicating typically rural or small-scale craft uses, whereas later on they were completely dominated by sales of pitwood and cordwood.

Details of individual sales and fellings are contained in the Glamorganshire Wood Account Books of the Plymouth estate,[22] four volumes covering the periods 1825-35, 1835-52, 1852-83, and 1883-1905, and showing five classes of entries: Timber Sold; Timber Used on the Estate; Pitwood Sold; Cordwood Sold; and Bark Sold. All wood sales are recorded in the account books. In the early years, the majority were small ones, and in aggregate they brought in more revenue than the few large sales. Later on the estate tended to organize operations with fewer but larger sales. The woods accounts were kept in such a way that it is not practicable to determine the annual income broken down by categories of produce, for example timber or cordwood. The accountancy years also overlap, sums being entered in the books one or two years after the actual felling had taken place. In general, 10% of an agreed purchase price was paid immediately and the balance later in one or two installments.

By the end of the century, simple calculations of the economics of forestry had been replaced by quite sophisticated economic forecasts including land rent, insurance and compound interest. Muir, the Scot in charge of the 2,000 acres of forest trees on the Margam estate, was one of the few professional foresters to give evidence to the Royal Commission on Land in Wales & Monmouthshire (1895). A strong advocate of European larch, thinned at four- or five-year intervals, on a fifty-year rotation, he proposed to the commission a scheme of state aid for forestry in the form of loans for planting. Muir presented a detailed statement of the economics of planting one hundred acres by such a scheme, including all costs, rent, insurance and compound interest at 3%. The loan would be repaid, with compound interest, during the last thirteen years of the rotation, and Muir calculated the profit to the owner at the end of the rotation as being of the order of £100 per acre.[23]

Tenancy and Leases

> The tenant shall protect all trees, plantations, brushwood, underwood . . .
> Wynnstay lease, 1896

Besides the major achievements in the afforestation of marginal land, most private estates in Wales also sought to preserve and increase the stock of wood, especially hardwood timber, on the farms on their estates. This was done either by the exhortation and example of progressive landowners, as exemplified by Thomas Johnes, or by compulsion through the insertion of planting clauses in leases. Planting clauses had been known in Wales since at least the sixteenth century, but landlords invariably reserved all timber trees and usually all the underwood on their estates. With the development of leasehold tenure, it became general to operate short-term leases, and in many instances leases from year to year. These short-term leases were by their very nature unsuited to the essentially long-term commitment involved in growing trees. Tenants in general were therefore deprived of security of long-term tenure and of any financial interest in the timber on their land; moreover, on estates where planting clauses were in force the tenants were obliged to procure, plant and maintain trees without any possibility of deriving any eventual pecuniary benefit themselves.

The net effect was to create a situation where tenants had no interest in promoting sound long-term management of woods and trees, and indeed had much to gain by eliminating or lopping tree growth on their land. This emerges clearly from the county reports to the Board of Agriculture in the 1790s which show that, in general, under the terms of the leases the landlord reserved the

77. Felling and primary conversion of large hardwoods in Glamorgan, *c.*1900.

right to fell and carry off any timber, paying equitable damages, and to enclose and fence coppices and plantations, the annual value of the land so enclosed being determined and deducted from the rent.[24] The terms of the leases required the tenant to prevent cattle or sheep from grazing in coppices or plantations set apart by the landlord, with a penalty (generally £5) for each offence; not to fell, shred (i.e. lop), top or otherwise damage trees, tops of pollards excepted, under a penalty (again generally £5 for each tree damaged); not to permit other people to cut any saplings nor any kind of underwood (penalty generally £1 per sapling and 15s. per load of underwood). However, tenants were generally allowed to cut underwood needed for repairing hedges and for fuel, though they were forbidden to sell any wood from the farm. A tenant farmer was therefore unwilling to raise a crop of young wood for his landlord's ultimate use, especially as he himself was already paying the landlord rent for the land. Accordingly, tenants regarded trees and woods growing on their land as unwanted intruders, and took care to destroy all young plants, before they attained the status of 'timber' and became reserved to the landlord. Any trees that did succeed in reaching maturity were surreptitiously lopped and topped. In Radnorshire these lopped and topped trees were known as 'rundles' and became the property of the tenant.

One method suggested to remedy this situation was to give tenants some financial interest in the well-being of trees and woods, as was the case in Ireland, where any leasehold tenant acquired a legally enforceable financial interest in any timber trees he had planted on the land he occupied. This enlightened recommendation was not put into effect in Wales, but a more radical method of

overcoming the neglect or abuse by tenants was practised in some areas early in
the nineteenth century. In the counties of Brecon and Radnor, for example, some
landowners separated the woodlands from the farms to which they had belonged,
and put them under the care and protection of 'professed woodmen' (i.e.
professional foresters), for proper fencing and management, including thinning
and pruning. Many estates, in an effort to stop abuses by tenants, recorded every
timber-tree standing on the property and painted its number on it, and also paint-
marked and counted the saplings and young trees in woods, fields and hedges.
On the Abbey Cwm Hir estate this measure was recommended in 1822 and had
been implemented by 1833.[25]

Summaries of agreements and leases operative on over a hundred estates in all
parts of Wales in the final quarter of the nineteenth century are summarized in
the report of the Royal Commission on Land in Wales & Monmouthshire.[26]
These leases were still generally of the same conservative and prohibitory nature
as a century earlier, though some contained positive clauses requiring tenants to
plant trees. The clauses relating to woods and trees in the leases tended to follow
a general pattern very similar to that outlined above for the early part of the
century. The following selection of more detailed or specific clauses in force on
Welsh estates large and small indicates the typical constraints imposed on the
tenants as regards utilization of trees, the penalties specified for infringements,
and the obligations for care and maintenance of existing trees and woods, and
for new planting. The tenants were required:

> not to lop any trees higher than they have been usually lopped, and to preserve all
> trees and saplings (Craigydon, Anglesey);
>
> the tenant shall protect all trees, plantations, brushwood, underwood (Wynnstay);
>
> to preserve all timber, growing trees, and underwood, not to lop any tree or sapling
> under a penalty of £10 for each tree or sapling (Rhiwlas);
>
> not to cut down, top, lop, or prune any timber tree, pole, or underwood . . . pay the
> sum of £10 in respect of each tree or pole which may be cut down or destroyed . . .
> in addition to the value of such tree or pole (Mostyn);
>
> £5 for every tree, holly bush, or sapling cut or injured, or for growing timber into
> which nails are driven (Brynkinallt, Flint);
>
> whenever the tenant shall new lay or cut any hedge or fence, he shall in all cases
> leave one timber tree or sapling of oak, ash, elm, or alder, a standard at every 25
> feet distance; and in case there shall be no such tree or sapling growing . . . the
> tenant shall . . . procure and plant therein, at his own expense, at the distance of 25
> feet apart, good and healthy saplings of oak, ash, elm or alder (Taliaris Park);
>
> to preserve all trees, fruit trees, timber trees, imps, saplings, and pollards now
> growing or hereafter to grow (St Athans);
>
> not to cut down, crop, or shred any timber tree, sapling, pollard, fruit or other tree
> or trees under a penalty of three times the value of such timber trees, and £10 for
> each of the said other trees, but to preserve all timber trees, saplings, or pollards,
> and also all fruit trees, and not to cut any sally or alder but for the use of the farm,
> and at the proper seasons of the year (Duke of Beaufort, Monmouthshire).

Game was another source of friction between landlord and tenant in Wales. Countless complaints were made about the depredations caused by the game itself, and the damage caused by hunting. Although the larger game animals such as red and roe deer had long been extinct in the wild, the interests of most estates in ground game, game birds and foxes took precedence over forestry in the later part of the century. Much estate planting was primarily for the establishment or renewal of game coverts, generally mixtures of hardwoods and softwoods. The planting stock was sometimes topped to promote bushy growth, and evergreen shrubs such as rhododendron or privet were introduced, together with individual specimens or clumps of Norway spruce, silver fir or Douglas fir to create good dry shelter for the game birds. Rides were cleared in the woods and kept regularly cleaned for the shooting parties.

Damage to Trees

> So many are the Infirmities and Sicknesses of Trees . . . that it were almost impossible to enumerate them.
>
> John Evelyn, *Sylva*

The pressures on some estates from trespass, poaching, theft and vandalism were considerable, especially in industrial areas, despite the severity of the legislation in force designed to protect landed property. For instance, in 1821 rewards were offered for information leading to the conviction of any person cutting down timber or young trees on the Glamorgan portion of the Plymouth estate. The posters announcing the rewards stated that: 'great Depredations have been committed upon the Estates of the Right Honourable the Earl of Plymouth in the County of Glamorgan, by the Tenants and others, cutting down Timber and young Trees; they are therefore hereby desired to desist from such practices, and informed also that the above Reward of Ten Guineas will be paid, on Conviction, to any Person or Persons giving information, it being in future intended to enforce the penalties of the Law for the above Offence'.[27]

Expenditure for printing and posting up notices warning against damage and trespass were regular items in the estate accounts during the nineteenth century, and the Plymouth estate did successfully prosecute transgressors.

Accidental fire damage was also a problem, especially in the spring, and particularly after the coming of the railways. For example, on 17 March 1893, sparks from a Taff Vale Railway engine caused a fire near Upper Boat, destroying about eight acres of young larch, oak, ash, birch, etc.; a claim was duly made against the railway for £80. Soon afterwards, on 30 March 1893, more serious damage occurred at the same place, when some twenty to thirty acres of 'fine young Larch from 6 to 16ft high, also Oak, Ash, Birch etc.' were burnt; again a claim was made against the railway for £300.[28]

In Wales the provision of shelter for dwelling-houses, livestock, field crops and for plantations was very important, both in the uplands and in areas exposed to sea winds. The value of shelter had been recognized from very early times in the Welsh Laws, where a relatively high value was assigned to trees deliberately planted for shelter. Considerable attention was paid to the optimum choice of tree species for shelter, and to the design and establishment of shelterbelt plantings in Rowlands' *Idea Agriculturae* (1764) and later in the reports submitted to the Board of Agriculture at the turn of the eighteenth century.

Sometimes artificial shelter was provided to give trees a start in very exposed places, in the form of stone walls, earth banks or mounds with wicker screens. Species recommended for shelter-planting in places exposed to the sea winds were black poplar, abele (white poplar), sycamore, hop willow, mountain ash, birch, Dutch elm, English elm, plane, beech and ash, and as hedge plants brown or Welsh willow, bullace and elder. In the uplands, the species recommended included sycamore, ash, alder, birch, elm and Scots pine.

The best shape for plantations in exposed places was deemed to be: 'parallelograms with their shorter sides to the west; by which means, the greater number would be protected with the loss of a few'.[29]

Although the need for shelterbelts on upland farms was manifest, comparatively little shelter-planting was in fact done in the uplands, and on most estates the planting was confined to sheltered places with the aim of ensuring good growth of timber. The situation was expressed clearly by T. Davies, district surveyor of the Aberaeron highway district in 1894: 'What is wanted is systematic planting in long beltings along the high ridges of the county of hardy trees for shelter only, that cannot be cut down . . . Some few landlords in the beginning of this century did a little of this, and it is astonishing to see the effect it has had on those neighbourhoods'.[30]

78. Clogmakers' camp at Rhostryfan (near Caernarfon), 1891, showing boles, cut logs, huts, tents and stacks of split blanks for clog soles.

Constant exposure to strong winds either prevents growth completely or reduces it, and results in crown and stem distortion or premature mortality. The other form of wind damage is windthrow or wind-breakage of established trees, and this is a recurring problem on wet upland sites in Wales with shallow soils and impeded drainage. Probably the earliest documented instance of storm damage to trees and woods in Wales was in 1236, when many woods were 'rent' by a storm on the night before Christmas eve.[31] Other examples are known: on 15 March 1757 a great storm at Mostyn uprooted over a hundred oaks and snapped or uprooted fir trees as well;[32] on 10 November 1810, 81 large oaks at Margam were overthrown;[33] the great gale of 14 October 1881 damaged trees of various species on estates from Carmarthenshire to Denbighshire and Caernarfonshire.[34] The gale on 26 January 1884 caused serious damage to a second-generation larch plantation near Castle Madoc in Breconshire, uprooting many trees and snapping others.[35] Some of these trees were growing on a spot where a previous larch plantation 60-70 years old had already suffered extensive windthrow in a summer storm in July 1853.

Most animal damage was caused by domestic livestock, especially goats and sheep (see p. 150). Rabbits were a constant problem in young plantations, at least until the advent of myxomatosis in the middle of the twentieth century. Wild deer had been absent from Wales for several centuries and, like the grey squirrel, would only start to become a problem towards the end of the twentieth century. Although a case of mass defoliation of trees had been recorded in Wales in the thirteenth century, insects would only become a real problem with the extensive planting of exotics.

79. Axemen rounding out hardwoods on Stanage estate, c.1904.

The Year's Programme

Calendar: table displaying the months . . . important to a particular
pursuit or occupation.
                                                                          SOED

On a well-managed Welsh estate that cared for its woodlands, the typical year's
work of the forest manager and forest labourer in the last quarter of the nineteenth
century, before the disappearance of the oak-bark harvest, was as follows:

January: Fell timber, thin and cut underwood; dispose of produce as early as
possible, getting timber out before the sap starts rising. Measure produce
preferably before removal from plantations. Plant only on driest and warmest sites.
Cut and remove all hedgerow timber.

February: Finish planting deciduous trees wherever possible. Finish thinning all
hardwood plantations except oak. Bind and stack faggots. Remove and transplant
young stock in nursery. Young oak may need careful root pruning. Prepare land for
planting by ploughing, draining, etc.

March: Beat up plantations 2-3 years old. Remove and transplant spruce, privet
and other evergreens to old and sheltered plantations for game cover. Young fir and
pine plantations can be thinned up to end of month. Fill up nursery with young
plants. Finish planting trees of all sorts.

April: Firm in recently planted trees, if blown about by wind. Get tools, etc. ready
for oak bark stripping, which can start if the weather is mild and warm. Finish
thinning of young plantations. Continue transplanting evergreens in nursery.

May: The main job is stripping and harvesting of the oak bark. Erect drying ranges
in the plantations, or on rides, and put bark outside upwards. Check young
plantations and newly transplanted trees, and straighten if necessary. Dig, hoe and
clean between plants in nursery.

June: Bark stripping now completed. If bark not sold, protect it against wet
weather. Dress all the oak timber and remove it carefully. Cord all branches for
sale, or for firewood, charcoal, etc. Prune hardwoods (lightly). Clear gorse, grass,
etc. from young plantations. Start site preparation for next planting season.

July: Finish dressing oak timber after peeling. Finish pruning hardwoods. Clear
gorse, grass, etc. from young plantations. Hoe and weed in nursery. Mow and clean
in pleasure grounds. Keep walks and carriage drives clean. Continue site
preparation (clearing, draining, fencing, etc.).

August and *September*: Little forest work done because most staff are released for
harvest work. Continue preparation of mountain ground for planting.

October: Continue enclosing and preparing ground for planting. On dry or drained
sites, plant towards end of month. Thin young softwood plantations, but defer
thinning hardwoods till end of month. Continue pruning. Select nursery stock for
planting; it should be 'well-feathered, clean and matured in its growth'.

November: (a busy month). Continue planting, fencing and thinning. This is one of
the best months for tree planting. Thin plantations, after they have been shot
through. Protect new plantations against rabbits and hares. Mark hedgerow trees
for felling. Continue enclosing and preparing ground for planting.

December: Continue fencing, draining, clearing and preparing ground, and
planting. Continue thinning plantations and cutting underwood. Fell and dispose of
hedgerow trees (except oaks). Check drains and fences.[36]

A few published studies have made passing mention of forestry on individual Welsh estates in the eighteenth and nineteenth centuries, for example Duffryn Aberdare,[37] Corsygedol[38] and Golden Grove,[39] and detailed studies, mostly unpublished, of forestry activity have been made for Baron Hill,[40] Hafod,[41] Crosswood, Nanteos and Dunraven[42] and Plymouth.[43] The overall picture of private estate forestry that emerges during the nineteenth century is as follows.

The first two decades, affected by the Napoleonic Wars, were a period when very high prices were obtained for wood and bark, and considerable investment went into the establishment of commercial plantations, principally of European larch and Scots pine, and also for the creation or embellishment of park landscapes. In general, forestry was regarded by the larger landowners as a sound investment in the first quarter of the century. Forestry and in particular the associated sporting interests of landowners were contributory causes in the deterioration of relations between landlords and tenants in Wales, which reached their nadir in the poverty and riots of the 1840s but continued to be generally poor thereafter.

From the middle of the century the oak-bark trade declined and virtually disappeared, and the market for naval oak timber received its death-blow in 1862 when, at the battle of Hampton Roads, iron ships proved decisively superior to wooden men-of-war. Though the demand for pitwood was large and increasing, the improvement of the communications (roads, canals and railways) and the systematic application of the Free Trade policy from 1846 onwards meant that unlimited cheap imports of softwood in the round and as sawn timber could become available in all parts of Wales, and commercial forestry at home became relatively unprofitable. Many landlords, often absentee, came to regard woodlands primarily as game covers, and preferred 'poverty with a gun on its shoulder to competence with no rabbits on the land'.[44] In the great agricultural depression of the final quarter of the century, most of the large estates started to experience financial difficulties, and from about 1870 onwards these difficulties resulted in the break-up of estates and the growth of freehold farming. These difficulties also coincided with the widespread and disastrous failures of European larch as a result of canker and dieback. This caused a general collapse of economic investment in woodlands towards the end of the century and at Crosswood, for example, by 1900 the woods were regarded as an economic liability. Despite this, arboriculture flourished, and some silvicultural experimentation was practised on a few estates. Conifers suitable for Welsh conditions were identified and grown on an increasing scale. During this period too the call grew for government support to private forestry, and for state involvement or commitment in forestry, in the form of a national forest policy, professional education and training in forestry, and development towards a state forest service.

Chapter XI

TOWARDS A NATIONAL FOREST SERVICE

If our statesmen, even thirty years ago, had shown equal foresight, most
of the timber required [to maintain naval coal supplies] could have been
grown on the Welsh hills.

Acland Committee Report, 1917; Cd. 8881

Since 1536 Wales had been treated for legislative purposes as part of England,
and national forest policy, insofar as it existed at all, was concerned mainly with
the Crown Forests, together with exhortations to landowners to plant and general
legislation aimed at preserving or protecting woodland. Wales had remained
unaffected by the major legislation promoting forestry in the great Crown
Forests in England, such as the acts for the increase and preservation of timber
within the Forest of Dean (1668) and the New Forest (1698), and the combined
act for these two forests in 1808. The forest policy which had developed during
the 'mercantilist' period from 1668 was discontinued in 1815 and replaced by a
laissez-faire policy, especially with the formal adoption of Free Trade in 1846,
and this had an adverse effect on forestry in England and Wales thereafter.

The Board of Agriculture Surveys carried out for the counties of Scotland,
England and Wales in the 1790s and in the early years of the nineteenth century
gave an account of the woods of each county but did not attempt any statistical
survey of woodland area. However, certain developments took place during the
last century that made it possible to obtain statistics of all the woods and forests
in the country, in addition to the Crown Forests. The first of these was the Tithe
Survey, carried out parish-by-parish in the period *c.*1835-50. Although these
surveys have been neglected by historians of forestry and have never been
comprehensively collated, they are in fact the first attempt at a systematic
national land-use survey since the Domesday survey, which in any case had
covered very little of Wales. The Tithe Surveys therefore provide the first
modern, fairly comprehensive and accurate set of statistics on land-use, and can
be used to make the first good estimate of the area of woodlands in Wales. The
Tithe Surveys give only the acreages of woodland in each parish, and contain no
information on species, type of management, standing volume, or increment.
Although woodlands were normally exempt from tithes by prescription, they
were generally recorded in the tithe apportionments. All the available tithe
apportionments were examined for two sample counties, Glamorgan as
representing a southern industrialized county and Merioneth as a northern rural
county, and the area recorded as woodland for each parish was abstracted and
totalled (Table 13).

Table 13. Woodland statistics from the Tithe Surveys for Glamorgan and Merioneth

	Glamorgan	Merioneth
No. of parishes	127	33
Total woodland area, acres	29,290	13,210
Total area of county, acres	516,955	427,811
Woodland as %	5.7	3.1

The recorded woodland area for Glamorgan is an underestimate because: (i) no apportionment was made for a few parishes, including the large parish of Margam which contained sizeable areas of woodland; (ii) no woodland at all was recorded in 33 parishes where apportionments were made, though some woods did exist, as for example in the parishes of Loughor and Penmark; here, woods were presumably left unrecorded as being exempt from tithes; (iii) some woods may be 'hidden' by being recorded as commons. Accordingly, the true woodland area in Glamorgan would certainly be over 31,000 acres, and perhaps substantially greater. The recorded woodland area for Merioneth is also an underestimate, perhaps substantially so, for the second and third reasons given for Glamorgan.

The systematic collection of agricultural statistics by the government in England and Wales began only in 1866. The Board of Trade was entrusted with the task, but the actual work of data collection was carried out from 1866 to 1918 by the officers of Inland Revenue (Surveyors of Excise).[1] The making of returns was voluntary until 1917, and especially in the early years many landowners were reluctant to provide information, so that estimates had to be made. Woodlands were included for the first time in the 1871 returns. The total acreages of woods and plantations for each of the counties of Wales from the returns made between 1871 and 1913 are collated in Table 14, and Table 15 shows the woodland acreages of each county as a percentage of total land area.[2]

Comparison of the underestimated figures of woodland area from the Tithe Surveys (Table 13) with the Agricultural Returns for 1871 (Table 14) indicates an apparent decrease in area of woodland over the period, amounting to over 9,000 acres in Glamorgan and 2,500 in Merioneth. The decrease is probably illusory because the data in the earliest Agricultural Returns are seriously suspect as a result of the number of 'estimates'. The returns from 1887 onwards, which are more accurate, indicate an apparent decrease of over 5,500 acres of woodland in Glamorgan and an apparent increase of some 1,800 acres in Merioneth between the Tithe Survey and the 1887 return.

The figures in Tables 14 and 15 indicate a substantial increase in woodland area during the 1870s, but this is certainly because the 1871 data are underestimates. From the 1887 return onwards, the figures show a fairly stable pattern, and towards the end of the century the figures are probably quite accurate. Therefore, the extremely low percentage area of 3.02% in 1871, which is commonly cited, did not correspond to the actual situation, and a woodland

Table 14. Total acreages of woods and plantations in Wales, from the Agricultural Returns

Counties	1871	1887	Years of the Returns 1888	1891	1895	1905	1913
Anglesey	1,198	1,769	1,693	1,853	2,193	2,422	2,409
Brecon	9,233	10,414	12,456	13,955	13,956	14,532	14,319
Caernarfon	6,746	10,938	11,015	11,654	12,593	11,716	15,978
Cardigan	11,257	14,738	15,650	15,758	15,989	16,341	18,437
Carmarthen	15,577	21,516	21,396	22,346	23,290	23,936	22,919
Denbigh	13,512	16,705	17,686	17,961	18,422	18,872	18,972
Flint	5,375	5,579	7,307	7,839	8,209	7,470	7,565
Glamorgan	19,864	23,687	23,195	25,694	27,206	25,712	25,830
Merioneth	10,635	15,049	15,771	13,750	14,407	15,912	15,270
Monmouth	28,484	29,856	32,037	33,415	32,733	32,149	29,839
Montgomery	18,775	22,744	22,090	23,728	24,730	25,776	23,866
Pembroke	5,930	10,064	9,116	9,776	9,689	10,105	10,330
Radnor	8,523	7,583	10,196	10,653	10,917	11,567	10,760
Wales, total	155,109	190,642	199,608	208,382	214,343	216,510	216,494

Table 15. The percentage areas under woods and plantations in selected years, from the Agricultural Returns

Counties	Total area* (acres)	Percentage of land under woods and plantations in 1871	1887	1891	1905	1913
Anglesey	175,836	0.68	1.00	1.05	1.37	1.37
Brecon	469,904	1.96	2.21	2.96	3.09	3.04
Caernarfon	360,137	1.87	3.03	3.23	3.25	4.43
Cardigan	443,186	2.54	3.32	3.55	3.68	4.16
Carmarthen	587,816	2.64	3.66	3.80	4.07	3.89
Denbigh	424,555	3.18	3.93	4.23	4.44	4.46
Flint	164,061	3.27	3.40	4.77	4.55	4.61
Glamorgan	516,955	3.84	4.58	4.97	4.97	4.99
Merioneth	427,811	2.48	3.51	3.21	3.71	3.56
Monmouth	349,119	8.15	8.55	9.57	9.20	8.54
Montgomery	510,111	3.68	4.45	4.65	5.05	4.67
Pembroke	392,595	1.51	2.56	2.48	2.57	2.63
Radnor	301,164	2.83	2.51	3.53	3.84	3.57
Wales, total	5,123,250	3.02	3.72	4.06	4.22	4.22

*From A.W. Ashby and I.L. Evans, *The Agriculture of Wales* (1944), p. 208.

percentage area of approximately 4%, as indicated by the earlier Tithe Surveys and by the later Agricultural Returns, is probably closer to the truth. Even so, the forest area of Wales had been reduced from a maximum of about 90% of the land area to about 4% in the space of a few thousand years. Within Wales, the percentage woodland area varied quite considerably by county, being little over 1% in Anglesey and as much as 9% in Monmouthshire. Most of the other counties had approximately 3 or 4%.

The earlier Agricultural Returns provided data only on woodland area by counties, but even these have been misquoted or misleadingly cited, even by authoritative sources. For example, the Forestry Commission's Census of Woodlands 1947-49 cites the nominal total area of woodland in Wales in successive surveys from 1871 to 1947; however, the figures tabulated for the 1871, 1887 and 1895 surveys do not include the acreage for Monmouthshire, whereas those for the surveys between 1905 and 1947 correctly include it.

Although the earlier Agricultural Returns provided statistics on woodland areas only, the later returns provided data on the area of forest nurseries, new plantations, and the major types of woods. Even so, the only data collected were acreages, and no attempt was made to collect statistical information on the proportions of individual species, age-classes, standing volume, or increment.

The area of forest nurseries within individual counties exhibits quite considerable fluctuations between 1887 and 1892 (Table 16), suggesting that the nurseries themselves were often temporary or short-lived enterprises.

Table 16. Areas of nurseries, and new plantations established in Wales

County	Acreages of nurseries		Acreages of new plantations in		
	1887	1892	1881-91	1881-95	1903-13
Anglesey	20	—	159	220	32
Brecon	13	7	1,212	1,540	948
Caernarfon	16	30	847	1,068	187
Cardigan	26	19	976	1,017	695
Carmarthen	46	34	1,720	2,099	1,546
Denbigh	29	24	528	1,111	421
Flint	7	8	179	202	164
Glamorgan	72	63	1,796	2,299	2,111
Merioneth	11	16	443	426	371
Monmouth	24	25	1,043	984	2,237
Montgomery	22	29	1,410	2,858	1,195
Pembroke	6	6	218	306	277
Radnor	9	4	230	507	879
Wales, total	301	240	10,761	14,637	11,063

The rate of new planting in the period 1881-1913 in the whole of Wales was only approximately 1,000 acres per annum (Table 16). The Rating Act (1874) had made the land, and not the timber or underwood it carried, the subject of assessment. For valuation purposes, woodland was divided under the act into three classes:

A. Land used only for a plantation or a wood: the value is estimated as if the land, instead of being a plantation or wood, were let and occupied in its natural and unimproved state;

B. Land used for the growth of saleable underwood: the value is estimated as if the land were let for that purpose;

C. Land used both for a plantation or a wood and for the growth of saleable underwood: the value is estimated either as A or as B, as the assessment committee may determine.

The rating of woodlands was generally thought to have deterred many landowners in England and Wales from planting, as indicated by witnesses giving evidence to various parliamentary committees and commissions. Evan Powell, land-agent and surveyor of Llanidloes, for example, made this point strongly to the Select Committee on Forestry in 1887.[3]

The area recorded immediately before the First World War as coppice was just under 20% of the total woodland area in Wales, and the area of young plantations (under 10 years old) formed slightly over 5% (Table 17). The percentage of coppice differed considerably by counties, being below 10% in all except for Glamorgan (17.9%), Radnor (23.7%), Carmarthen (23. 9%) and Monmouth (71%). The very high proportion of coppice in Monmouthshire accounted for over half of all the recorded coppice in Wales. It is possible, however, that differences of definition of coppice and coppice-with-standards may account for some of the striking differences between the counties.

Table 17. Acreages of major types of woods, by counties, in 1913

County	Coppice, acres	Plantations (under 10 years old) acres	Other woods, acres	Total acres
Anglesey	41	32	2,336	2,409
Brecon	849	948	12,522	14,319
Caernarfon	455	187	15 336	15,978
Cardigan	1,845	695	15,897	18,437
Carmarthen	5,473	1,546	15,900	22,919
Denbigh	480	421	18,071	18,972
Flint	139	164	7,262	7,565
Glamorgan	4,615	2,111	19,104	25,830
Merioneth	1,178	371	13,721	15,270
Monmouth	21,193	2,237	6,409	29,839
Montgomery	1,706	1,195	20,965	23,866
Pembroke	924	277	9,129	10,330
Radnor	2,550	879	7,331	10,760
Wales, total	41,448	11,063	163,983	216,494

The 1901 Census Returns give the number of foresters and woodmen employed in Wales.[4] These figures refer to persons in full-time employment, and take no account of casual labour employed for seasonal jobs such as the bark harvest. The total number of workers classed as foresters and woodmen (all male) in Wales in 1901 was 978, representing just under 1% of the total agricultural labour force.

It is also possible to derive an estimate of the intensity of forest management in the various counties at the beginning of the twentieth century from the data of the Agricultural Returns and the Census Returns by dividing the area of woods and plantations in 1905 by the number of foresters/woodmen in 1901, to give the average woodland acreage per forester/woodman (Table 18).

Table 18. Forest management intensity (woodland acreage per forester) in Wales

County	No. of foresters & woodmen (1901)	Area of woods & plantations, acres (1905)	Average woodland area, in acres per forester
Anglesey	14	2,422	173
Brecon	64	14,532	227
Caernarfon	66	11,716	177
Cardigan	29	16,341	563
Carmarthen	75	23,936	319
Denbigh	99	18,872	190
Flint	46	7,470	162
Glamorgan	139	25,712	184
Merioneth	39	15,912	408
Monmouth	271	32,149	118
Montgomery	73	25,776	353
Pembroke	33	10,105	306
Radnor	30	11,567	385
Wales, total	978	216,510	221

Monmouthshire, the county with the greatest area of woodland, the greatest percentage area of woodland and the greatest proportion of coppice, was clearly the most intensively managed county (118 acres/forester), and Cardiganshire by far the least intensively managed (563 acres/forester).

During the nineteenth century the increasing sense of professionalism in forestry resulted in the formation of a number of societies devoted to its furtherance in Britain. The Scottish Arboricultural Society was founded in 1854, the English Arboricultural Society in 1881 and the Irish Forestry Society in 1901. Despite their names, these Scottish and English societies were concerned from the start with forestry proper as well as with arboriculture. The English Arboricultural Society eventually became the Royal English Arboricultural Society and in 1931 changed its name to the Royal English Forestry Society, but it was not until after 1947 that it became officially the Royal Forestry Society of England, Wales and Northern Ireland. No professional forestry society has ever been formed in Wales, though many landowners and their foresters, usually expatriate Scots, were members of either or both the Scottish and English societies. The journals of these societies, and many books written by individuals, provided a medium for expressing the growing need for an appropriate forest policy, including such developments as professional forestry education, government support for private forestry, research and experimentation, large-scale state afforestation schemes, and the formation of a state forest service.

As a result of this pressure, a certain amount of government activity took place towards the end of the nineteenth century. A Select Committee of the House of Commons was set up in 1885 to consider 'whether, by the establishment of a Forest School, or otherwise, our woodlands could be rendered more remunerative'. In its report in 1887, it referred to the desirability of establishing forest schools in England and Scotland and also in Ireland, and to the economic and social benefits of extensive planting schemes in many parts of the kingdom. Evan Powell, land-agent and surveyor of Llanidloes, in giving evidence to the committee suggested that 'there is probably a larger area of unplanted land in Wales that would pay for planting than in any other portion of the kingdom'.[5]

Another Select Committee was appointed in 1889 to inquire into the administration of the Department of Woods and Land Revenues of the Crown. In the same year the Board of Agriculture was empowered to undertake various measures for assisting and promoting forestry.

The particular problems of land in Wales were recognized in the report of the Royal Commission on Land in Wales & Monmouthshire published in 1896. In evidence to this commission J. Muir, the forester of the Margam estate, proposed a scheme for state aid to assist landowners by lending the capital necessary to plant and enclose the land at a low rate of interest, and also an amount of money sufficient to recoup the rent lost during the early unproductive years of the plantation.[6]

In 1902, a Departmental Committee was appointed 'to inquire into and report as to the present position and future prospects of forestry, and the planting and management of woodlands in Great Britain, and to consider whether any measures might with advantage be taken ... for their promotion and encouragement'.[7] One practical outcome of the committee's recommendations was the award of a grant of £250 per annum by the Board of Agriculture and Fisheries for the establishment of a lectureship in forestry at the University College of North Wales at Bangor. This led, in 1904, to the establishment of a School of Forestry, and the appointment of Fraser Story as lecturer. This lectureship was soon raised to the status of a chair, and in 1907 Professor Story started a full degree course, Bangor thus becoming the first place in Britain to offer a university degree in forestry. In 1912 the School was further strengthened by the appointment of Thomas Thomson as assistant to Professor Story. The first woman to graduate in forestry at Bangor was Mary Sutherland (1895-1955).

At the very end of the century the Crown purchased one substantial area of land for planting and another substantial area of established woods in Wales.[8] Hafod Fawr (Merioneth), consisting of 1,369 acres of hill sheep land, was bought in 1899, and a resident woodman was put in charge soon after; 210 acres were enclosed and planted by 1915, mainly with Scots pine but also with Japanese larch and Sitka spruce. In 1901, nearly 4,000 acres of established woods at Tintern, mainly coppice-with-standards, were bought from the Duke of Beaufort. Both these Crown woods were subsequently transferred to the Forestry Commission under the Forestry (Transfer of Woods) Act of 1923. The Hafod Fawr experiment proved valuable in species selection for exposed peatland sites, and it also focused attention on the importance of sheep damage, the costs of land acquisition, the problem of evicting tenant farmers, and the expense of labour.

In addition to Hafod Fawr, another experimental scheme of species trial plots was started near Chirk early in the twentieth century.[9] This was an upland area of fifty acres at 900-1,200ft, donated to the council by John Mahler of Penisa'r Glyn, and planted up as species trial plots under the direction of the young Forestry Department of the University College, Bangor.

Large-scale corporate afforestation schemes in the late nineteenth century and early in the twentieth century were carried out by various water boards in the catchment areas of major reservoirs, notably around Lake Vyrnwy by Liverpool Corporation and the Elan valley reservoirs by Birmingham Corporation. At Lake Vyrnwy, for example, in 1893 the catchment contained 172 acres of old native hardwoods, 25 acres of old plantations, mainly larch, and 273 acres of new plantations, again mainly larch, but also spruce and several species of pine.[10]

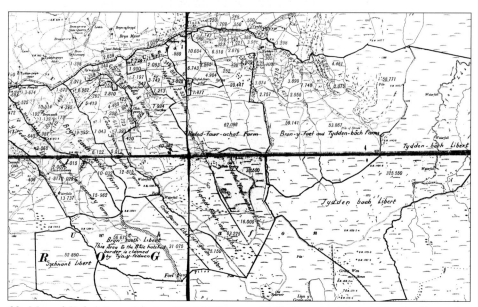

80. Map of Hafod Fawr (Merioneth): 1,369 acres of hill sheep land, bought by the Crown for afforestation in 1899.

In the Elan valley catchment, over 1,000 acres were planted before 1918, mainly with Scots pine and European larch, but also with Japanese larch, Douglas fir, Sitka spruce and Corsican pine. One plantation of European larch, with Scots pine for shelter at the higher elevations, planted in 1904-05, was awarded the Silver Medal at the Royal Agricultural Society's show in 1919.[11]

The Rt. Hon. Lloyd George, as Chancellor of the Exchequer, in introducing his 'People's Budget' in 1909, referred at length to the question of afforestation: 'there is very general agreement that some steps should be taken in the direction . . . of reafforesting the waste lands of this country', but he concluded with caution: 'there is a good deal of preliminary work which ought to be undertaken in this country before the Government could safely begin planting on the large scale . . . to rush into planting on a huge scale without first of all making the necessary experiments, organizing a trained body of foresters and taking all other essential steps to secure success when you advance, would be to court disaster, which might discourage all future attempts'.[12]

Despite the growing climate of informed opinion for major state involvement in forestry, no definite measures were taken until the pressure of the First World War forced rapid action. In 1914, over 90% of Britain's supplies of wood were imported, and per capita consumption had recently risen quite considerably. The critical supply position was not fully realized until 1916, when a Timber Supplies Department was hastily created; also, a Women's Forestry Corps was formed, and overseas units such as a Canadian Forestry Corps came into operation to accelerate the felling and utilization of home timber supplies. A team of Portuguese labourers, for example, was employed at Presteigne producing ash for coachwork and pit-props for the South Wales coalfield. A whole series of orders governing the sale and prices of timber, pitwood and fuelwood was issued by the Controller of Timber Supplies and by the Board of Trade.

During the war, felling operations were conducted on no fewer than 114 estates in Wales, and more than two thousand people were employed. The following account by Gertrude M. Painter, who was in charge of a Women's Forestry Corps contingent in Breconshire, gives a vivid first-hand picture of the forestry conditions at the time and the urgency of the war effort:

> The country is of the wildest, hilly and mountainous, with deep valleys and narrow gorges, and while this renders it very beautiful and picturesque it makes it very difficult for the work in hand, the task of removing timber from the wooded slopes and precipices. Some of the valleys where we are felling timber are very remote and far removed from railway stations, with roads never intended for heavy traffic, and with inclines so steep that it is not possible to use horses to drag the trees out of the wood. But by means of traction engines placed on the roadside the felled timber is removed by the use of wire ropes. Sometimes it is possible to run a tramline through the wood; sometimes a brook rushing madly through the bottom of the ravine is dammed and the trees are floated downstream.
>
> In the case of pitwood the trees are cross-cutted and in lengths of six, nine and thirteen feet, placed ready for loading on the roadside, whence a motor lorry takes

81. Timber fellers working in conifers at Glanusk, near Crickhowel, during the First World War.

them direct to the nearest station for consignment to the collieries. Should the valley hold a great quantity of big timber, saw mills are set up directly the felling has progressed sufficiently, and camps spring up like mushrooms in the most isolated parts of the county – camps of busy men and women, occupied in getting converted timber ready for France for use in the construction of huts and dug-outs and gateposts, and as sleepers for the railway companies. Some of the timber is sent to the dockyards and some to the arsenals, camp depots, and railway and post office departments. The big larch and scotch trees are used for keeling boats; the willow trees are used largely for artificial limbs, while the wood of the ash is utilised in the construction of aeroplanes, in munition works, and in the manufacture of tool handles. The industry of bark stripping has been greatly revived, and while the bark continued to run well a large quantity was harvested in this county.

It is difficult to give an impression of the enormous rate at which timber is being felled, owing to the urgency of the orders which we have to execute. An incredible quantity has already been cut. Every wood is either felled or has been bought for that purpose in the county. The work is hard and the strain is great. The difficulties of transport, the remoteness of the woods, and the lack of skilled labour all add to the arduousness of our task. I must not forget the Welshwoman, for we have a gang of timber girls doing excellent work. Not all, I must confess, are Welsh, but a fair proportion belong to the Principality.

There is a sadness in the destruction of the beauties of the countryside which this work entails, but it is counter-balanced by the pleasure of finding what a dignity the bare hills acquire.[13]

It is difficult to quantify the amount felled in Wales during the war, but felling was certainly heavier in percentage terms in Wales than in England and Scotland (see next chapter).

Amazingly, some afforestation was actually undertaken during the war. A fairly large area was planted by women's labour on the catchment area of Lake Vyrnwy. Small areas were also planted on the following estates: Crosswood (Cardiganshire), Coed Coch (Abergele), Hafodunos (Denbighshire) and Nantclwyd (near Rhuthun). Women also planted up an experimental area of 25 acres at Corsygedol (Merioneth) in connection with the UCNW Forestry Department at Bangor.

However, thousands of plants which became overgrown in the nurseries had to be burnt because of the lack of labour for planting. Another difficulty was the shortage of wire netting to protect young plantations from damage by rabbits.

In July 1916 the Prime Minister appointed a Forestry Sub-Committee of the Ministry of Reconstruction 'to consider and report upon the best means of conserving and developing the woodland and forestry resources of the United Kingdom, having regard to the experience gained during the war'. In 1917 this sub-committee, commonly called the Acland Committee after its chairman, the Rt. Hon. F.D. Acland M.P., recommended the adoption of an adequate forest policy, including a large long-term state afforestation programme and the creation of an appropriate state forest service. In its report, the committee commented, with reference to the conifer afforestation of wasteland in France in the nineteenth century: 'If our statesmen, even thirty years ago, had shown equal foresight, most of the timber required [for maintenance of naval coal supplies] could have been grown on the Welsh hills'.[14]

The Acland Committee recommended one central forest authority for Britain, with separate consultative committees for England, Wales, Scotland and Ireland. Authoritative voices such as W. Craven Llewelyn (of the Forestry Supplies Department), and W.R. Fisher, chief editor of the Royal English Arboricultural

82. Timbermen's bridge over the river Teifi at Henllan falls, c.1916.

Society's journal, had for some time urged the formation of an autonomous Welsh Forestry Board.

In due course, after the Acland Committee's report had been submitted and debated, a forestry bill was drafted and passed rapidly through its various stages: it was introduced into the House of Lords on 7 July 1919 and as the Forestry Act received the Royal Assent on 19 August 1919. Under its provisions the Forestry Commission was established, but Wales was not accorded equal status with Scotland and Ireland: three Assistant Commissioners were appointed, one (Hugh Murray) responsible for England and Wales, one for Scotland, and one for Ireland.[15] The work in Wales under the Assistant Commissioner was carried on by two Divisional Officers responsible respectively for North Wales (D.W. Young, operating from Shrewsbury) and South Wales (W.H. Lovegrove, operating from Hereford). Consultative committees were provided for each of the four countries. The committee for Wales, under the Rt. Hon. the Lord Kenyon, K.C.V.O. as Chairman and Col. F.D.W. Drummond, C.B.E., D.L. as Vice-Chairman, consisted of: G.B. Bovil, Alderman T.W. David, J.P., Lt.-Col. J.R. Davidson, C.M.G., Major David Davies, M.P., Capt. J.D.D. Evans, Col. W. Forrest, D.S.O., D.L., J.P., Vernon Hartshorn, M.P., G.A. Humphreys, C. Bryner Jones, C.B.E., M.Sc., John Jones, Lt.-Col. W.N. Jones, J.P., Col. Chas. Venables Llewellyn, F. J. Matthews, the Rt. Hon. the Earl of Powis, D.L., J.P., L.R. Pym, D.C. Roberts, J. Roberts, Major-Gen. A.E. Sandbach, C.B., D.S.O., J.I. Storrar, the Rt. Hon. the Lord Tredegar, H.C. Vincent, Percy Wilkinson, and Col. Sir H.L. Watkin Williams-Wynn, Bart., C.B.; H.A. Pritchard, O.B.E. served as secretary to the committee.[16]

This then was the embryo executive organization and consultative body responsible for ushering in the new era of state forestry involvement in Wales alongside the existing private interests.

The national forest policy, defined by the Acland Committee and accepted by parliament fell under two heads: The *ultimate objective* was to create 'reserves of standing timber sufficient to meet the essential requirements of the nation over a limited period of three years in time of war or national emergency' (this would require the state to afforest 1,770,000 acres of land previously unplanted, of which 1,180,000 acres should be planted in forty years, and the whole in eighty years). The *immediate objective* was a ten-year scheme, based on a block grant, for state afforestation of 150,000 acres of new land, plus assistance to local authorities and private owners for afforestation or reforestation of 110,000 acres.[17]

Chapter XII

1919-45: Mutton *versus* Trees

> The afforestation of land . . . is bound to cause inconvenience and even hardship to existing owners and occupiers: the cry of mutton versus trees will be raised.
>
> *Forestry Commission Annual Report,* 1919/20

As shown in the previous chapter, in addition to drafting and introducing the Forestry Bill into parliament, the Interim Forest Authority had carried out much valuable preparatory work, and accordingly when the Forestry Commission was formally created on 29 November 1919 it was able to start its programme of work immediately.

After a meeting of the Forestry Commissioners in London on 7 December 1919, a dramatic race ensued between noble lords travelling on overnight express trains to undertake the symbolic planting of the Commission's first trees.[1] Lord Lovat, as chairman, had intended to make the first planting himself at Monaughty in Scotland. However, on arrival at Elgin station on the morning of 8 December, Lord Lovat was greeted by a telegram from Lord Clinton, informing him that he, Clinton, had already planted the Forestry Commission's first trees, a few beech and larch, earlier that very morning, at Eggesford Forest in North Devon. However, this was a two-horse race between England and Scotland: Wales was a non-starter, and the first Forestry Commission planting in Wales did not come until fifteen months later.

One of Lord Lovat's first moves was to arrange a working weekend at Llanthony Abbey, for Commissioners and senior officials to discuss their tasks, and especially the problems of land acquisition and planting stock. During its first year of operation, to 30 September 1920, the Forestry Commission acquired its first land in Wales at Margam and at Gwydyr, but no actual planting was undertaken that year. During the next forest year, October 1920-September 1921, the Forestry Commission acquired more land at Llantrisant (Glamorgan), Llanover (Monmouthshire) and Vaughan (Merioneth), and also made its first plantings in Wales as follows:

Gwydyr	320	acres	(reforestation; all conifers)
Llanover	93	acres	(new planting; 92 acres conifers)
Llantrisant	71	acres	(new planting; 69 acres conifers)
Margam	156	acres	(new planting; 152 acres conifers)

It seems to be generally agreed that the first new plantings in Wales were actually carried out in early February 1921, at Llantrisant on land acquired from the Marquis of Bute's estate. The bulk of the new plantings at Llantrisant and Llanover was Douglas fir, and at Margam Scots and Corsican pine, European and Japanese larch, Douglas fir, and Norway and Sitka spruce, while at Gwydyr well over half the replanting was with spruce.[2]

In 1922 the infant Forestry Commission was nearly terminated by the cost-cutting Geddes Commission, and it was only the most spirited defence by Lord Lovat that rescued it from extinction by the infamous Geddes 'axe'. Even so, the effects of the enforced financial cutbacks did cause serious disruption in the early work of the Forestry Commission, notably the closure of the Cardiff office.

In 1923 the Crown Woods at Hafod Fawr and Tintern were formally transferred to the Forestry Commission,[3] and during the 1920s the Commission's acquisitions of new land in Wales gathered pace, as did the annual planting rate, though during those difficult years the Commission was never able to do much to assist and promote private forestry.

The Forestry Commission carried out a complete Census of Woodlands in Great Britain in 1924.[4] In Wales most of the actual data collection was done on a voluntary basis by private individuals (County Organisers) selected for their extensive knowledge of the woodlands in their particular districts. The 1924 Census revealed that the total area of woodland in Wales amounted to 253,461 acres, i.e. 5% of the land area (Table 19). This woodland was classified as follows: high forest 113,003 acres, coppice 35,331 acres, scrub 34,934 acres, felled or devastated 64,182 acres, and uneconomic (including amenity woods and shelterbelts) 8,011 acres. Some two-fifths of the area of high forest was conifers, two-fifths hardwoods, and one-fifth was mixed.

However, the stark fact is that soon after the First World War 41.5% of the total area of woodland in Wales was classified as scrub, felled or devastated, and uneconomic (as compared with only 24% for England).

Great differences in the amount and the condition of the Welsh woodlands become apparent when the 1924 Census figures are analysed by counties:

Table 19. Area and condition of woodlands in Wales, 1924 Census

County	Woodland area, acres	Woodland as % of land area	Scrub + felled/ devastated + uneconomic as % of the total woodland area
Anglesey	2,068	1.2	56.6
Brecon	28,150	6.0	56.3
Cardigan	13,126	3.0	59.9
Carmarthen	22,920	3.9	49.9
Caernarfon	13,145	3.6	39.6
Denbigh	17,447	4.1	23.4
Flint	7,170	4.4	24.5
Glamorgan	29,177	5.7	43.5
Merioneth	18,639	4.5	47.2
Monmouth	44,497	12.8	18.1
Montgomery	33,141	6.6	50.7
Pembroke	9,431	2.4	49.8
Radnor	14,550	4.9	45.9
Wales, total	253,461	5.0	41.5

The administrative territorial divisions of the Forestry Commission frequently changed their boundaries and designations in the early years. From 1922 South Wales was amalgamated with SW England until 1936, when South Wales was again recognized as a division, and the divisional office was set up in Cardiff, where it was to remain until final closure and transfer of functions to Aberystwyth in 1984. North Wales continued to form a part of a larger division comprising also several English midland counties and with its divisional office in Shrewsbury, where it remained right up until its move to Aberystwyth in 1962/63. This long location in Shrewsbury may well have contributed to the Forestry Commission being perceived as a rather alien authority in North Wales.

Initially, the official figures published by the Forestry Commission for land acquisition and annual planting in England and Wales were lumped together, and it is difficult to separate out the figures for Wales. This situation persisted right up until 1946, and was rendered worse by the fact that some of the expanding forest units, for example Dean, Mortimer and eventually Kerry, straddled the border between Wales and England.

However, by extracting from the Forestry Commission annual reports the planting figures for individual forests within Wales, it is possible to gain a picture of the progress of land acquisition and planting in Wales during the 1920s and 1930s: annual planting increased fairly steadily from 1,128 acres in 1922 to some 4,200 acres in 1930. With some fluctuation the annual planting rate remained at about this level during the 1930s, but in fact exceeded 5,000 acres per annum in 1939 and again in 1940.

The year 1924 saw the start of the Forestry Commission's policy for combining forestry with the creation of small part-time forest holdings. This was thought to be an excellent policy particularly for the poor hill areas of Wales, and was strongly supported by H.A. Pritchard, Assistant Commissioner for England and Wales from January 1924 until his death in 1932.[5]

Henry Ambrose Pritchard, a Welshman of humble origins, had worked as a lad in the estate office of the Earl of Plymouth at St Fagans, where he qualified as a member of the Surveyors' Institute, with its special forestry diploma. He then taught forestry at the Agricultural College, Cirencester, and during the 1914-18 war he was in charge of a large timber supply division, responsible for maintaining wood supplies to the South Wales coalfield. In November 1919 he had been appointed Chief Technical Adviser to the Assistant Commissioner for England and Wales. By all accounts an irascible man, Pritchard spared neither his staff nor himself, and his drive and energy were vital in the infant years of the Forestry Commission.

83. H.A. Pritchard, *c*.1922, drawn by G.B. Ryle.

The forest worker holdings set up by the Forestry Commission in the early years were usually existing cottages, refurbished as necessary. In the process of land acquisition, many remote hill farmhouses came into the hands of the Forestry Commission, with outbuildings and a few acres of moderate meadow adjoining. These were readily adaptable as smallholdings, while the *ffridd* (nearby sheepwalk) and the remote mountain sheepwalk were enclosed for afforestation. There was no shortage of potential tenants willing to become woodmen, but few of these houses were fit for occupation without repairs and renovation.[6]

The quality of the houses built by the Forestry Commission improved steadily in their amenities between 1924 and 1939 – from simple brick houses with kitchen-parlour, two bedrooms, boxroom and scullery with a single cold tap, to quite good three-bedroom houses with bathroom and hot and cold water. Later on, these houses were often grouped together.

With the high unemployment in the coalfields in the 1920s and 1930s, the Ministry of Labour asked the Forestry Commission to set up forestry camps under the Distressed Areas (soon renamed Special Areas) scheme.[7] Residential camps were set up in the new forests of Gwydyr, Dovey, Brechfa and Mortimer (Radnor/Hereford), for example, and a non-residential camp at Rheola Forest in the Vale of Neath. These camps, commonly known as 'reconditioning' camps, were initially for training men for settlement overseas, but this element of the training soon gave way to rehabilitation works to refit the men for tough work at home. Manual road-making was one of the main tasks, and many unemployed miners were trained at these camps. At Rheola, for instance, men were bussed in each day from the mining townships, and provided with strenuous work under conditions of reasonable outdoor hardship, but importantly they started the day

84. Unemployed Welsh miners at a forest reconditioning camp near Presteigne in the 1930s.

off with a good hot snack and they had a really nourishing hot midday meal. These training courses generally lasted for sixteen weeks.

The development of the several separate forests such as Margam, Rheola and Cwmogwr which eventually came to form parts of the huge forest later named Coed Morgannwg has been described by George Ryle. The forest of Rheola (Glamorgan), started in 1922, was over 13,000 acres by 1949, of which nearly 7,000 acres were already under plantations, with over 4,000 acres still to be planted.[8]

In north Wales Coed-y-Brenin (Merioneth), started as Vaughan Forest in 1923, totalled over 18,000 acres by the mid 1950s, with nearly 10,000 acres planted.[9]

However, the best and most accessible account of the acquisition and subsequent development of a major new forest in Wales is Donald Shaw's *Gwydyr Forest in Snowdonia: A History*.[10] In 1920 the Forestry Commission initially acquired 6,000 acres from the Gwydyr estate. The acquisition officers' report for the area included an important and far-sighted statement on amenity: 'Owing to the popularity of the district as a tourist centre a large proportion of the woods will be displayed to the full view of visitors. Careful planning of plantation layout and choice of species will be a capital advertisement of the Forestry Commission's intentions and activities – and this is a place where we must not fail, as scenic effects are jealously observed'.

Planting in Gwydyr began in 1921, but initially this was only the reforestation of areas that had been felled and cleared during the First World War. The much more difficult task of creating new forest by afforesting the moorland *ffridd* slopes and the bare plateau-land would come later. Shaw's history covers five decades of forest expansion at Gwydyr, including the problems of sheep, fire and war, the developments in nursery work, planting and mechanization, the growing timber yields and the importance of amenity, recreation, education and wildlife.

In 1966 Gwydyr Forest was split into three separate units: Gwydyr, Lledr and Machno. As at 30 March 1961 these three units had a total forest area of over 20,000 acres, the area actually under trees exceeding 14,000 acres (95% conifers, 4% broadleaves, 1% mixed).

During the period between the two world wars, under a government-imposed stop-go policy, the Forestry Commission was learning by often bitter experience many important lessons associated with the problems of afforesting bare hill land, which heroic pioneers such as Thomas Johnes had faced a century and a half earlier at Hafod. These concerned particularly the correct choice of species; the crucial importance of site preparation and drainage; atmospheric pollution; the ever-present problem of marauding sheep; and especially in south Wales, fire. In some years Wales had the unenviable record of recording more forest fires than all the rest of Great Britain together. Ryle and Shaw both give graphic accounts of fighting major fires in the early years at Margam in 1929, and at Gwydyr in 1938.[11]

Remarkably, the Forestry Commission was always able to acquire adequate land in Wales, in parcels large and small, and almost always without recourse to their statutory power of compulsory purchase. Through the 1920s and 1930s many thousands of acres of land were acquired throughout Wales, to extend the first young forests and to create new ones.

Both before and after the Second World War there has always been a strange ambivalence in Wales towards 'the forestry': the Forestry Commission was buying up farms which would otherwise have been difficult or impossible to sell, from anxious but willing vendors. However, in so doing it was changing the old way of life in the mountains of Wales. As George Ryle put it: 'It meant change, and that was wrong'.[12]

During the difficult inter-war years the Forestry Commission was unable to do much to assist private forestry, as the planting grants available were too small. However, an alternative to planting grants was available, namely the proceeds-sharing scheme. The only instance of this being implemented was the joint scheme for afforestation of the Lake Vyrnwy catchment area, whereby the Forestry Commission and Liverpool Corporation shared the costs and profits.[13]

By 1939 Wales boasted nearly forty new state forests. The roll-call reads: Beddgelert, Brechfa, Brecon, Brynmawr, Caio, Chepstow, Clocaenog, Coed-y-Brenin, Coed-y-Rhaiadr, Crychan, Cwmeinion, Cwmogwr, Cynwyd, Dovey (Dyfi), Dyfnant, Glasfynydd, Gwydyr, Hafod Fawr, Hafren, Hay, Itton, Kerry (Ceri), Llanover, Llantrisant, Margam, Mathrafal, Michaelston, Mortimer (part), Myherin, Mynydd Du, Pembrey, Radnor, Rheola, St Gwynno, Tarenig, Tintern, and Usk. The names of some new Welsh forests had already changed – Vaughan had become Coed-y-Brenin. Later on many new names would be added to the list, and familiar old ones lost as a result of reorganization, mergers and renaming.

Well over 90% of all the new planting in Wales was of conifers. Fast-growing spruces, Norway and especially Sitka, have always been the main species, especially for the wetter areas at higher altitudes. Larches, mainly Japanese and hybrid larch, were quite widely planted on mineral soils. Douglas fir, which requires good rich soil at lower altitudes, was chosen on the better sites, and was often used to underplant and convert oak. Corsican pine, the best growing pine, came to be planted on drier areas, especially sand-dune sites such as Pembrey and, later, Newborough (Anglesey) and Harlech.

Young plants by the million were needed for the new Welsh forests. Initially, small nurseries were set up, but by the 1930s it was realized that a large specialist nursery would be preferable. A suitable site was eventually decided upon, namely Tair Onen (more correctly Onnen), ten miles west of Cardiff. Tair Onnen nursery, established in 1936, soon became one of the largest forest nurseries in Britain, in its heyday employing up to a hundred people and producing millions of plants each year. Much of the nursery work was done by women and girls, and some forty houses were built at Tair Onnen for the nursery staff.[14]

Another major development in the late 1930s was the formation of two National Forest Parks, one wholly and one partly within Wales. The first was the Snowdonia National Forest Park, initially based mainly upon Gwydyr Forest but including Beddgelert main block. It was established in 1937, encouraging open-air recreation and giving public access to the hills and lakes above the new plantations. In 1938 the Forest of Dean was established as a National Forest Park; it included the Tintern and Chepstow forests, west of the Wye, and was later renamed the Dean & Wye Valley Forest Park. With the post-war creation of National Parks (Snowdonia in 1951, and the Brecon Beacons in 1957) the Forestry Commission changed the name from National Forest Parks to Forest Parks.

The government instructions to the Forestry Commission to create work in the Special Areas had led to the reopening of the South Wales divisional office in Cardiff in 1936, and a drive to acquire more land for planting in the south Wales valleys.

Thus, by the end of the 1930s the annual planting rate by the Forestry Commission in Wales had built up to over 5,000 acres in 1938/39 and again in 1939/40. In 1938 the Forestry Commission started a new census of woodlands, but progress was slow and by the middle of 1939 it was clear that urgent action was needed in order to get data on available wood supplies before the outbreak of war. Accordingly, rough-and-ready 'flying surveys' were carried out by local staff to provide at least some basis for the emergency wartime fellings that would obviously soon be required.

Forests at War, 1939-45

> the creation of . . . reserves of standing timber . . . to meet the essential requirements of the nation in time of war.
>
> *Forestry Commission Annual Report,* 1919/20

Sealed orders to be opened on the outbreak of war (3 September 1939) split the Forestry Commission in two to form the Timber Production Department and the Forest Management Department. Some conflicts inevitably arose between these two departments, and with the Timber Control of the Ministry of Supply. However, in general it was agreed that wartime felling should concentrate on crops that could be felled at once, as and when needed, viz. plantations 20-35 years old, part of crops already mature, and coppice of pitwood size. Next in priority came crops which could be felled 'if necessary', i.e. plantations 15-20 and 35-40 years old, and the remaining mature timber. Other crops could be felled only in 'extreme emergency', viz. very young plantations, and middle-aged crops (conifers 40-60 years old and big hardwoods under 100 years old).[15]

The 'flying surveys' of forest resources that had been carried out in Wales in summer 1939 were soon put to use, as the Home Timber Production Department started its work.

Improvisation was the order of the day. For example, the front-axle units of old Cardiff Corporation buses were turned into two-wheel forestry trailers for wood extraction, and a rather ramshackle light railway was cobbled together to extract old coppice oak from Brechfa Forest. Charcoal burning in steel drums also witnessed a renaissance in Wales during the war, as did oak-bark stripping for tanstuffs.

By the end of the war, the motley fleet of vehicles in the South Wales division consisted of 10 articulated timber wagons, 57 heavy lorries, 28 crawler tractors, 2 bulldozers, 61 wheeled tractors, 14 small vans, 6 narrow-gauge steam trains, about 70 trams adapted from colliery tubs, and 17 motorcycles.

The function of the Forestry Commission, and later of the Home Timber Production Department, was to supplement the efforts of the timber trade in order to produce in quantity and kind what the timber merchants could not. Military units were also employed, for example a detachment of the Royal Engineers Forestry Company worked near Penhow on a pitwood operation. The Women's Timber Corps (WTC) was also active in Wales, and the 'lumber jills' or 'timber jills' of the WTC, with their distinctive green beret and badge, performed a wide range of forestry tasks during the war. Mrs Eileen Rawlinson (née Burton) of Cardiff recalled working in various forests in England, and later in Carmarthenshire, where she was billeted in Bryn Cothi house, requisitioned by the Ministry of Supply for the Women's Timber Corps. Their work at Abergorlech and Brechfa involved felling with axes and cross-cut saws, and the

85. Eileen Burton of Cardiff in Women's Timber Corps uniform, 1943.

86. 'Timber jills' of the Women's Timber Corps stripping oak bark, 1943.

stripping of oak bark for local tanneries. Italian and German POWs, conscientious objectors and Irish volunteer labour also worked in Welsh forests, but it must be remembered that the bulk of the forest workers employed during the war consisted of British civilian labour.

In his book *Timber at War* (1965) F.H. House gave a detailed account of the organization and activities of the Timber Control in Great Britain during the period 1939-45. The whole country was divided into areas, North Wales coming within Area 9 with the area office in Liverpool, while South Wales was Area 17 with the area office in Cardiff. Sometimes the Welsh language obviously proved something of a problem to Timber Control:

> In many parts of the Welsh counties the only language used is the native tongue, and it was necessary to have the Control Orders translated into Welsh and to obtain authority for them to be reprinted in this state in some of the West and mid-Wales local papers, where to a large extent English is a foreign language. This language problem remained throughout the period of the Control and was a common source of misunderstanding, not only of the Orders and procedure, but also in ordinary correspondence.[16]

Russell Meiggs of the Home Timber Production Department of the Ministry of Supply gave a detailed account of the importance of British woodlands to the war effort in his book *Home Timber Production 1939-1945*. Unfortunately, the production figures for England and Wales were always lumped together, and it is not easy to determine the Welsh contribution. The total volume of home-grown

87. Charcoal kilns, Wentwood, 1940, drawn by G.B. Ryle.

88. A gang of the Women's Timber Corps, 1943.

timber produced from September 1939 to December 1945 in England and Wales was 588.8 million cubic feet (after conversion). This represents a standing volume of some 750 million cubic feet (Hoppus measure over bark) – approximately one-third of the total volume of woodland, park and hedgerow timber estimated to be standing at the outbreak of war.

However, by using the figures of the 1947 Census it is possible to get some idea of Wales' contribution by adding together the devastated area (i.e. stands from which the best timber had been removed) plus the area felled (i.e. more or less completely clear-felled) since September 1939. This gives a figure of at least 49,408 acres of woodland felled, which is equivalent to a quarter of the total woodland area of Wales. Almost all of this area felled came from the private sector, for the war had come too soon for the Forestry Commission: it had not had enough time to fulfil its primary objective of creating a strategic reserve of timber for time of emergency. Only 1,828 acres of state forests were felled in Wales during the war.

The following two paragraphs are abridged from Meiggs[17] and give a succinct account of wartime timber production in Wales.

In England, Wales and Northern Ireland the Home Timber Production Department's special responsibility lay in the maintenance of supplies to the South Wales coalfield, which, when imports from France and Portugal were cut off, became almost exclusively dependent on home grown production for an annual consumption which through the war averaged nearly 500,000 tons. In peace time the home timber merchants could not compete with the French and Portuguese prices. The pitprop trade was therefore generally unfamiliar in the South and South West. During the war the trade contribution to the South Wales supply never exceeded 20 per cent of the total requirement, and though small parcels of imported props were from time to time diverted to South Wales, the large gap had to be filled primarily by the Department, whose deliveries in fact rose from 130,700 tons in 1940 to 402,000 tons in 1944. To maintain deliveries on this scale extreme measures had to be taken. The natural sources of supply were Wales and the Forest of Dean. A flying start could be made in the Dean and by the end of the first fortnight of war over 2,000 tons had been despatched, including a stock of some 200 tons prepared before the war. Young plantations, mainly from 20 to 35 years old, which according to the peace time working plan would have been periodically thinned to carry a mature crop, were clear felled. They were growing well and provided high yields. A high rate of production was maintained over a long period from the Dean with an economic use of labour.

The position in Wales was very different. In the critical years from 1916 to 1922 the cutting in Wales to feed the mines had been particularly heavy, and almost all the Forestry Commission plantations, though growing well, were too young to provide props. Highly productive plantations were the exception, and oak coppice was the dominant type of woodland. Its peace-time market value had been drastically reduced with the fall in the price of bark and the decay of the charcoal trade, and only a small proportion of the stands had been maintained in good condition. However, the Department was able at the outset of the war to make three substantial acquisitions of good quality pitwood reasonably near the mining district. As the war developed, production in Wales relied increasingly on oak coppice and small scattered parcels of conifers.

These two sources of supply, Wales and the Dean, were insufficient to meet requirements, and from the outset wood for south Wales was obtained from all parts of England and eventually even from Scotland. No colliery in south Wales ever had to cease production for lack of round timber.

Surprisingly, the Forestry Commission was able to continue its planting programme, albeit on a greatly reduced scale, throughout the war. Over 5,000 acres had been planted up in Wales during the forest year 1939/40, but naturally enough the planting rate thereafter decreased quite sharply year by year until 1945, when it fell below 1,000 acres for the first time since the early 1920s.

During the war a report on *Post-War Forest Policy* (1943) was produced by H.M. Forestry Commissioners which would reinvigorate state forestry and also provide a firm foundation and incentives for private forestry, once the hostilities had ceased.

Ryle summed up the situation at the end of the war in the following words: 'In all, between 1939 and 1946 we had cut down very nearly a third of the measurable living trees in Great Britain, and that destruction had been necessary. We had cut down the best and much which, though immature, was suitable for many of the urgent needs. We had left behind many thousands of acres of devastation. It was going to be a prodigious task for the government and the private landowner . . . to make good that loss'.[18]

89. 'Mutton versus trees': sheep in an oak wood in north Wales.

Chapter XIII

THE NEW LOOK: 1946-99

an all-out effort to rehabilitate and to increase the country's wood
reserves.
G. Ryle, *Beating about the bush*, p. 140

Following the reorganization and devolution of the Forestry Commission
enshrined in the Forestry Act of 1945, the old consultative committees were
replaced by national committees for England, Scotland and Wales, each country
had its own director of forestry, and Wales was divided into two conservancies,
North and South. The national headquarters for Wales was located at
Aberystwyth, though the two conservancy offices remained at Cardiff (South
Wales) and Shrewsbury (North Wales).

The Wales National Committee consisted of Lloyd P. Owen, W.L. Taylor, Sir
Richard Cotterell, Sir Cadwaladr Bryner Jones, Lt.- Col. J.C. Wynne Finch and
Alderman W. H. ('Billy') Vaughan.

Following this administrative reorganization and devolution, figures for
England and Wales are separated in the Forestry Commission's reports, making
it easier to trace developments in Wales.[1]

As Ryle put it, intensive tree-farming with sporadic 'social' expansions to
relieve unemployment, had almost wholly governed state policy from 1919 to
1939. After 1946 this policy was intensified for the Forestry Commission, and
incentives were greatly increased for private landowners, in an all-out effort to
rehabilitate and to increase the country's wood resources.[2] As we shall see, this
policy of producing more wood at a controlled cost became progressively more
successful.

On the basis of the Post-War Policy papers for state and private forestry, an
ambitious five-year plan was drawn up for forestry in Wales from 1946/47 to
1950/51, which envisaged total land acquisition of 176,000 acres over the five-
year period.[3] The state forestry planting programme was to increase annually,
and plant a total of 48,200 acres over the period. In fact, the Forestry
Commission came quite respectably close to fulfilling this planting programme.
In addition, the target for private forestry in Wales was to plant over 10,000 acres
over this same five-year period.

As soon as possible after the war, the Forestry Commission undertook a
complete survey of Britain's woodlands of five acres and over. This *Census of
Woodlands, 1947-1949* was published in 1952.[4]

In Wales the small, straggling and relatively inaccessible nature of many of
the woods made for slow progress. Survey took from August 1947 until May
1948 and occupied about 600 man-weeks. 1,755 six-inch Ordnance Survey

quarter-sheets were issued, and 22,133 Stand Data Forms completed. Only 3% of the maps published covered more than 500 acres of woodland apiece; another 71% had more than 5 acres each. The results for Wales are shown in Table 20.

Table 20. Total woodland area 1947-48

County	Private, acres	State, acres	Total acres	% of land area
Anglesey	1,979	81	2,060	1.2
Brecknock	23,668	8,557	32,225	7.0
Cardigan	13,188	5,613	18,801	4.2
Caernarfon	10,480	9,202	19,682	5.5
Carmarthen	23,192	14,622	37,814	6.5
Denbigh	20,624	5,546	26,170	6.1
Flint	7,924	—	7,924	4.9
Glamorgan	26,272	12,529	38,801	7.5
Merioneth	17,513	12,782	30,295	7.2
Monmouth	26,644	10,615	37,259	10.7
Montgomery	29,811	9,509	39,320	7.7
Pembroke	9,938	—	9,938	2.5
Radnor	12,975	3,214	16,189	5.4
Wales, total	224,208	92,270	316,478	6.2

Within the total area of Welsh woodlands, coniferous high forest made up 31%, broadleaved high forest 25%, and mixed high forest just 3%. Simple coppice accounted for 5%, and coppice-with-standards only 1%. The remaining categories were scrub 13%, devastated 4%, and felled 18%, totalling 35% (as compared with 41.5% in 1924). Of the total area, 71% was in private and 29% in state ownership.

Curiously, the 1947 Census also showed that Wales had lost a relatively large amount of woodland: 10,740 acres. Woodland was recorded as 'Disafforested' or 'Lost' if, though shown as woodland on the most recent 6-inch Ordnance Survey map, it was found in the census to be already converted or obviously under conversion to other uses. Most of this loss had taken place during the twentieth century, much of it indeed since the 1914-18 war. In the words of the census it appears that 'the small and scattered woods characteristic of the Welsh valleys, have tended to be converted rather rapidly to other forms of land use, mainly grazing'.

After hostilities ceased in 1945, the private woodlands of Wales, amounting to 224,208 acres, were again in a sadly ravaged condition, just as they had been after the First World War. Only 66% of private woodlands in Wales were classed as suitable for economic management, and 11% as doubtful. As the *Census of Woodlands 1947-1949* report put it: 'here most of the woods are small and scattered, or straggle across rocky hillsides and along winding dingles, with irregular boundaries and varying greatly in accessibility'. Moreover, by no means all of the productive woodlands were being managed efficiently.

90. Women working in Tair Onnen nursery, Glamorgan, in the 1950s.

91. Planting up a felled area in the 1950s.

To remedy this rather desperate situation, the Dedication of Woodlands Scheme was introduced in 1948.[5] Its basic principle was that woodland owners would receive state assistance if they were prepared to dedicate their land specifically to timber production in perpetuity and also provide adequate assurances for subsequent good management under a Forestry Deed of Covenant. The owner would receive grant aid provided he worked to an approved plan of operations, kept the essential records and ensured skilled supervision. To assist those owners not wishing to enter into a formal covenant, an alternative Approved Woods Scheme was also introduced, offering a lower level of grant aid.

Though initially greeted with some suspicion by private owners, the Dedication Scheme, which remained in operation until the 1980s, had a very significant effect in increasing the area and improving the standard of management of private woodlands in Wales. By 1972, for example, some five hundred private estates in Wales, with a total area of 80,000 acres, had come into the Dedication Scheme or had undertaken to manage their woods under the Approved Woods Scheme.

At the end of the 1950s and during the 1960s, the rules under which woodlands were treated for tax purposes encouraged the investment of capital in the afforestation of marginal and hill land. This gave a tremendous impetus to private planting, and forestry companies such as EFG, Tilhill and Fountain acted as agents, undertaking land acquisition, site preparation, planting and subsequent management of the plantations.

Another important development was the formation of cooperatives of private owners to promote forestry, for example Dovey Woodlands, Usk Woodlands, Towy Woodlands and Flintshire Woodlands.

With all this development, it is rather strange that forestry never became a popular career choice in Wales. Despite the existence of the university forestry department at Bangor since 1904, and the forester training school at Gwydyr (1948-69), relatively few Welsh people have chosen to make their career in forestry.

In Wales, most planting by private owners (i.e. new planting or restocking) since the war has been grant-aided under the various Dedication, Approved Woodlands and Small Woods Planting Grant schemes. Private planting averaged well over 1,000 hectares per annum during the 1960s, rising to about 1,500 hectares per annum during the early 1970s. It then fell quite sharply to less than half that figure in the mid 1970s, because of a combination of low business confidence, withdrawal of tax allowances and the decline in relative value of some of the grants. With the new Forestry Grant Scheme, planting increased once more to about 1,000-1,100 hectares per annum during the 1980s, but the removal of forestry tax reliefs in the March 1988 budget caused a drop in the level of private (mainly grant-aided) planting for a few years; however, private planting rates (new planting and restocking) soon recovered in Wales, and have generally exceeded 1,000 hectares per annum during the 1990s.

Assisted by increasingly powerful machinery for site preparation and road-building, the Forestry Commission's annual planting rate built up steadily during the 1950s and 1960s. It exceeded 13,000 acres for the first time in 1954, and peaked in 1960 with 13,167 acres (5,486 hectares). The activities of the Forestry Commission were literally transforming the face of much of rural and industrial Wales.

Figures for the numbers of persons directly and indirectly employed in forestry are a matter of some debate. In fact, the level of direct industrial employment by the Forestry Commission in Wales peaked quite early, in 1955, with 3,326 persons employed. Since then it has decreased very considerably, as the forests matured, with increasing mechanization, greater use of contractors, etc.

A Forester Training School, established in 1948 on the premises of the former labour 'reconditioning' camp that had been built near Capel Curig in 1935, ran two-year courses until its final closure in 1969.

New houses were built by the Forestry Commission for its workers. Llwyn-y-gog (Hafren Forest) was an entirely new forest hamlet, but forestry houses were more successful socially when built as extensions to old villages, as for example at Brechfa.

The Forestry Commission was not allowed to buy properties without first getting the agreement of the Ministry of Agriculture that the change of land-use would be unimportant from the point of view of food production. In practice this meant that the pressure to relegate forestry to the poorest land was always very strong.

Land acquisitions for forestry peaked in the 1950s. As before the war, there was an ambivalent attitude in Wales to the Forestry Commission buying up land from willing sellers. Forestry was changing the old way of life in the Welsh mountains. It was felt that 'dark trees by the million could never compare with good mountain lamb: six or ten woodmen drawing regular pay packets could never equal one shepherd. It meant change and that was wrong'.[6]

The long-running 'mutton *versus* trees' debate came to a head during the 1950s with the 'Battle of the Upper Towy' – a scheme to afforest the vast watershed of the upper Tywi and its tributaries the Camddwr and Doethïe, and also the Irfon.[7] Compulsory purchase of an initial block of 20,000 acres was agreed upon by the Forestry Commissioners, the Welsh National Committee and the Ministry of Agriculture. Local feelings ran high, a public enquiry was held under Sir Wynn Wheldon in Llandovery, and the vociferous opposition was such that the whole scheme for compulsory purchase was dropped. Later, an open forum at Tregaron helped restore some degree of understanding between the two sides. By 1965 the battle had been both won and lost: willing purchases of land provided not only the Forestry Commission but also several private forestry investors with plenty of land for afforestation of the hill catchments of the rivers and streams that now fill the great reservoir of Llyn Brianne. In fact, the total sold voluntarily over a 15-year period was more than double the area originally proposed for compulsory acquisition.

The depth of feeling against 'the forestry', and the sadness at the passing of the traditional way of life and abrupt alteration of the environment were poignantly expressed by Gwenallt (David James Jones, 1899-1968) who in

92. Conifers in Coed-y-Brenin and National Trust oakwoods in the Ganllwyd valley, near
    Dolgellau, 1970s.

Rhydcymerau lamented the planting of trees on bare Welsh hillsides by the Forestry Commission, regarded as an alien London-based authority:

Ac erbyn hyn nid oes yno ond coed	(And by now there is nothing there but trees
A'u gwreiddiau haerllug yn sugno'r hen bridd:	Their impudent roots sucking the old soil:
Coed lle bu cymdogaeth	Trees where there was neighbourliness
Fforest lle bu ffermydd	Forest where there were farms)

It was indeed farewell to Hafod Elwy and to many another Welsh upland farm: *y coed mawr a'i ceidw hi mwy* (the great woods will keep it now).

On 8 May 1962 the Forestry Commission celebrated the planting of a quarter of a million acres in Wales. The ceremony was held, appropriately enough, at Llantrisant Forest, where the Commission's very first planting in Wales had taken place back in February 1921.[8]

Of all the fine stands of exotic conifers now growing in Wales, one merits a special mention.[9] This is the Redwood Grove at Leighton, near Welshpool, donated by Charles Ackers to the Royal Forestry Society for England, Wales and Northern Ireland in 1958. The original main grove contains 33 coastal redwoods (*Sequoia sempervirens*) planted in 1857; in addition there is a larger area of *S. sempervirens* planted in 1935, and a pinetum of mixed age, containing many individual wellingtonias (*Sequoiadendron giganteum*) all well over 100 years old. The tallest of the old coastal redwoods is 40m high, and over 1.25m in diameter. The standing volume is approaching 3,000m³/ha.

In 1958, however, forest policy was modified. Instead of the unambiguous creation of strategic reserves of wood for time of war or national emergency, the main objective was the commercial production of timber for industry; the expansion of forestry was seen as a help in stemming rural depopulation, in improving recreation, and in enhancing the amenities of the countryside.

Although it had initiated the formation of the Dean/Wye and Snowdonia Forest Parks before the war, the Forestry Commission was rather slow to appreciate the growing demands of the recreation and landscape lobbies in the late 1950s. In fact, the Law Lords had given opinion that the Forestry Commission was acting 'outwith its remit' in providing recreational facilities at all, and so clauses were inserted in the Countryside Act of 1968 to legalize what the Forestry Commission had been doing ever since the creation of Forest Parks in 1938.

In Wales especially, the large-scale planting of pure blocks of conifers, with insensitive boundary lines and straight rides and roadways, coupled with the wholesale coniferization of low-grade broadleaved semi-natural woodlands, mainly oak, was giving forestry a bad name.

Eventually moved to action in 1963, the Forestry Commission appointed Dame Sylvia Crowe as its Landscape Consultant. From her long and unique experience in landscaping forests, she drew up a set of principles on landscape design which were adopted as the Commission's official policy. This led to the forest design plans now being routinely applied.[10] Essentially her principles

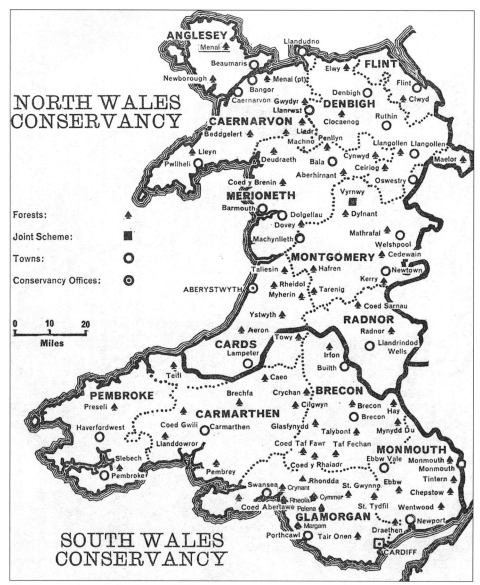

93. Forestry Commission forests, 1970.

involve a detailed analysis of the landscape and site; planting appropriate to the topography as regards species choice and plantation shape; the integration of forestry and agriculture; and utilizing the felling programme as the opportunity to create an enhanced forest landscape.

The beneficial effects of this enlightened approach are increasingly being seen throughout Wales, as the stark and uncompromising pure conifer blocks of the early years are gradually giving way to sensitively contoured and varied forest landscapes. Trunk-road and motorway planting, especially of broadleaves, has also had a significant effect in enhancing the Welsh landscape.

In the state forests of Wales, the provision of recreation facilities expanded greatly during the 1970s. As at 31 March 1995 forest recreationists had at their disposal 93 picnic places, 98 forest walks and nature trails, 11 cycle and 5 horse trails, 11 wayfaring and orienteering courses, 6 visitor centres, 4 arboreta and forest gardens, one forest drive (Cwmcarn), and one caravan and camping site (Beddgelert).[11]

Along with recreation came increasing public awareness of the environment, which foresters ignore at their peril. Conservation is the concern of countless individual members of the public, as well as a multitude of organizations such as the Woodland Trust, CPRW, Friends of Hafod, CCW, CLA, Nature Conservancy, National Trust, National Parks, Ramblers' Association, county wildlife trusts, RSPB, Coed Cymru, etc. Otters and red kites are notable conservation success stories; the black grouse is not.

The status of the semi-natural broadleaved woodlands, alluded to several times already, is now the prime concern of Coed Cymru, established in 1986 as a joint project in order to promote the good management of the remaining broadleaved woodlands of Wales.[12]

After the great census of 1947-49, further sample-based censuses were carried out by the Forestry Commission in 1965 and in 1979-82.[13] The actual basis of each of these three censuses differed, making comparison difficult, and metrication was officially adopted by the Forestry Commission on 15 February 1971. Accordingly, in the following table the figures shown in the third column are officially adjusted (by adding an allowance for small woods of 0.25-2.0ha to the 1947 results, and 0.25-0.4ha to the 1965 results) and rounded, in order to bring the results to a common basis.

Table 21. Woodland area in Wales in successive censuses

Year of Census	Area of woodland, hectares	Actual total area of all woodland over 0.25ha, hectares	Woodland as a percent of land area %
1947	128,300	141,000	6.8
1965	200,603	202,000	9.7
1980	240,784	241,000	11.6

The proportion of coniferous high forest increased from 33% of the Welsh woodland area in 1947 to 70% in 1980. The increase was most rapid between 1947 and 1965, when the actual area under conifers almost trebled.

The 1980 Census concluded that the total area of broadleaves in Wales was not less than it had been thirty years previously, but that the area of oak had decreased by some 7,000 hectares while that of sycamore, ash and birch had increased.

The 1980 Census also covered non-woodland trees over 7cm at breast height, a category which is of major importance for the rural and urban landscapes of Wales. This category comprises isolated (solitary) trees, small clumps and linear features such as avenues and shelterbelts, and is almost entirely in private ownership. The total number of live non-woodland trees in Wales was 12.6 million, of which conifers accounted for 11% and broadleaves 89%. The main broadleaved species is oak (20%), followed by alder and ash (17% each), sycamore and birch (12% each), and beech (6%). Elm had declined considerably, and accounted for only 2% in terms of numbers.

94. Ancient beech woodland, Coed Ffyddlwn, Clydach gorge, near Gilwern, 1998.

Oak, accounting for 41% of the volume, most of it in the larger size classes and with apparently adequate recruitment potential, is the most important non-woodland species in Wales, and seems likely to remain so for the foreseeable future.

The ratio of state forest to private forest in Wales has changed dramatically during the twentieth century. From virtually 0/100 in 1919, it grew to 5/95 in 1924, 29/71 in 1947, and 58/42 in 1965. Since the privatization disposals of recent years, the area and the proportion of state forests has declined a little.

Although the Conservative government decided, after some acrimonious argument and strong lobbying, against the wholesale privatization of the Forestry Commission, the Forestry Act 1981 did widen the powers of ministers to dispose of Forestry Commission land and plantations in order to reduce dependence on public funds for the management of the forest estate.

The total area of Forestry Commission plantations in Wales peaked in the year 1982/83, with 136,849 hectares. Table 22 shows the total area of plantations, the annual area of new planting and restocking, and the volume of production (thinnings plus fellings) at 5-year intervals from 1975 to 1995.

Table 22. Forestry Commission plantation area, annual planting and production in Wales

Year	Total area of plantations, hectares	New planting, hectares	Restocking, hectares	Volume production '000 m³o. b.
1975	132,300	1412	649	289
1980	135,902	797	1241	480
1985	134,407	161	1300	621
1990	127,029	96	1364	689
1995	118,863	0	1972	912

This table shows how the total area of plantations peaked in the early 1980s and then declined as disposals took place during the era of privatization in the eighties and nineties, up until the recent moratorium on large sales. It also shows how new planting (i.e. afforestation of bare land) has virtually stopped, while restocking of felled areas and volume production have increased steadily and inexorably as the forests approach maturity.

The number of named Forestry Commission forests in Wales increased from forty-four in 1946 to nearly eighty in the 1960s. Then began an apparently never-ending series of administrative reorganizations of the forests throughout the 1970s and 1980s, resulting in fewer but ever larger forest units. In 1984 the South Wales Conservancy office at Cardiff closed, administration for all Wales being concentrated at Aberystwyth. The forest unit was replaced by the district unit in 1984, and after nearly seventy years of existence and achievement, the two conservancies disappeared, Wales being run for the first time as a single unit.

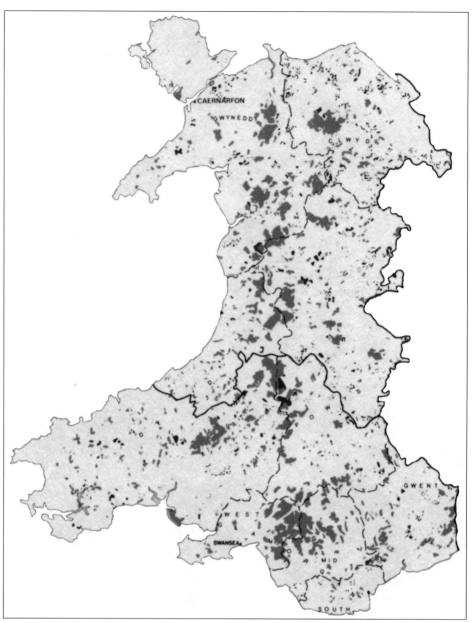

95. Forests in Wales, 1978.

The development of forest research, and the mechanization of forestry are subjects too large to feature in this book. Likewise, the economic arguments on the wisdom or folly of investment in forestry will form no part of this history. Suffice it to say that the state forests of Wales are now yielding nearly a million cubic metres of wood per annum, a figure expected to double in the next few decades. In the year ended 31 March 1995 the total volume of timber felled and thinned was 912,000 m^3 standing volume over-bark.

96. European larch, planted at Llanthony in 1835 by Walter Savage Landor.

It is doubly ironical that these Welsh forests, initially created deliberately to produce a strategic reserve of mining timber against time of war, now produce no mining timber whatsoever. As our forests grew, the demand for mining timber in Welsh pits withered away and disappeared. The bulk of forest sales now go as sawlogs, pulpwood and boardmill material to major industrial consumers such as BSW at Newbridge-on-Wye, Shotton and Sudbrook pulpmills, and Chirk MDF.

In summing up it will be of interest to examine the change in the total area of woodland in Wales from the low point in 1871 to the 1990s. Here it must be remembered that the earliest published returns for Wales are underestimates, and some did not routinely include Monmouthshire. Indeed, the 1947 Forestry Commission Census failed to appreciate this, and so their published figures significantly understated the true position in the nineteenth century.

97. Stone in Llantrisant Forest, unveiled 5 December 1994, commemorating the 75th anniversary of the founding of the Forestry Commission.

In the following table, all the area data for Wales from 1871 to 1992 always include Monmouthshire; for ease of comparison all areas have been converted to hectares; and the figures used for 1947 and 1965 are officially adjusted and rounded to include all woodlands over 0.25ha in area.

Table 23. Total woodland area of Wales, 1871-1992

Year	Area in hectares	Area as % of land area of Wales	Year	Area in hectares	Area as % of land area of Wales
1871	62,797	3.02	1938/39	127,530	6.2
1887	77,182	3.72	1947(actual)	128,128	6.2
1891	84,365	4.06	1947(adjusted)	141,000	6.8
1895	86,778	4.17	1965(adjusted)	202,000	9.7
1905	87,655	4.2	1980	241,000	11.6
1913/14	87,649	4.2	1992	248,000	11.9
1924	102,615	4.9			

Wales now has 12% of its land area under woodlands, and is certainly much better wooded than at any time since the Middle Ages. For comparison, the figure for England is only about 7.5% and for Scotland 14.5%, while for Denmark it is 12%, France 27%, Ireland 5%, Netherlands 9% and Sweden 70%.

On 1 July 1999 the Welsh Assembly assumed full power for funding and directing the Forestry Commission in its activities in Wales. Henceforward, forestry policies and programmes in Wales will be tailored to take account of Welsh issues, independent of policies and programmes in Scotland or England. A separate and distinct forest strategy is being developed for Wales. The UK government, jointly with the Assembly as regards Wales, will continue to ensure an overall strategic approach for forestry in the UK, and Welsh policies must fulfil and be consistent with the UK's international and European Union obligations.

ABBREVIATIONS

The following abbreviations are used in the references:

CFI	Commonwealth Forestry Institute, Oxford
ClRO	Clwyd Record Office, Mold
CPL	Cardiff Public Library
CRO	Dyfed (Carmarthen) Record Office, Carmarthen
GRO	Glamorgan Record Office, Cardiff
GwRO	Gwent Record Office, Cwmbrân
NLW	National Library of Wales, Aberystwyth
NMW	National Museum of Wales, Cardiff
PRO	Public Record Office
RCAMW	Royal Commission on Ancient and Historical Monuments in Wales
UCNW	University College of North Wales, Bangor
WFM	Museum of Welsh Life, St Fagans

Agric. Hist. Rev. Agricultural History Review. British Agricultural History Society.

Ann. Agric. Annals of Agriculture.

Arch. Camb. Archaeologia Cambrensis. Journal of the Cambrian Archaeological Association.

Bull. Bd. Celtic Studies. Bulletin of the Board of Celtic Studies.

Carm. Antiq. The Carmarthen Antiquary.

Cymm. Record Ser. Cymmrodorion Record Series. Honourable Society of Cymmrodorion.

Flint. Hist. Soc. Publ. Flintshire Historical Society Publications.

Hist. Soc. W. Wales Trans. West Wales Historical Records. The Annual Magazine of the Historical Society of West Wales.

J. Ecol. Journal of Ecology.

J. For. Estate Mgmt. Journal of Forestry & Estate Management.

J. Merion. Hist. Rec. Soc. Journal of the Merioneth Historical & Record Society.

J. Roy. Agric. Soc. Journal of the Royal Agricultural Society of England.

Mont. Coll. The Montgomeryshire Collections. Journal of the Powysland Club.

Nat. Lib. Wales J. National Library of Wales Journal.

Q. J. For. Quarterly Journal of Forestry.

S. Wales Mon, Rec. Soc. Publ. South Wales & Monmouth Record Society Publications.

Trans. Anglesey Antiq. Soc. Transactions of the Anglesey Antiquarian Society and Field Club.

Trans. Caerns. Hist. Soc. Transactions of the Caernarvonshire Historical Society.

Trans. Cardiff Nat. Soc. Transactions of the Cardiff Naturalists' Society.

Trans. Carm. Antiq. Soc. Transactions of the Carmarthenshire Antiquarian Society and Field Club.

Trans. Denb. Hist. Soc. Transactions of the Denbighshire Historical Society.

Trans. Hon. Soc. Cymm. Transactions of the Honourable Society of Cymmrodorion.

Trans. Radn. Soc. Transactions of the Radnorshire Society.

Trans. Roy. Soc. Arts. Transactions of the Royal Society of Arts.

Trans. Scott. Arb. Soc. Transactions of the Scottish Arboricultural Society.

Welsh Hist. Rev. Welsh History Review.

Welsh J. Agric. Welsh Journal of Agriculture.

BIBLIOGRAPHY

The following select bibliography of books, articles and theses consists of works which are referred to frequently in the notes.

Albion, R.G., *Forests and sea power* (Harvard University Press, 1926)

Anderson, M. L., *A history of Scottish forestry* (Edinburgh, 1967)

Ashby, A.W., and Evans, I.L., *The agriculture of Wales and Monmouthshire* (Cardiff, 1944)

Black Book of St. Davids. An extent of all the lands and rents of the Lord Bishop of St. Davids . . . 1326. (*Cymm. Record Series* No. 5, 1902)

Board of Agriculture, *Agricultural Returns of Great Britain* (London, 1871-1913)

Bradney, J.A., *A history of Monmouthshire* (London, 1904-1933)

Clark, John, *General view of the agriculture of the County of Brecknock* (London, 1794)

Clark, John, *General view of the agriculture of the County of Radnor* (London, 1794)

Darby, H.C., and Terrett, I.B., *The Domesday geography of Midland England* (Cambridge, 1954)

Davies, Hugh, *Welsh botanology* (London, 1813)

Davies, J.C., *The Welsh Assize Roll 1277-1284* (Cardiff, 1940).

Davies, Walter, *General view of the agriculture and domestic economy of North Wales* (London, 1810)

Davies, Walter, *General view of the agriculture and domestic economy of South Wales* (London, 1815)

Edwards, I. ab Owen, *A Catalogue of Star Chamber proceedings relating to Wales* (Cardiff, 1929)

Edwards, J.G., *Calendar of Ancient Correspondence concerning Wales* (Cardiff, 1935)

Ellis, T.P. *The first extent of Bromfield and Yale, AD 1315* (*Cymm. Record Series* No. 11, 1924)

Elwes, H.J., and Henry, A., *The trees of Great Britain and Ireland* (Edinburgh, 1906-13, 7 vols.)

Emery, F. V., *The world's landscapes – Wales* (London, 1969)

Evans, J.A., *Comparative studies in the historical geography of woodlands in south-east England and Wales, 1790-1919* (Ph.D. thesis London, 1970)

Evelyn, J., *Sylva; a discourse of forest trees* (London, 1664)

Finberg, H.P.R. (ed.), *The agrarian history of England and Wales, A.D. 43-1042* (Cambridge, 1972)

Fisher, R., *Heart of oak, the British bulwark* (London, 1763)

Fox, Cyril, *Offa's Dyke* (Oxford, 1955)

Fox, John, *General view of the agriculture of the County of Monmouth* (Brentford, 1794)

Fox, John, *General view of the agriculture of the county of Glamorgan* (London, 1796)

Frere, S., *Britannia – a history of Roman Britain* (London, 1967)

Garsed, John, *Records of the Glamorganshire Agricultural Society, from the date of its establishment in 1772 to the year 1869* (Cardiff, 1890)

Gibson, J., *Agriculture in Wales* (London, 1879)

Gilpin, W., *Observations on the River Wye* (London, 1782)

Giraldus Cambrensis, *The itinerary of Archbishop Baldwin through Wales; Description of Wales* (Everyman ed., 1908)

Godwin, H., *The history of the British flora* (Cambridge, 1975)

Griffiths, R.A., *The Principality of Wales in the later Middle Ages, The structure and personnel of government. 1. South Wales, 1277-1536* (Cardiff, 1972)

Hall, E.H., *A description of Caernarvonshire 1809-1811 (Caerns. Hist. Soc. Record Series* No. 2)

Hart, C.E., *Royal Forest: a history of Dean's woods as producers of timber* (Oxford, 1966)

Hart, C.E., *The industrial history of Dean* (Newton Abbott, 1971)

Harvey, J.H., *Early nurserymen* (London, 1974)

Hassall, Charles, *General view of the agriculture of the county of Carmarthen* (London, 1794)

Hassall, Charles, *General view of the agriculture of the county of Pembroke* (London, 1794)

Hassall, Charles, *General view of the agriculture of the county of Monmouth* (London, 1812)

Heath, Charles, *Historical and descriptive accounts of . . . Monmouth* (Monmouth, 1804)

Hodgson, L.M., *The distribution of woodland, present and past, in the Nant Ffrancon valley and other parts of Caernarvonshire* (M.A. thesis, University of Wales, Bangor, 1933)

Hyde, H.A., *Welsh timber trees native and introduced* (4th ed., revised by S.G. Harrison, Cardiff, 1977)

Holinshed, *Chronicles* (1586). *The description of England* (London, 1807)

James, N.D.G. *A history of English forestry* (Oxford, 1981)

Johnes, Thomas, *A Cardiganshire landlord's advice to his tenants* (Hafod, 1799)

Jones, E.G., *Exchequer proceedings (equity) concerning Wales Henry VIII - Elizabeth* (Cardiff, 1939)

Jones, P. d'A., and Simon, E.N., *Story of the saw* (Sheffield, 1961)

Jones, Thomas, *Brut y Tywysogion or The Chronicle of the Princes Peniarth MS.20 version* (Cardiff, 1952)

Jones, T.I. Jeffreys, *Exchequer proceedings concerning Wales in tempore James I* (Cardiff, 1955)

Jones T.I. Jeffreys, *Acts of Parliament concerning Wales, 1714-1901* (Cardiff, 1959)

Kay, George, *General view of the agriculture of North Wales* (Edinburgh, 1794)

Leland, J., *The itinerary in Wales of John Leland in or about the years 1536-1539* (ed. L. Toulmin-Smith, London, 1964)

Lewis, E. A., *Welsh Port Books 1550-1603 (Cymm. Record Series No. 12*, 1927)

Lewis, E.A., *An inventory of the early Chancery proceedings concerning Wales* (Cardiff, 1937)

Lewis, E.A., and Davies, J.C., *Records of the Court of Augmentations relating to Wales and Monmouthshire* (Cardiff, 1954)

Lewis, W.J., *Lead mining in Wales* (Cardiff, 1967)

Lhuyd, Edward, *Parochialia* (Suppl. to *Arch. Camb.* 1909-11)

Linnard, W., 'Thomas Johnes (1748-1816) – pioneer of upland afforestation in Wales', *Forestry* 44 (1971), 135-43; also in *Ceredigion* (1970), 309-19

Linnard, W., 'Forestry in Wales at the turn of the 18th century', *Q.J. For.*, (1972), 208-218

Linnard, W., *History of forests and forestry in Wales up to the formation of the Forestry Commission* (Ph.D. thesis, University of Wales, Bangor, 1979)

Linnard, W., *Welsh woods and forests: history and utilization* (Cardiff, 1982)

Lloyd, J., *The Great Forest of Brecknock* (London, 1905)

Lloyd, J.E., *A history of Wales from the earliest times to the Edwardian conquest* (London, 1948)

Lloyd, Thomas, and Rev. Turnor, *General view of the agriculture of the county of Cardigan* (London, 1794)

Loudon, J.C., *Arboretum et fruticetum Britannicum* (London, 1838)

Mabinogion, The (transl. by G. and T. Jones, Everyman ed., 1966)

McCracken, E., *Irish woods since Tudor times* (Newton Abbott, 1971)

Madge, S.J., *The Domesday of Crown Lands* (London, 1938)

Matheson, C., *Changes in the fauna of Wales within historic times* (Cardiff, 1932)

Matts, R.S., *A century of timber management at Baron Hill, Anglesey, 1734-1835* (Diploma Dissertation, UCNW, Bangor, 1977)

Mitchell, A., *A field guide to the trees of Britain and Northern Europe* (London, 1974)

Morris, J.E., *The Welsh wars of Edward I* (Oxford, 1901)

Myddleton, W.M. (ed.), *Chirk Castle Accounts AD 1605-1666* (St. Albans, 1908); *AD 1666-1753* (Manchester, 1931)

Nisbet, J. *The forester* (Edinburgh, 1905)

Orwin, C.S., *History of British agriculture 1846-1914* (Newton Abbott, 1971)

Owen, Aneirin, *Ancient laws and institutes of Wales* (London, 1841)

Owen, D.H. (ed.), *Settlement and society in Wales* (Cardiff, 1989)

Owen, George, *Description of Pembrokeshire 1603* (*Cymm. Record Series,* 1892)

Owen, G.D., *Agrarian conditions and changes in West Wales during the sixteenth century* (Ph.D. thesis, University of Wales, Aberystwyth, 1936)

Owen, Henry (ed.), *A calendar of the public records relating to Pembrokeshire II, III* (*Cymm. Record Series,* 1914, 1918)

Phillips, D.R., *The history of the Vale of Neath* (Swansea, 1925)

Pugh, T.B., *The Marcher Lordships of South Wales 1415-1536* (Cardiff, 1963)

Rackham, O., *Trees and woodland in the British landscape* (London, 1976)

Rackham, O., *The history of the countryside* (London, 1986)

Rees, William, *South Wales and the March, 1284-1415. A social and agrarian study* (Oxford, 1924)

Rees, William, *The historical map of South Wales and the Border in the Fourteenth Century* (4 sheets, ½ inch/mile, Ordnance Survey, 1933)

Rees, William, *A survey of the Duchy of Lancaster Lordships in Wales 1609-1613* (Cardiff, 1953)

Rees, William, *The Great Forest of Brecknock – a facet of Breconshire history* (Brecon, 1966)

Rees, William, *Industry before the Industrial Revolution* (Cardiff, 1968)

Rees, William, *Calendar of Ancient Petitions relating to Wales* (Cardiff, 1975)

Reports of the Commission on Woods, Forests, and Land Revenues of the Crown (1787-1793)

Report of the Royal Commission on Land in Wales and Monmouthshire (1896)

Report of the Select Committee on Forestry (Hansard, 1887)

Rhys, Myfanwy, *Ministers' Accounts for West Wales 1277 to 1306* (*Cymm. Record Series* No. 13, 1936)

Roberts, R.A. (ed.), *The Court rolls of the lordship of Ruthin or Duffryn-Clwyd of the reign of King Edward the First.* (*Cymm. Record Series* No. 2, 1893)

Robinson, J. (Surveyor General of Woods & Forests), *Letter to Sir John Sinclair, Bart. on waste lands and commons* (London, 1794)

Rowlands, H., *Idea Agriculturae* (Dublin, 1764) (in *Trans. Anglesey Antiq. Soc.* 1934-1936)

Ryle, G., *Forest service* (Newton Abbott, 1969)

Savine, A., *English monasteries on the eve of the dissolution* (Oxford, 1909)

Schubert, H.S., *History of the British iron and steel industry* (London, 1957)

Shaw, Donald L., *Gwydyr forest in Snowdonia: a history* (HMSO, 1971)

Stamp, I.D., and Hoskins, W.G., *The common lands of England and Wales* (London, 1963)

Sylvester, D., *The rural landscape of the Welsh Borderland* (London, 1969)

Tansley, A.G., *The British Islands and their vegetation* (Cambridge, 1939)

Taylor, A.J., *The King's works in Wales, 1277-1330* (HMSO, 1974)

Thirsk, J. (ed.), *The agrarian history of England and Wales, 1500-1640* (Cambridge, 1967)

Thomas, David, *Agriculture in Wales during the Napoleonic Wars* (Cardiff, 1963)

Turner, J.G., *Select pleas of the forest* (Selden Society, 1901)

Vinogradoff, V., and Morgan, F., *Survey of the honour of Denbigh, 1334* (London, 1914)

Waters, I., *Leather and oak bark at Chepstow* (Chepstow, 1970)

Watkins, W., *A treatise on forest trees* (London, 1753)

White, K.D., *Agricultural implements of the Roman world* (Cambridge, 1967)

Wilkins, C., *The history of the iron, steel, tinplate, and other trades of Wales* (Merthyr Tydfil, 1903)

Williams, D.H., *The Welsh Cistercians* (Pontypool, 1969)

Williams, D.H., *White monks in Gwent and the Border* (Pontypool, 1976)

Williams, Glanmor, *The Welsh Church from Conquest to Reformation* (Cardiff, 1962)

Wyndham, H.P., *A tour through Monmouthshire and Wales* (London, 2nd ed., 1781)

Wynn, Sir John, *The history of the Gwydir family* (Cardiff, 1927)

Yarranton, A., *England's improvement by sea and land* (London, 1677)

Young, Arthur, *A six weeks tour through the southern counties of England and Wales* (London, 2nd ed., 1769)

Young, Arthur, *A tour in Wales* (in *Annals of Agriculture* 8 (1787) 31-89)

Zukowski, A.A., *The relation between forest policy and economic development* (D. Phil. thesis, Oxford, 1951)

REFERENCES

Chapter I: The Woodlands of Wales: Ice Age to Norman Conquest

1. References to the methodology of pollen analysis and the various published studies for Wales are too numerous to list here. Readers are referred to the syntheses and extensive bibliographies in the following works: H.J.B. Birks & H.H. Birks, *Quaternary Palaeoecology* (1980); H. Godwin, *The History of the British Flora* (Cambridge, 1975); H.A. Hyde & S.G. Harrison, *Welsh Timber Trees* (Cardiff, 1977); W. Linnard, *Welsh Woods and Forests: History and Utilization* (Cardiff, 1982); W. Pennington, *The History of British Vegetation* (1974); O. Rackham, *Ancient Woodland* (1980); J.P. Savidge, 'The Effects of Climate, Past and Present, on Plant Distribution in Wales' in R.G. Ellis (ed.), *Flowering Plants of Wales* (Cardiff 1983); A.G. Tansley, *Britain's Green Mantle* (revised by M.C.F. Proctor; London, 1968); J.A. Taylor (ed.), *Culture and Environment in Prehistoric Wales* (BAR British Series 76, 1980); and D. Walker & R.G. West (eds.), *Studies in the Vegetational History of the British Isles* (Cambridge, 1970).

2. H.A. Hyde, *Welsh Timber Trees* (Cardiff, 1961 ed.), 11.

3. The editor's 'Environmental Changes in Wales during the Holocene Period' in J.A. Taylor (ed.), *Culture and Environment.*

4. W. Linnard, op. cit.

5. J.A. Taylor, *Culture and Environment*, 113.

6. F. Rose, 'The Vegetation and Flora of Tycanol Wood', *Nature in Wales,* 14 (1975), 178-85.

7. H.J.B. Birks et al., 'Pollen Maps for the British Isles 5000 Years Ago', *Proceedings of the Royal Society of London* (B), 189 (1975), 87-105.

8. Gwyn Jones and Thomas Jones (eds.), *The Mabinogion* (Everyman, 1966), 113.

9. C.B. Crampton, 'A History of Land-use at Aberduhonw, near Builth Wells', *Brycheiniog*, 14 (1970), 41-52.

10. R.E. Hughes, 'Environment and Human Settlement in the Commote of Arllechwedd Isaf, *T.C.H.S.*, 2 (1940), 1-25.

11. Gwyn Jones & Thomas Jones, op. cit., 125.

12. John Leland, *The Itinerary in Wales in or about the years 1536-9* (ed. L. Toulmin-Smith, 1964), III, 122-4.

13. W. Linnard, 'Historical distribution of beech in Wales', *Nature in Wales,* 16(3) (1979), 154-9.

14. W.F. Grimes & H.A. Hyde, 'A Prehistoric Hearth at Radyr, Glam.' *Trans. Cardiff Naturalists' Society,* 68 (1935), 46-54.

15. N.L.W. Bute Box 104, MS. 1, 96, 163.

16. R.T. Gunther, *Early Science in Oxford. Vol. XIV. Life and Letters of Edward Lhuyd* (Oxford, 1945), 106, 315.

17. For discussion and references, see e.g. H.A. Hyde, *Welsh Timber Trees,* 59; and Linnard, *Welsh Woods and Forests,* 8.

18. Ifor Williams (ed.), *Canu Aneirin* (Cardiff, 1938), 26, 233.

19. Ifor Williams & T. Roberts (eds.), *Cywyddau Dafydd ap Gwilym a'i Gyfoeswyr* (Cardiff, 1935), 124; E.D. Jones, *Lewys Glyn Cothi* (UWP, 1984), 87-8.

20. R.H. Richens, *Elm* (Cambridge, 1983).

21. R.H. Richens & J.N.R. Jeffers, 'The Elms of Wales', *Forestry,* 58 (1985), 9-25; see also R.H. Richens, 'The History of the Elms of Wales', *Nature in Wales,* 5 (1986), 3-11.

22. personal communications, Dr C. Earwood and Dr A. Gibson.

23. Caesar, *De Bello Gallico*, V, 12.

24. Tacitus, *Annals*, XIV, 30.

25. Pliny, *Naturalis Historia*, XVI, 95.

26. Tacitus, *Agricola*, 34, 37.

27. W. Ll. Morgan, 'Report on the excavations at Coelbren', *Arch. Camb.*, (1907), 129-74.

28. R.F.M. Wheeler, 'Segontium and the Roman occupation of Wales', *Y Cymmrodor,* 33 (1923).

29. M. Devèze, *La vie de la forêt française au XVIe siècle* (Paris, 1961).

30. P. d'A. Jones and E.N. Simon, *Story of the saw* (Sheffield, 1961).
31. White, *Agricultural implements of the Roman world.*
32. *Mabinogion*, p.ix, 113.
33. B. Seddon, 'Report on the organic deposits in the pool at Dinas Emrys', *Arch. Camb.*, 109 (1960), 75-7.
34. *Mabinogion*, 125.
35. G.R.J. Jones, 'Post-Roman Wales' in *Agrarian history of England and Wales* edited by Finberg (Cambridge, 1972), 291-2.
36. C.B. Crampton, 'A history of land-use at Aberduhonw, near Builth Wells', *Brycheiniog*, 14 (1970), 41-52.
37. Fox, *Offa's Dyke*, 122-3.
38. Sylvester, *The rural landscape of the Welsh Borderland*, 84-96.
39. G.R.J. Jones, op.cit., 320-49, 381-2.
40. J.G. Evans & J. Rhys (eds.), *The text of the Book of Llan Dav* (Oxford, 1893).
41. Rackham, *Trees and woodland in the British landscape*, 115-17.
42. For detailed studies of the Welsh Laws as sources of information on trees and woods, see W. Linnard, 'Forests and forestry in the ancient Welsh Laws', *Q.J. For.*, (1976), 38-43; 'Trees in the Law of Hywel', *Pamphlets on Welsh Law* (Aberystwyth, 1979); 'Beech and the lawbooks', *Bull.Bd. Celtic Studies*, 28 (1980), 605-7.
43. W. Linnard, 'Coed Cadw', *Bull.Bd. Celtic Studies*, 27 (1978), 558-9.
44. A. Jones, *The history of Gruffydd ap Cynan* (Manchester, 1910), 154-5.
45. F. Kelly, 'The Old Irish Tree List', *Celtica*, 11 (1976), 107-124; M. Devèze, op.cit., 57.
46. Cyril Fox and Lord Raglan, *Monmouthshire houses, Part 1* (Cardiff, 1951), 37-9.
47. See, for example, the chapters on Shropshire, Herefordshire and Gloucestershire in *The Domesday geography of Midland England* edited by Darby & Terrett, especially 32, 53, 111, 158, and 433; J. Tait, 'Flintshire in Domesday Book', *Flint. Hist. Soc. Publ.*, 11 (1925), 1-37; C. Venables-Llewelyn, 'Domesday Book in Radnorshire and the Border', *Trans. Radn. Soc.*, 2 (1932), 14-17.

Chapter II: Military Significance of Forests in the Norman Conquest

1. Giraldus Cambrensis, *The itinerary through Wales, The description of Wales*, especially 30, 38 . . . 45, 58, 72-3, 91-2, 129, 155, 161, 184, 199-200.
2. Thomas Jones, *Brut y Tywysogion*, 19, 20, 59, 158.
3. J.G. Edwards, 'Henry II and the fight at Coleshill – some further reflections', *Welsh Hist. Rev.*, 3 (1967), 251-3.
4. Thomas Jones, op.cit., 24, 63.
5. *Cal. Patent Rolls* (8 Henry III), 414.
6. *Cal. Patent Rolls* (8 Henry III), 424.
7. M. Paris, translation cited in *Mont. Coll.*, 44 (1889), 354-5.
8. *Cal. Close Rolls*. Henry III 1251.
9. *Cal. Patent Rolls*. 1278, 270.
10. William Rees, *Calendar of Ancient Petitions*. 1281/82, 216.
11. For details of the campaigns, see J.E. Morris, *The Welsh wars of Edward I*. Also, J.G. Edwards, *Calendar of Ancient Correspondence relating to Wales*, 66-7, 108. *Cal. Welsh Rolls*, 171 . . . 319.
12. L.F. Salzmann, *Building in England down to 1540* (Oxford, 1952), 244-5.
13. PRO. S.C., 925/18 (see *Arch. Camb.*, 105 (1956), 104).
14. *Pipe Rolls* 1184-1185 (*Cartae Munim. Glam.* Vol. 1, 171).
15. *Hist. Soc. W. Wales Trans.*, 4 (1914), 37-9.
16. C.R. Peers, 'Carnarvon Castle', *Trans. Hon. Soc. Cymm.*, (1915-16), 1-74.
17. *Flint. Hist. Soc. Record Series*, (1913), 33-7, 45.
18. *Y Cymmrodor*, 27 (1917), 96.

Chapter III: Forests and Woods in Medieval Times

1. The account of forest organization is based mainly on Turner, *Select pleas of the forest*, and Nisbet, *The forester*, I, 6 . . . 14.
2. J. Lloyd, *The Great Forest of Brecknock*. W. Rees, *The Great Forest of Brecknock a facet of Breconshire history.*
3. W. Rees, *The historical map of South Wales and the Border in the fourteenth century*.
4. C.A. Gresham, 'The Forest of Snowdon in its relation to Eifionydd', *Trans. Caerns. Hist. Soc.*, 21 (1960), 53-62; R. Griffiths, *The Governance of Gwynedd*, 52.
4a. E.D. Jones. *Lewys Glyn Cothi* (1984), 33.
5. R.A. Griffiths, *The Principality of Wales in the later Middle Ages*, 393-400.
6. R.I. Jack, 'Welsh and English in the medieval lordship of Ruthin', *Trans. Denb. Hist. Soc.*, 18 (1969), 23-49.
7. R. A. Roberts (ed.), *The court rolls of . . . Ruthin*, 10.
8. F.A. Lewis, 'The proceedings of the Small Hundred Court of the commote of Ardudwy', *Bull. Bd. Celtic Studies*, 4 (1928), 153-66.
9. *Caernarvon Court Rolls 1361-1402* (*Caerns. Hist. Soc. Record Series*, No. 1 (1951), 50-1, 91).
10. H.J. Randall, 'Landscape and history in Mid-Glamorgan', *Arch. Camb.*, (1928), 316-29.
11. J.C. Davies, *The Welsh assize roll 1277-1284*, 190-1, 262-3.
12. W. Rees, *Calendar of Ancient Petitions relating to Wales*, 340-1; H. Owen (ed.), *A calendar of public records relating to Pembrokeshire* (*Cymm. Record Series* No. 7, 1918, III, 105).
13. A. Owen, *Ancient laws and institutes of Wales*, II, 460-1.
14. W. Rees, *Calendar of Ancient Petitions relating to Wales*, 74.
15. See also W. Rees, *South Wales and the March*.
16. H. Owen, *Cymm. Record Series*, No. 7, III, 173.
17. *Flint. Hist. Soc. Record Series*, No. 2, 22 (*Flintshire Ministers' Accounts 1328-1353*).
18. NLW. Bettisfield MS. 1306.
19. *Flint. Hist. Soc. Record Series*, No. 2, 76-7.
20. *Cartae Munim. Glam.*, III, 847.
21. Vinogradoff & Morgan (ed.), *Survey of the honour of Denbigh, 1334*, xl, 27.
22. Vinogradoff, op. cit., 231.
23. *Flint. Hist. Soc. Record Series*, No. 2, xxxvi, xxxvii.
24. Vinogradoff, op. cit., 51.
25. D. H. Williams, *White monks in Gwent and the Border*, 115.
26. I. Waters, *Leather and oak bark at Chepstow*, 10.
27. *Flint. Hist. Soc. Record Series*, No.2.
28. ibid.
29. *Cal. Patent Rolls*. 1281-1292, 133.
30. *Trans. Hon. Soc. Cymm.*, (1925/6), 25-110.
31. *Flint. Hist. Soc. Record Series*, No. 2, 34, 58-9.
32. W. Rees, *South Wales and the March*, 119.
33. *Flint. Hist. Soc. Record Series*, No. 2, xxxvii.
34. R.A. Roberts (ed.), *The court rolls of . . . Ruthin*,10.
35. T.P. Ellis, *The first extent of Bromfield and Yale*, AD 1315.
36. *Black Book of St. Davids*, 166-7.
37. E.J.L. Cole, 'Maelienydd 30-31 Edward III', *Trans. Radn. Soc.*, 34 (1964), 31-8.
38. *S. Wales Mon. Record Soc. Publ.*, No. 2, 103.
39. W. Rees, *South Wales and the March,* 122 . . . 126.
40. M. Rhys, *Ministers' Accounts for West Wales AD 1277-1306*, 433.
41. *Flint. Hist. Soc. Record Series*. No. 2, 2, 3, 9.
42. W. Rees, *South Wales and the March*, 114-18.
43. *Black Book of St Davids,* 166-7, 220-1.
44. M. Rhys, op. cit., 186-7.

45. ibid., 266-7.
46. *Flint. Hist. Soc. Record Series,* No. 2. 31.
47. *Hist. Soc. W. Wales Trans.*, XIII, 47, 84.
47a. D.R. Phillips. *History of the Vale of Neath*, (1925) 475-6.
48. M. Rhys, op. cit., 403.
49. *A catalogue of manuscripts relating to Wales in the British Museum (Cymm. Record Series,* No. 4, 151).
50. W. Rees, *South Wales and the March,* 119.
31. D.H. Williams, op. cit., 130.
52. R.I. Jack, 'The seigneurial charters of the borough of Ruthin', *Nat. Lib. Wales J.,* 16 (1969/70), 77-86.
53. R.I. Jack, 'The medieval charters of Ruthin borough', *Trans. Denb. Hist. Soc.,* 18 (1969), 16-22.
54. *Cartae Munim. Glam.* I, 136-138.
55. G.G. Francis, *Charters granted to Swansea* (1867). (Translation: W. H. Jones, *History of Swansea* (1920), 304-12).
56. *Cartae Munim. Glam.* III, 998.
57. E.A. Lewis, 'The development of industry and commerce in Wales during the Middle Ages', *Trans. Roy. Hist. Soc.,* (n.s.) 17 (1903), 143.
58. Sir John Wynn, *The history of the Gwydir family,* 52.
59. ibid. 53.

Chapter IV: Deer Parks

1. *Inventory of Ancient Monuments, Glamorgan.* RCAHM, iii, Pt. II, 381-2.
2. Vinogradoff op. cit. 51.
3. G. Owen, *The Taylor's Cushion.*
4. *Records, Court of Augmentations,* 71-2.
5. op. cit. 361-2.
6. T. Dinely, *Account of the progress of the Duke of Beaufort through Wales in 1684,* 313.
7. W. Linnard, 'Llantrithyd deer park', *Deer,* 1988, 257.

Chapter V: Monastic Woods

1. Glanmor Williams, *The Welsh Church front Conquest to Reformation,* 559-61.
2. See, for example, D.H. Williams, *The Welsh Cistercians,* especially 47-51, and 'The Cistercians in Wales – some aspects of their economy', *Arch. Camb.,* 114 (1965), especially 12-18.
3. R.W. Hays, *The history of the Abbey of Aberconway 1186-1537* (Cardiff, 1963), 18-9.
4. Giraldus Cambrensis, *Opera* (Rolls Series), *Speculum Ecclesiae,* III, 12.
5. D.H. Williams, *The Welsh Cistercians*, 48.
6. D.H. Williams, 'The Cistercians in Wales – some aspects of their economy', *Arch. Camb.,* 114 (1965), 14.
7. S.F. Hockey (ed.), *The account book of Beaulieu Abbey* (Camden 4th Series, Vol. 16, 1975). See also W. Linnard, 'A forester's manual of the thirteenth century', *Q.J. For.,* (1979), 95-9.
8. Glanmor Williams. 'The dissolution of the monasteries in Glamorgan', *Welsh Hist. Rev.,* 3 (1966), 41.
9. A. Savine, *English monasteries on the eve of the dissolution,* 210-1.
10. D.H. Williams, *The Welsh Cistercians,* 50.
11. *Hist. Soc. W. Wales Trans.*, 8 (1919/20), 157.
12. *Mont. Coll.,* 27 (1893), 84.
13. D. H. Williams, *The Welsh Cistercians,* 50.

Chapter VI: Forest Decline and Estate-building

1. T.B. Pugh, *The Marcher Lordships of South Wales 1415-1536*, 170, passim.
2. *Arch. Camb.*, (1864), 15-17.
3. I. Bowen, *The Statutes of Wales* (London, 1908), 69-72.
4. J. Leland, *The Itinerary in Wales* (edited by Toulmin-Smith, 1964), III, 118 . . . 124.
5. UCNW. Mostyn MS. 379.
6. E. Owen, 'The fate of the structures of Conway Abbey, and Bangor and Beaumaris Friaries', *Y Cymmrodor*, 27 (1917), 70-114.
7. *Letters & Papers, Foreign & Domestic*, XX, Pt. 1, 674; XXI, Pt. 1, 769.
8. G. Williams, 'Landlords in Wales: the Church', in *Agrarian history of England and Wales* edited by Thirsk (Cambridge, 1967), 384-5.
9. *Letters & Papers, Foreign and Domestic*, XX, Pt. 1, 665.
10. *Letter & Papers, Foreign & Domestic*, XX, Pt. 1, 222.
11. *Cartae Munim. Glam.* V, 1940.
12. Glanmor Williams, 'The dissolution of the monasteries in Glamorgan', *Welsh Hist Rev.*, 3 (1966), 37-8.
13. *Mont. Coll.*, 27 (1893), 84-5.
14. E.A. Lewis and J.C. Davies, *Records of the Court of Augmentations*, 98, 124, 132, 110, 121.
15. Lewis and Davies, op. cit., 124.
16. Lewis and Davies, op. cit., 216.
17. Lewis and Davies, op. cit., 361.
18. A.D. Powell, 'The Brilley Remembrance, 1590', *Trans. Radn. Soc.*, 34 (1964), 23-30.
19. W.J. Slack, *The Lordship of Oswestry, 1393-1607* (Shrewsbury, 1951), 69.
20. J. Lloyd, *Historical memoranda of Breconshire* (Brecon, 1903), I, 156.
20a. George Owen. *Extent of Cemais 1594* (Pembs. Record Series, 1977, No.3, 63).
21, NLW. Coed Coch MS. 1023.
22. Lewis, op. cit., 359, 368 . . . 374.
23. J. Lloyd, *Historical memoranda of Breconshire*, 76.
24. G. Owen, *Description of Pembrokeshire 1603*, 145-6, 149.
25. R.C. (Rocke Church), *An olde thrift newly revived* (London, 1612), 8.
26. Linnard, Ph.D. thesis, Table 12, 133-4.
27. *Montgomeryshire Records* (suppl. to *Mont. Coll.*), 412, 616.
28. ibid., 328 611.
29. B.M. Evans, 'The commote of Cyfeiliog in the late 16th century', *Mont. Coll.*, 60 (1967/68), 40.
30. Matheson, *Changes in the fauna of Wales within historic times*.
31. Holinshed, *Chronicles*, 'The description of England', 1586 (1807 ed., 355-9).
32. T. Churchyard, *The worthines of Wales* (1587).
33. T.I. Jeffreys Jones, *Exchequer proceedings concerning Wales in tempore James 1*, 318.
34. ibid., 6.
35. ibid., 30.
36. E.G. Jones, *Exchequer proceedings (equity) concerning Wales, Henry VIII Elizabeth*, 59.
37. T.I. Jeffreys Jones, op. cit., 103.
38. ibid., 121.
39. ibid., 157.
40. ibid., 204.
41. I. ab Owen Edwards, *Catalogue of Star Chamber proceedings relating to Wales*, 181.
42. ibid., 185.
43. T.I. Jeffreys Jones, op. cit., 257.
44. *Mont. Coll.*, 44 (1936), 1-31.
45. E.G. Jones, op. cit., 309-310.
46. T.I. Jeffreys Jones, op. cit., 318.
47. Transcript in *Trans. Carm. Antiq. Soc.*, 11 (1916), 24.
48. *House of Commons Journal*, 47 (1792), 284-6.

49. T.I. Jeffreys Jones, op. cit., 310.
50. H. Owen, *Calendar of public records relating to Pembrokeshire*.
51. W. Rees, *A survey of the Duchy of Lancaster Lordships in Wales 1609-1613*.
52. S.J. Madge, *The Domesday of Crown Lands*.
53. H.R. Davies, *A review of the records of the Conway and Menai ferries* (Cardiff, 1942), 96.
54. *The garden book of Sir Thomas Hanmer* (1659, publ. London, 1933).
55. Rev. H. Rowlands. *Antiquitates Parochiales* (*Arch. Camb.* (1848), 297).
56. J.A. Bradney, *History of Monmouthshire* (Part II, Abergavenny, 217).
57. R.T. Gunther, *Life and letters of Edward Lhwyd (Early Science in Oxford*, XIV, 75).
58. W.M. Myddleton (ed.), *Chirk Castle Accounts 1605-1753* (1908, 1931).
59. E. Lhuyd, *Parochialia*.
60. F.V. Emery, 'A map of Edward Lhuyd's Parochial Queries'. *Trans. Hon. Soc. Cymm.*, (1958), 41-53.

Chapter VII: Forest-based Industries (Charcoal)

1. W.J. Lewis, *Lead mining in Wales*; W. Rees, *Industry before the Industrial Revolution*.
2. *Cal. Patent Rolls* Henry VII 1485-1494, 69.
3. Stat. I Eliz. c.15,
4. *Cal. Patent Rolls* 1566-1569 (1910).
5. *State Papers* V Henry VIII. 1531-2. 118-9.
6. W. Rees, op. cit., 1, 265.
7. T.I. Jeffreys Jones, *Exchequer proceedings concerning Wales in tempore James I*, 101.
8. For *Coed Marchan* (by Robin Clidro) and *Coed Glyn Cynon* (anon), see Gwyn Williams, *The burning tree* (London, 1956), 162-9; for the *cwndid* mentioning Coed Mwstwr, see L.J. Hopkin-James and T.C. Evans, *Hen gwndidau* (Bangor, 1910), 30.
9. W. Gilpin, *Observations on the river Wye* (London, 1782), 22.
10. Yarranton, *England's improvements by sea and land*, 60.
11. R.F. Tylecote, 'Blast furnace at Coed Ithel, Llandogo', *Monmouthshire Antiquary*, 2 (1967), 149-60.
12. *Sidney Ironworks Accounts 1541-1573* (Camden 4th Series, Vol. 15, RHS, 1975).
13. ibid., 232-243.
14. W. Rees, op. cit., I, 292.
15. CPL. MS. Glam. Deed 1657/8 (Jan. 14); GwRO MS. D.43. 5499.
16. Schubert, *History of the British iron and steel industry*, 423-30.
17. Wilkins, *History of the iron. steel, tinplate and other trades of Wales*, 50.
18. M.C.S. Evans, 'Cwmdwyfran forge, 1697-1839', *Carm. Antiq.*, 11 (1975), 146-76.
19. CPL. MS. 1.503
20. A. Webster, 'Manufacture of charcoal at Penrhyn Castle', *J. For. Estate Mgmt.*, 5 (1881), 473-5. See also L. Armstrong, *Woodcolliers and charcoal burning* (Horsham, 1978).
21. Rice Lewis, *A breviat of Glamorgan, 1596-1600* (*S. Wales Mon. Rec. Soc. Publ.*, No. 3, 104, 108).
22. A.S. Davies, 'The charcoal iron industry of Powys Land', *Mont. Coll.*, 46 (1939/40), 31-66.
23. GRO. D/D Pl. 797/1.
24. NLW. Penrice & Margam MS. 3666.
25. CRO. Derwydd MS. D 180.
26. UCNW. Nannau MS. 536.
27. UCNW. Nannau MSS. 1185-1188; I. ab Owen Edwards. *A catalogue of Star Chamber proceedings concerning Wales*, 185; B.R. Parry, 'A sixteenth century Merioneth ironworks', *J. Merion. Hist. Rec. Soc.*, 4 (1963), 209-11.
28. W. Rees, op. cit., 615-7; E.G. Jones, *Exchequer proceedings (equity) concerning Wales*, 256 . . . 263.
29. Nathan Rogers, *Memoirs of Monmouthshire* (London, 1708).

30. J. Evans and J. Britton, *A topographical and historical description of . . . Monmouth* (London, 1810), 34-5.
31. W. Davies, *General view of . . . North Wales* (1810), 415.
32. D.R. Phillips, *History of the Vale of Neath*, 308-9.
33. GRO. MS. Gn/E 171, 172.
34. CRO. Mansel Lewis MS. 2145.
35. *Trans. Scot. Arb. Soc.*, 6 (1872), 152.
36. D.J. Williams, *Hen Dŷ Ffarm* (Aberystwyth, 1953), 80; W. Linnard, *Folk Life*, 1986/87 (25), 68.
37. Dafydd Morganwg, *Hanes Morganwg* (Aberdare, 1874), 68.
38. Webster, op. cit.

Chapter VII: (Shiptimber)

1. R.G. Albion, *Forests and sea power.*
2. C. Hart, *The industrial history of Dean.*
3. See, e.g. Rackham, *Trees and woodland in the British landscape,* 99-102.
4. Report of the Commissioners of Crown Lands (Vol. 2), (1792) Appendix No. 12, 124-6.
5. Albion, op. cit., 98.
6. NLW. MS. 9719E. See also W. Linnard, 'A glimpse of Gwydyr forest and the timber trade in North Wales in the late 17th century', *Nat. Lib. Wales J.*, 18 (1974), 397-404.
7. G.M. Ashton (ed.), *Hunangofiant a llythyrau Twm o'r Nant* (Cardiff, 1964), 44-5.
8. R. Fisher, *Heart of oak, the British bulwark*, 33.
9. NLW. Penrice & Margam MSS. 6677, 6680,
10. *Bye-gones* 1888 (Feb. 1), 25; W. Davies, *General view of . . . North Wales* (1810), 241.
11. *Mont. Coll.* 13 (1880), 425.
12. NLW. MS. 13089 E. See also W. Linnard, 'The Cefn Mabli giant', *Country Quest*, Nov. (1978), 35.
13. *Mont. Coll.*, 18 (1885), 383.
14. *Q.J. For.*, (1933), 151-2.
15. W. Davies, op. cit., 234.
16. R. Fisher, op. cit., 32-4.
17. R. Fisher, op. cit., 50.
18. Report, Committee of House of Commons, (1803) III.
19. 11th report, Board of Land Revenue (*House of Commons Journal*, 47 (1792), 314).
20. London *Star* (26 Jan. 1804), Swansea *Cambrian* (4 Feb. 1804). (Morien, *History of Pontypridd and the Rhondda valleys* (1903), 37).
21. *Mont. Coll.*, 47 (1941/2), 211.
22. CRO. MS Cawdor 1/235.

Chapter VII: (Tanbark)

1. Heath, *Historical and descriptive accounts of . . . Monmouth.*
2. *Q.J. For.*, (1933), 151-2.
3. D.H. Williams, *The Welsh Cistercians*, 80.
4. NLW. MS. 9719E. See also W. Linnard, 'A glimpse of Gwydyr forest and the timber trade in North Wales in the late 17th century', *Nat. Lib. Wales J.*, 18 (1974), 397-404.
5. *Kilvert's Diary* 5 July 1872 (1939 ed., Vol. 2, 232).
6. J. Evelyn, *Sylva* (1664), 93.
7. WFM. MS. 1650/12 (translated from Welsh).
8. WFM. Tape No. 226 (Rees Price, Merthyr Cynog).
9. E.A. Lewis, *The medieval boroughs of Snowdonia* (London, 1912), 192.
10. *J. For. Estate Mgmt.* (1877-1884).

11. *Kilvert's Diary*, 24 April 1872 (1939 ed., Vol.2, 190).
12. WFM. Tape No. 226.
13. Photo in WFM. See also *Gwynedd Archives Service Bulletin*, 1975, No. 2, 34.
14. *Trans. Scott. Arb. Soc.*, 1 (1858), 228.
15. WFM, MS 1650/12.
16. GRO. MS. D/D Pl. 570/1-6.
17. UCNW. Mostyn MS. 6774; C. Hassall, *General view of . . . Monmouth* (1812), 65; W. Davies, *General view of . . . North Wales* (1810), 244.
18. *Cardiff Records* (Cardiff, 1900), II, 432-43.
19. Heath, op. cit.; I. Waters, *Leather and oak bark in Chepstow*, 11-12.
20. GRO. D/D Pl. 336-9.
21. See also W. Linnard, 'Bark stripping in Wales', *Folk Life*, 16 (1978), 54-60.

Chapter VII: (Pitwood)

1. W. Davies. *General view of . . . North Wales* (1810), 239.
2. C. Hassall, *General view of . . . Monmouth* (1812), 62.
3. 'Pembrokeshire Life 1572-1843' (*Pemb. Record Series*, No. 1, 57).
4. BM Add. MS. 14923, ff.17-36 (see *Arch. Camb.*, 93 (1938), 25).
5. C. Hassall, *General view . . . of Pembroke* (1794), 27-8.
6. W. Davies, *General view of . . . South Wales* (1815), II, 20.
7. M.I. Williams, 'The port of Aberdyfi in the 18th century', *Nat. Lib. Wales J.*, 18 (1973), 95-134.
8. *Transactions of the Aberafan & Margam District Historical Society*, 5 (1932-33), 52.
9. NLW. MS. 1340C.
10. *J. Roy. Agric. Soc.*, 80 (1919), 346.
11. Private communication, Mr H. Sims.
12. *Trans. Scott. Arbor. Soc.*, 1 (1858), 228; 6 (1872), 152.
13. CRO. Mansel Lewis Muniments MS. 2145.
14. GRO. D/D Pl. 336-339.
15. Annual supplements to *J. For. Estate Mgmt.*, 1876/77-1883/84.
16. GRO. D/D Pl. 336-339.
17. W. Rees, *Cardiff, a history of the city* (Cardiff, 1969), 293.
18. W. Little, 'The agriculture of Glamorganshire', *J. Roy. Agric. Soc.*, (1885), 196.
19. *South Wales Coal Annual 1919*, 224.
20. *J. Roy. Agric. Soc.*, 80 (1919), 359-60, cxliv.

Chapter VIII: Famous Trees and Big Trees

1. I. Williams, *BBCS*, 5, 19-24.
2. *Arch. Camb.*, 1865, 33-7; also R. Denning (Ed.), *The Story of St. Donats* (1983), 25-7.
3. A. Roderick, *The Folklore of Gwent* (1983), 8-9; also J.H. Wilks, *Trees of the British Isles in History and Legend* (1972).
4. *The Book of Llan Dâv* (1893), 166, 207, 250.
5. *Arch. Camb.*, 1914, 430-40.
6. R.J. Thomas, *Astudiaeth o Enwau Lleoedd Cwmwd Meisgyn* (M.A. thesis (Wales), 1933).
7. Bradney, *History of Monmouthshire*, IV, 1, 190; J.H. Clark, *Usk past and present*, 1891, 104.
8. T.H. Thomas, *Trans. Cardiff Nat. Soc.*, 1880, 16.
9. W. Linnard, *Country Life* (1981), 978-9.
10. *Q.J. For.* (1933), 151-2.
11. T.H. Thomas, *Trans. Cardiff Nat. Soc.* (1880), 15-24.

Chapter IX: Conifers, Nurseries and Planting

1. T.I. Jeffreys Jones, *Acts of Parliament concerning Wales, 1714-1901*.
2. E.P. Thompson, *Whigs and hunters: the origin of the Black Act* (London, 1975), esp. 255, 270-7.
3. NLW. Penrice & Margam MSS. 3812, 5226.
4. *Q.J. For.*, (1913), 67.
5. Arthur Young, 'A tour in Wales', *Ann. Agric.*, 8 (1786), 45.
6. Wyndham, *A tour through Monmouthshire and Wales*, 100.
7. Hyde, *Welsh timber trees*, 53-4.
8. J.H. Davies (ed.), *The letters of Lewis, Richard, William and John Morris of Anglesey*, (Oxford, 1907).
9. ClRO. Rhual MSS. D/HE/285.
10. W.M. Myddleton, *Chirk Castle Accounts*, II, 449.
11. For references to these nurseries and plantation schemes, see Linnard, Ph.D. thesis, 1979, Table 22.
12. C. Hassall, *General view of . . . Carmarthen*, 30-1.
13. W. Davies, *General view of . . . North Wales*, 243.
14. W. Linnard, 'The first treatise on forest trees in Wales', *J. Welsh Bibl. Soc.*, 11 (1975/6), 247-50.
15. H. Rowlands, *Idea Agriculturae* (in *Trans. Anglesey Antiq. Soc.*, (1936), 63).
16. W. Watkins, *A treatise of forest trees*, 38-9.
17. J. Fox, *General view of . . . Glamorgan*, 47.
18. W. Watkins, op. cit., 20.
19. W.M. Myddleton, *Chirk Castle Accounts*, II, 396.
20. Paper by Rev. H.W. Jones (1814). (NLW XSD 141 J 76).
21. Linnard, 'Thomas Johnes . . .', *Forestry*, 44 (1971), 135-43.
22. *Ann. Agric.*, 29 (1797), 290-1; 31 (1798), 317-9.
23. *Brycheiniog*, 2 (1956), 77.
24. *Ann. Agric.*, 29 (1797), 302-3; 31 (1798), 329-30; 33 (1799), 484; (1804), 135.
25. *Trans. Roy. Soc. Arts*, 39 (1821), 14-25.
26. W. Davies, *General view of . . . North Wales*, 243.
27. C. Hassall, *General view of . . . Carmarthen*, 30-1.
28. W. Davies, *General view of . . . South Wales*, II, 35-8.
29. E.A. Williams, *Hanes Môn yn y XIX ganrif* (Llangefni, 1927), 120-1.
30. W. Davies, *General view of . . . South Wales*, II, 35.
31. NLW. MS. 13,115B, 360.
32. D.J. Williams, *Hen dŷ ffarm* (Aberystwyth, 1953), 78.
33. *Trans. Radn. Soc.*, 12 (1942), 38.
34. *Trans. Hon. Soc. Cymm.*, (1966), 198-200.
35. J.H. Harvey, *Early gardening catalogues* (London, 1972); 'Forest trees and their prices before 1850', *Q.J. For.*, 67 (1973), 20-37.
36. W. Watkins, op. cit.
37. *Trans. Roy Soc. Arts*, 19 (1801), 78-80.
38. W. Watkins, op. cit., 8.
39. R.T. Gunther, *Life and letters of Edward Lhwyd* (Oxford, 1945) 'Early science in Oxford', XIV, 106, 315.
40. NLW. MS. 'Tour in Wales 1799 by E.W.' See *Trans. Denb. Hist. Soc.*, 16 (1967), 82-99; *J. Merion. Hist. Rec. Soc.*, 5 (1967), 239-50,
41. E.H. Hall, *A description of Caernarvonshire 1809-1811*, 222-5.
42. ibid.
43. ibid.
44. W. Davies, *General view of . . . North Wales*, 247-9.
45. *Trans. Roy. Soc. Arts*, 18 (1800), 81-2.
46. E.H. Hall, op. cit., 221.

47. *Trans. Radn. Soc.*, 12 (1942), 60.
48. G. Kay, *General view of . . . North Wales* (Merioneth, 8).
49. UCNW. Mostyn MS. 6774.
50. *Trans. Roy. Soc. Arts*, 18 (1800), 81-2.
51. NLW.XSD 141 J 76.
52. *Trans. Roy. Soc. Arts*, 39 (1821), 14-25.
53. *Trans. Radn. Soc.*, 12 (1942), 60; *J. For. Estate Mgmt.*, 1 (1878), 491.
54. *Trans. Roy. Soc. Arts*, 20 (1802), 182-90.
55. NLW.XSD 141 J 76.
56. *Trans. Roy. Soc. Arts*, 20 (1802), 182-90.
57. Linnard, 'Thomas Johnes . . .', *Forestry,* 44 (1971), 139-40.
58. *Trans. Roy. Soc. Arts*, 39 (1821), 14-25.
59. E. H. Hall, op. cit., 221-6.
60. NLW.MS. 13,147A.
61. GRO.D/D Pl. 1-5.
62. W. Davies, *General view of . . . South Wales*, II, 52.
63. Linnard, Ph.D. thesis, Table 28.
64. Linnard, 'Thomas Johnes . . .', *Ceredigion* (1970), 309-19; *Scottish Forestry* (1988), 3, 181-4.
65. ibid., 312.
66. C. Coltman Rogers, 'Monograph of Stanage trees', 1924 (typescript in Botany Dept., NMW); *Trans. Roy. Soc. Arts*, 39 (1821), 14-25; *Q.J. For.*, (1918), 204-12.
67. *House of Commons Journal*, XLVII (1792), 314-6.
68. GRO. D/D Gn/E/7.
69. NLW.MS. 13,147A. 413-28.
70. *J. Merion. Hist. Rec. Soc.*, 5 (1967), 243.
71. ibid.
72. R. Fenton, *Tours in Wales 1804-1813* (suppl. to *Arch. Camb.*, 1917), 34, 172-3, 92, 174.
73. J. Byng, *Tour in North Wales 1793* (Torrington Diaries, III, 279, 291).
74. W. Bingley, *North Wales . . . 1798 and 1801* (London, 1804), I, 384.
75. J. Byng, op. cit., 279, 291.
76. J. Fox, *General view of . . . Glamorgan*, 47-8.
77. W. Davies, *General view of . . . South Wales*, II, 51.
78. ibid., 26.
79. NLW.MS. 5446 B, 91-3.
80. See e.g. *J. For. Estate Mgmt.*, 3 (1880), 626-8, 783-5, 848-50; 4 (1881), 721-3; *J. Roy. Hort. Soc.*, 14 (1892), 484-6.
81. Hyde, *Welsh timber trees*, 45.
82. T. Thomson, 'The Douglas fir in North Wales', *Welsh J. Agric.*, 2 (1926), 234-9.
83. T. Thomson, 'Douglas fir plantation at Llandinam, Montgomeryshire, Wales', *Empire Forestry Journal*, 2 (1923), 236-42.
84. WFM.MS. 1800/1.
85. W. Linnard, 'The woods at St. Fagans', *Amgueddfa* (*Bulletin of the National Museum of Wales*), 24 (1976), 30-7.

Chapter X: Professional Foresters and Private Estate Management in the Nineteenth Century

1. J. Byng, *South Wales 1787* (Torrington Diaries, I, 298).
2. Linnard, 'Thomas Johnes . . .', *Forestry* 44 (1971), 139, 141.
3. W. Linnard, 'Scots foresters in Wales in the l9th century', *Scottish Forestry*, 29 (1975), 270.
4. Anon, 'The education of young foresters', *J. For. Estate Mgmt.*, 3 (1880), 614.
5. I. Niall, *The forester* (London, 1972); D.L. Shaw, *Tales from the Gwydyr woods* (Forestry Commission, 1977).

6. GRO, Notes to Plymouth estate schedule. Also, GRO.D/D Pl. 215, 240, 255.

7. GRO.D/D Pl. 823/57.

8. Anon, 'The education of young foresters', *J. For. Estate Mgmt.* 3 (1880), 614.

9. They include: Anon, *Cyfarwyddiadau i Fesurwyr* (Instructions to Measurers) (Shrewsbury, 1700); John Roberts, *Arithmetic: mewn trefn hawdd ac eglur* (Arithmetic in a clear and easy way) (1768; 2nd ed. Dublin, 1796); Mathew William, *Y Mesurwr Cyffredinol* (The General Measurer) (Carmarthen, 2nd ed. 1785; 3rd ed. 1810); Lewis Morris, *Rhodd Meistr i'w Brentis* (A Master's Gift to his Apprentice) (Bala, 1776; 2nd ed. 1812); Anon, *Cyfarwyddiad i Fesurwyr* (Instructions to Measurers) (Wrexham, 1784); Anon, *Y Mesurydd Tir a Choed* (The Land and Timber Measurer) (1816; Denbigh, 3rd ed. 1858); and William Griffith, *Y Ddwy Droedfedd* (The Two-Foot Rule) (Caernarfon, 1830).

10. CRO. MS. Derwydd D 180.

11. NLW MS. 13089E. See also W. Linnard, 'The Cefn Mabli giant', *Country Quest*, Nov. (1978), 35.

12. Linnard 'Thomas Johnes . . .', *Forestry* 44 (1971), 141-2; A. Mitchell, *A field guide to the trees of Britain and Northern Europe*, 119-20.

13. W. Linnard, 'The Pen-pont larches', *Brycheiniog*, 18 (1978/79), 100-2.

14. CRO. Cawdor MS. 108/8189.

15. CRO. Cawdor MS. 1/235.

16. UCNW. Mostyn MS. 6043.

17. CRO. Taliaris MS. 166.

18. GRO. D/D Pl. 572.

19. GRO.D/D Pl. 810/63.

20. W. Davies, *General view of . . . South Wales*, II, 44-5.

21. For details see Linnard, Ph.D. thesis, 253-77.

22. CRO. D/D Pl. 336-39.

23. Report of Royal Commission on Land in Wales & Monmouthshire (1896), 540-1.

24. See e.g. *General views of . . . Carmarthen* (C. Hassall, 1794, 49), *Monmouth* (C. Hassall, 1812, 64), *Brecknock* (J. Clark, 1794, 25-6), *Radnor* (J. Clark, 1794, 28), *South Wales* (W. Davies, 1815, I, 170-7; II, 25), *North Wales* (W. Davies, 1810, 102, 106).

25. *Trans. Radn. Soc.*, 35 (1965), 49.

26. D. Lleufer Thomas, *Abstracts of agreements and leases in use upon Welsh estates* (Appendix F to Report of Royal Commission on Land in Wales & Monmouthshire (1896), 300-39).

27. GRO. D/D Pl. 36.

28. GRO. D/D Pl. 339, 47.

29. W. Davies, *General view of . . . North Wales*, 232.

30. Report, Royal Commission on Land . . . (1896), III, 631.

31. T. Jones, *Brut y Tywysogion*, 104.

32. Hugh Owen, *Additional letters of the Morrises of Anglesey* (London, 1949), 909.

33. W. Davies, *General view of . . . South Wales*, II, 30-1.

34. *J. For. Estate Mgmt.*, 5 (1881), 517-8.

35. *Forestry (J. For. Estate Mgmt.)*, 8 (1884), 381.

36. Summarized from 'Forest work of the month in Wales', *J. For. Estate Mgmt.*, (1877-86).

37. H.M. Thomas, 'Duffryn Aberdare', *Morgannwg*, 21 (1977), 9-41.

38. C. Thomas, 'The Corsygedol estate during the age of improvement', *J. Merion. Hist. Rec. Soc.*, 6 (1971), 303-10.

39. F. Jones, 'The Vaughans of Golden Grove', *Trans. Hon. Soc. Cymm.*, (1964), 208-13.

40. Matts, *A century of timber management at Baron Hill, Anglesey, 1734-1835* (Diploma Dissertation, UCNW, 1977).

41. Linnard, 'Thomas Johnes . . .', *Forestry*, 44 (1971), 135-43.

42. Evans, *Comparative studies in the historical geography of woodlands . . .* ' (Ph.D. thesis).

43. Linnard, *History of forests and forestry in Wales . . .* ' (Ph.D. thesis).

44. J. Gibson, *Agriculture in Wales* (London, 1879), 91.

Chapter XI: Towards a National Forest Service

1. A.W. Ashby and I.L. Evans, *The agriculture of Wales*, 283.
2. Board of Agriculture, *Agricultural Returns of Great Britain* (1871-1913).
3. Report, Select Committee on Forestry (Hansard, 1887).
4. Census 1901 (cited in Ashby and Evans. op. cit. 228).
5. Report, Select Committee on Forestry (Hansard, 1887).
6. Report, Royal Commission on Land in Wales & Monmouthshire (1896), 539-42.
7. J. Nisbet, *The Forester*, I, 37-42.
8. G. Ryle, *Forest service*, 164-7; W. Linnard, *J. Merion. Hist. Soc.*, 1981, IX, 89-94
9. *Q.J. For.*, (1907), 15-18.
10. W.R. Fisher, *Report on the woods and plantations around Lake Vyrnwy* (Liverpool, 1897; in CFI Library).
11. *Q.J. For.*, (1919), 226-8.
12. D. Lloyd George, *The People's Budget* (London, 1909), 14-16.
13. I. Nicholson & T. Lloyd-Williams. *Wales, its part in the war* [1919], 215-7.
14. Cd. 8881 (G. Ryle, op. cit., 26).
15. *Forestry Act 1919* (9 & 10 Geo 5, Ch. 58).
16. *Q.J. For.*, (1920), 215.
17. Forestry Commission Annual Report 1919-20, 13.

Chapter XII: 1919-45: Mutton *versus* Trees

1. N.D.G. James. *History of English Forestry*, 1981, 216.
2. Forestry Commission Annual Reports, 1919/20, 1920/21.
3. Forestry (Transfer of Woods) Act, 1923, 13 & 14 Geo. 5, Ch. 21.
4. Report on Census of Wodlands . . . 1924. (HMSO, 1928); see especially 36-7.
5. G. Ryle, *Forest Service* (1969), and *Beating about the Bush* (unpublished typescript, 1972).
6. Ryle, op. cit.
7. Ryle, *Forest Service*, 52 . . . 8.
8. Rheola, HMSO (1949).
9. Hanes Coed-y-Brenin, HMSO (1956).
10. D. Shaw, *Gwydyr Forest in Snowdonia*: *A History* (HMSO, 1971).
11. Ryle, *Forest Service*, 52; D. Shaw, *Tales from the Gwydyr Woods* (1977), 99-110.
12. Ryle, *Beating about the Bush*, 143.
13. Ryle, *Forest Service*, 266-8.
14. Glamorgan Forests (HMSO, 1961), 42-4.
15. This section on the war is based mainly on Ryle *op. cit.*, R. Meiggs *Home Timber Production 1939-45* (1949); and the unpublished F.C. Annual Reports.
16. F. House, *Timber at War* (1965), 306.
17. Meiggs, *Home Timber Production 1939-45*, 91-3.
18. Ryle, *Beating about the Bush*, 107.

Chapter XIII: The New Look: 1946-99

1. This chapter is based mainly on F.C. Annual Reports and other publications, including J.W.Ll. Zehetmayr *Forestry in Wales* (1985).
2. G. Ryle, *Beating about the Bush*, 140.
3. F.C. Annual Report 1946/47, 11-12.
4. F.C. Census of Woodlands 1947-49 (HMSO, 1952).
5. F.C. booklet, *The Dedication of Woodlands* (1948, and subsequent editions).
6. Ryle, op. cit. 143.
7. Ryle, *Forest Service*, 123-5; R. Phillips, 'Y bugail a'r coedwigwr', *Gwyddor Gwlad* (1963), 5, 24-37.

8. Commemorative leaflet (F.C. 1962).
9. D. Williams, *Q.J. For.* 1995, 106-10.
10. S. Crowe. *Forestry in the landscape,* and *The landscape of forests and woods* (F.C. Booklets No. 18, 1966, and No. 44, 1978).
11. F.C. Annual Report 1994/95, 97.
12. *Broadleaved woodlands in Wales*, Coed Cymru, 1985.
13. F.C. Census of Woodlands 1965-67 (1970); F.C. Census of Woodlands and Trees 1979-82, Cymru/Wales (1983).

APPENDIX 1: GLOSSARY OF SPECIAL TERMS

(Abbreviations: L. = Latin; W. = Welsh)

abele: white poplar

abradico (L.): to uproot

acer (L.): maple

aelwyd cols (W.): charcoal hearth

aethnen (W.): aspen

afforest: to place an area under forest law and administration (in medieval contexts); to establish a tree crop on an area that has not carried wood for some time (in more recent contexts)

afforestatio (L.): *see* afforest

agistator: see agister

agister: forest officer responsible for agistment

agistment: herbage of a forest or the right to it; grazing dues or income front agisting

allt (W.): see gallt

alnetum (L.): alder wood

amputo (L.): to fell, to poll, to lop

arles: alder grove, alder wood

assart: land newly cleared from the waste, to clear land

avesagium (L.): pannage

bavenum (L.): faggot

bedwen (W.): birch tree

billa (L.): pick

black coal: charcoal

blattro (L.): see blettro

blettro (L.): sapling, branch

bollo (L.): to strip branches from trees

borda (L.): board, plank

bosca (L.): wood, firewood

boscus (L.): wood, woodland

broche: twigs and debris of trees

brueria (L.): heath, heathland

brulla (L.): small wood, coppice

brusca (L.): brushwood, scrub

bunga (L.): faggot

burda (L.): *see* borda

busca: *see* bosca

cablicium (L.): windfall wood

cadeirio (W.): to sprout (coppice); coppice sprouting

carbo (L.): charcoal

carbonarius (L.): charcoal-burner

carbonator (L.): charcoal-burner

carpentarius (L.): carpenter

cartbote: right of tenants on a manor to take wood for repair of carts

celli (W.): grove, small wood

celynnen (W.): holly

cerddinen (W.): mountain ash, rowan

chace: tract of land reserved for hunting but not subject to forest law and administration

cheminage: *see* cheminagium

cheminagium (L.): toll paid for passage through a forest

cineres tinctorum (L.): dyer's ashes

cipher: suppressed, thin or unsaleable stem (included with timber in a sale)

cippus (L.): tree stump, stock

cissores bosci (L.): sawyers, wood-cutters

coal: charcoal; to make charcoal

coed (W.): wood, woodland, timber, trees

coed cadw (W.): reserved forest, preserved woods

coedcae, coetgae (W.): woodland grazing, field recovered from forest, fenced enclosure (cf. ffridd)

coeden (W.): tree

coediog: *see* coedog

coediwr: *see* coedwr

coedlan (W.): copse, wood, plantation

coedo (W.): to erect timber (mining)

coedog (W.): wooded, woody

coedwig (W.): forest

coedwigaeth (W.): forestry

coedwigwr (W.): forester

coedwr (W.): woodman; timberman (mining)

cog, cogs: roundwood or squared wood used in building up a support for the roof of a mine

cogge: small boat

cogwood: *see* cog

cogyn (W.): *see* cog

colier coed (W.): charcoal-burner

cols (W.): charcoal

collen (W.): hazel

cols (W.): charcoal

compass timber: crooked and curved assortments for shipbuilding

coperones (L.): twigs of trees, lop and top

copare (L.): to top, trim

coppice: a wood regularly cut for regrowth

coppicing: cutting trees close to ground level to produce regrowth of coppice shoots

copusa (L.): coppice

cord: stacked measure of round or cleft wood

cordwood: wood cut into short lengths and sold by the cord for charcoal-burning, fuel, etc.

cortex (L.): bark
coti (L.): billets
coupiatores (L.): wood-cutters
courbe: *see* curba
crachgoed (W.): coppice shoots
criafolen (W.): mountain ash, rowan
croppae (L.): twigs, lop and top
crusts: slabs, i.e. outer pieces removed first in log conversion
curba (L.): cruck
cynnud (W.): firewood, fuelwood
cypher: *see* cipher

deafforestatio (L.): *see* disafforest
dean: wooded valley
decorticatio (L.): to bark
dene: *see* dean
derwen (W.): oak
disafforest: to release land from forest law
dodders: old pollards (senescent)
dolabra (L.): hatchet
dolabella (L.): small short-handled hatchet
dotters: *see* dodders
dozen: charcoal measure (12 loads = 1 dozen)

essart: *see* assart
estovers: right of tenants to take wood for repair of buildings, hedges, carts, etc.
exotics: trees introduced from abroad
extent: survey, measurement and evaluation of land

faculare (L.): to cut up, grub up
fagetum (L): beechwood
fagus (L.): beech tree
falx (L.): billhook
falx lumaria (L.): thorn cutter, slasher
falx putatoria (L.): tree-pruning billhook
fasciculus (L.): bundle, faggot
ffannys: regeneration (seedlings, sprouts)
ffawydden (W.): beech tree; used colloquially in N. Wales for pine/fir
fforest (W.): *see* forest
ffridd (W.): woodland, forest; enclosed mountain pasture, sheepwalk
firebote: right of tenants on a manor to take wood for fuel
fleakes: cleft hurdles
floats: rafts
flottmaster: man in charge of raft
flotts: *see* floats
forest: 1. extensive area of woodland 2. hunting preserve of the king or lord-marcher, subject to forest law but not necessarily woodland

forks: crucks; forked (Y-shaped) pieces
fossatores (L.): diggers, ditchers
fraxina (L.): ash tree
frith: *see* ffridd
fustum (L.): log
futtock: one of the middle timbers in the frame of a ship

gad: faggot wood
gallt (W.): wood, wooded slope
garsanese: *see* grasanese
gelli: *see* celli
germens: coppice sprouts (of oak)
gistae (L.): joists
glans (L.): acorn
glo (W.): coal; charcoal
golosg (W.): charcoal
grasanese: obligation of bondmen to feed their swine in the lord's wood
gwern (W.): alder trees, alder grove
gwernen (W.): alder tree
gwig (W.): wood, forest
gwinllan (W.): wood, copse, plantation, grove
gwŷdd (W.): trees, wood, forest

hachia (L.): hatchet, axe, mattock, hack
haia (L.): *see* hay
haie (F.): *see* hay
hand-sets: young plants from nurseries
hay: enclosure in the forest
haybote, heybote: right of tenants on a manor to take wood for making fences
hedgebote: *see* haybote
helygen (W.): willow tree
high forest: a stand of trees generally of seedling origin
hodd: charcoal measure, ¼ load
holo cols (W.): charcoal hearth
housebote: right of tenants on a manor to take wood for making and repairing buildings

imp: young plant, grafted plant
impertone (L.): enclosure for saplings

knee: piece of timber having a natural bend for using in shipbuilding

lappata (L.): loppings
launds: pasture, forest pastures
lea: woodland clearing
lignum (L.): wood
ligo (L.): mattock
llannerch (W.): glade, clearing
llwyfen (W.): elm

llwyn (W.): grove

load: wood measure (usually 50 cu. ft); charcoal measure (variable)

loppis et toppis (L.): lop and top

loppo (L.): to lop

maeremium: *see* meremium

maiden: a tree that has been neither lopped, pollarded nor coppiced

maisremium: *see* meremium

masarnen (W.): maple

materies (L.): timber

mast: fruits of oak and beech (used for fattening swine in autumn)

meremium (L.): timber

merym: *see* meremium

modulus (L.): standard measure of wood

moket: pannage

mongwode: mixed wood

morbosium (L.): dead wood

nemora (L.): groves

onnen (W.): ash tree

orles: *see* arles

pannage: feeding swine in the woods in autumn; payment for so doing

pannagium (L.): *see* pannage

parc (W.): park, field

pawnage: *see* pannage

paxillus (L.): stake

peel: to bark, to strip off bark

pesso(na) (L.): acorns; beechmast

pilbren (W.): barking iron

pilo (W.): to bark

pit-sawing: conversion of roundwood by hand-sawing in a saw-pit

planhigfa (W.): plantation

plannu (W.): to plant

ploughbote: right of tenants on a manor to take wood for making and repairing ploughs

powderwood: wood used for manufacture of gunpowder charcoal

pren (W.): tree, timber, wood

pren tafod y ferch (W.): aspen

prysg (W.): thicket, brushwood, scrub

prysgoed (W.): brushwood, scrub

purlieu: land afforested (in the legal sense) and subsequently disafforested

purpresture: enclosure of or encroachment upon land

quadriga (L.): 4-wheel cart

quercus (L.): oak

quisquilliae (L.): chips of wood

ramalia (L.): small branches, lopwood

regardatores (L.): regarders, supervisory officers

rhisgl (W.): bark

rinbold: cropped, topped or polled trees

rundle: cylinder or roller of wood, a lopped and pollarded stem

sally: sallow willow

sartum: *see* assart

scapulo (L.): to trim and square timber (by adze)

schrido: set, shredding

scissores: *see* cissores

securis (L.): axe, woodman's axe

securis dolabrata (L.): double-bladed axe, mattock

sepes (L.): hedge

serrula (L.): small saw

shreading: *see* shredding

shredding: pruning, especially heavy high pruning

shrouding: *see* shredding

shrowding: *see* shredding

sigillo (L.): marking iron

silva (L.): wood, forest

silvae caeduae (L.): coppices

silvae glandiferae (L.): pannage woods

silvae materiariae (L.): high forest

silvae vulgares (L.): forests where wood was the most important product

slang: strip of land (used as a measure of coppice)

smokesilver: payment for the right of gathering firewood

spere (L.): sapling

spina (L.): thorn tree

sprag: short pit-prop

spring: coppice, coppice shoot

springoed: *see* spring

spring wood: *see* spring

spurn: spur root, main root

squarro (L.): to square (timber)

stadell: *see* standard

staggard: wilding transplanted into a hedge

standard: a tree selected to remain standing after the rest of the stand has been felled

standil: *see* standard

stathelus (L.): young tree left standing

stipes (L.): tree trunk

stock: to clear ground of stumps
storer: *see* standard
strip: to bark, to peel off bark
subboscus (L.): underwood
summer: large beam
swinemote: court of the pannage

teller: *see* tiller
tempus pessun (L.): pannage season
thickstuff: planking over 4 inches thick
tiller: stool shoot, coppice shoot, sucker
tornator (L.): wood-turner
traba (L.): beam
treenails: wooden pegs or pins (used in shipbuilding)
trennals: *see* treenails
truncus (L.): trunk, stem
trychwr (W.): wood-cutter

ulmus (L.): elm

venison: game animals
vert: vegetation of a forest (including trees and herbage)
viridarii (L.): verderers

waste: unclaimed land; damage or destruction of trees, etc.; see also crusts
weeding: frequently used in the sense of early thinning
Welsh quicksets: wildings
weygafol: *see* cheminagium
white coal: chopped wood, slivers
white wood: broadleaved species (not oak) for charcoal-burning
windfalls: windthrown trees or branches
wodegavell: *see* woodgavol
wodekevyll: *see* woodgavol
woodachet: wooden utensils
woodasken: *see* woodachet
woodgafol: money given in lieu of wood carrying services
woodhen: hen given in payment for right to gather wood
woodsilver: *see* woodgafol
woodward: forester, man in charge of or caring for woods
wormtak: payment due for compulsory feeding of swine of bond tenants in the lord's wood in autumn
wyndfal: *see* windfalls
wyures: large beams

APPENDIX 2: NAMED WOODS AND FORESTS IN SOUTH WALES, FOURTEENTH CENTURY

(W. Rees, *The historical map of South Wales and the Border in the Fourteenth Century,* 1933)

Monmouth/Skenfrith/White Castle/Grosmont
Bucknolt Wood
Coed Anghred
Coed Belod
Coed Broyn
Coed Bycha
Coed Llanveyr
Coed Llifos
Grosmont Wood
Hodnach Wood
Bergavenny
Bloreys (the Forest)
Lyngoed
Moelyfan Forest
Tillery Forest
Usk/Caerleon/Strigoil/Trelech
Cattershaies
Coed Cwnwr Forest
Earls Wood
Forest of Weloc
Paynes Wood
Rodge Wood
Strigoil Wood
Trellech Wood
Wastacoyt
Wentwood
Wyeswood
Glamorgan
Glyntaff Wood
Glyntaff Forest
Llwynperdeit Wood
Old Forest
Pencoed Forest
Crug Wood
Coed Franc
Gwynllwg
Coed Meredydd
Glyn Eboth Wood
Glyn Rempny Wood
Glyn Sirhowy Wood
Moelvan Forest

Gower
Kilvey Forest
Mynydd Gellionen
Tulchyclydwen Forest
Blaen Olchfa
Forest Fychan
Crow Wood
Clyne Forest
Ewyas Lacey
Forest of Ewyas
Maescoed
Forest of Monnow
Forest Hen
Forest Ollon
Carmarthen, Iscennen etc.
Pedol Forest
Brenaye Forest
Glyn Amman Forest
Maes Cathelog Forest
Glyncothi Forest
Pennant Forest
Killardun Forest
Wenallt Wood
Pencoed Forest
Cefngorach Forest
Gellyfeisant Forest
Penrhyn Forest (submerged)
Glynneiskin Forest
Forest of Glynne
Wenallt Forest
Coed y Brenin
Treskech
Glynistyn Forest
Coed yr Arglwydd
Emlyn
Garth Gyddyll Forest
Cilgerran
Cefn Drym Forest
Elfael
Old Forest
Buellt
Talyfan Forest

Blaenllynfi
Dinas Forest
Grono Wood
Brecon
Brychlyd Forest
Cadelan Forest
Great Forest
Little Forest
Lower Forest
Upper Forest
Cantref Bychan
Crugyblaidd Forest
Forest Cefngelevarth
Pembroke
Penkelly Forest
Loydarth Forest
Narberth Forest
Coytrath Forest
Coytkellas
Kingeswood
Preskely Forest
Radnor/border
Forest of Brilley
Kingswood Common
Bradnor Forest
Norwood Forest
Commergron Wood
Ackwood
Forest Fach
Knucklas Forest
Kingestell Wood
Portloke Forest
Clun Forest
Glyntoloch Forest
Hirthowel Forest
Le Tablaborn Forest
Montgomery
Forest of Cornedune
Le Lucley Forest

APPENDIX 3: NAMED FORESTS AND MAJOR WOODS IN THE MAPS OF SAXTON AND SPEED, AND GEORGE OWEN'S *DESCRIPTION OF WALES*

County	Saxton 1578	Owen* 1602	Speed 1610
Anglesey		Coedkadw	
Brecon		Forest y Brenin	
		Dyvynnog	
Cardigan	The Forest (Llanbeder)		The Forest (Llanbeder)
	Rescob Forest	Forest yr Esgob	Rescob Forest
		Coedmor	
		Coedyllys	
Carmarthen	Cardyth Forest	Caerdyth	Cardyth Forest
		Parkryn	
Denbigh		Coed or llwyn	
Glamorgan	Forest Coidfrank	Coed phrank	Coidfrank Forest
		Coed iarlh	
Merioneth	Benrose Wood	Berwyn	Benrose Wood
Monmouth	Erleswood	Earles woodde	Erles Wood
	Wensewood	wentes woodde	Wense Wood
	Wiesewood Chase	Wyes woodde	Wiesewood Chase
		Monckes woodde	
		Grismond	
Pembroke	Coidrath Forest	Coed traeth (Coed yr haf)	Coidrath Forest
	Narbarth Forest	Narberth (Arberth)	Narbarth Forest
		Kilgarran	
		Ki1rhyth	
		Penkelli	
		Mynwer	
		Picton wodde	
		Pentre Ivan woode	
Radnor	Forest of Knukles	Knukles Forrest	Knockles
	Radnor Forest	Radnor Forrest	Radnor
	Forest of Blethuagh	Blethuach Forrest	Blethvaugh

*For discussion of these woods and forests, see Henry Owen's notes in *Cymmrodorion Record Series* No. 1, Parts III & IV.

APPENDIX 4: NAMED FORESTS AND WOODS
IN GLAMORGAN (1578) AND PEMBROKESHIRE (1603)

Glamorgan*	Pembrokeshire*	

Forests	**The best standing woods**	**Smaller woods**
Cefn y Fid.	Narberth forest	Picton
Cefn Onn	Killgarran	Boulston
Coed Marchan	Coed Traeth	Wiston
Gelynnog	Caneston	Throstlwoode
Glyn Taff	Mynewer	lloyn gwayr
Llwydcoed	Penkelly	western Trewgarne
Glyn Cynon	Killreth	Estern Trewgarne
Garth Maelog	hook wood	Coed kynles
Garthgriffith	Vpton	llannerche
New Forest	**Forests & woods now destroyed**	Killkythed
Old Forest	lloydarch forest	Diffryn gwayn
Bery	Rywgian	Argoed
Woods	Moelgrove	Henllis
Llanishen	Coed Cadw	Wenallt
Caerau	Coed llong	Beinton
Leckwith	Mouncton park	Rams Bushe
Pencoetre	The wood by Newe gall	Perskyly
St Fagans	Cron lloyn	vper Talch
Rhydlafar		Nether Talch
Pentrebane		Creswell
Riglin		Mote
Yechan		Walton
Gwerndegay		Woodstock
Coed Mawr		lloyn y gorres
Y Cotrel		Drym
Y Kynehed		Nashe
Hornby		langom
Barry		
Penmark		
Carnllwyd		
Llanvithyn		
Cadw		
Brynhelygen		
Tal-y-fan		
Wern Fraith		
Crabla		
Sor		
Landavan		
Coed y Mwstwr		
Coed Melwas		
Coed Ffranc		

*For identification of these woods see Brian Ll. James's notes in Rice Merrick, *Morganiae Archaiographia* (1983), and Henry Owen's notes in *Cymmrodorion Record Series* No. 1 Part I, 86-7.

APPENDIX 5: WOODS NAMED IN EDWARD LHUYD'S
PAROCHIAL QUERIES, 1696

Parish	Woods	Parish	Woods
Llanelltyd (Merion.)	Koed y Ganlhwyd	Bryneglwys (Denb.)	Koed Bryn Tangor
	Koed y Berthlwyd		Koed y Plas yn Ial
	Koed Dol y Melynlhyn	Llantysilio (Denb.)	Koed y Geveliae
	Koed yr Hengwrt	Bangor (Flint)	Tir y Prenniae
	Koed y Vanner	Hanmer (Flint)	Halghton Wood
Llanrwst (Denb.)	Koed Karreg y Walch		Hanmer wood
	Koed Bryn Sylhty		Betchfield
	Koed y Gweilch	Gresford (Denb.)	Koed y Person
	Koed Nant Goron		Koed Trevor
Llanddoged (Denb.)	Koed Gronant		Koed y Brain
	Koed y Gorswen		Koed y Kopi
	Koed Kaer hyn		Koed yr Akrae
	Koed havod y Klawdd		Koed y Kox
Abergele (Denb.)	Koed y Plas ycha	Llanfair Dyffryn	Koed Kochion (alias
	Koed Syrrie	Clwyd (Denb.)	K. Plas ennion)
	Keivronnydh		
St Asaph (Flint)	Koed Kil Owen	Llannefydd (Denb.)	Koed yr Henvron
Dyserth (Flint)	Koed Gwylim		K. pen Porchell
Prestatyn (Flint)	Koed yr Esgop	Aberllynfi (Brec.)	Coed bolyn
Llanasa (Flint)	Coed gwilim	Glasbury (Rad.)	Coed y marchog
	Coed pant y Lhawndy		Gerndhover
Caerwys (Flint)	Koed y Pwlh gwyn	Bleddfa (Rad.)	Koed y forest y
Bodfari (Flint)	Park		mynachdy
	Koed pont Ryffydh	Llanddewi Ystradenny	Fforest y Knucklas
	Koed y Lhan	(Rad.)	
Holywell (Flint)	Greenfield Wood	Llangollen (Denb.)	Forrest y Krygnant
	Bagylht Wood		Koed Pengwern
Ysceifiog (Flint)	Coed Bron Vadog	Corwen (Merion.)	Park Glyndowerdwy
Nannerch (Flint)	Koed y Gelhi	Llanfor (Merion.)	Koed Rhiwedog
Cilcain (Flint)	Koed Plas newydd		Koed y Rhiwlas
	Koed Merklas		Kam yr wyll
Flint (Flint)	Koed onn	Llangower (Merion.)	Koed y vron
	Koed Bryn y Garreg	Llanfrothen (Merion.)	Koed du
Hawarden (Flint)	Ewlo wood		Koed y rharad
Henllan (Denb.)	Koed Panton		Y Keunant koch
	Koed yr Eivied		Koed Tyddin y sais
	Koed Lhannerch	Trelech (Monm.)	Wisewood
	Koed Lhyweni	St Clears (Carm.)	Priory Wood
	Koed Gwaenynog	Llantilio Pertholey	Gwern pen y clawth
	Koed Bod Eliog	(Monm.)	
	Koed Rhyd Goch	Walwyn's Castle	Sichwood
Llanrhaiadr yn	Koed Lhywesog	(Pemb.)	
Cinmerch (Denb.)	Koed Nant-Mawr		
	Park Koed orlhwyn		
	Y Koed dyon		
	Y Koed ystig		
	Koed Syl		
	Koed Kae'r havod		
	Koed maes Annod		

APPENDIX 6: PRE-DECIMAL CURRENCY AND METRIC CONVERSION TABLE FOR OLD IMPERIAL WEIGHTS AND MEASURES

Pre-decimal currency

12 pence (12*d*.)	= 1 shilling (1*s*.)		
20 shillings (20*s*.)	= £1		
£1	= 240 pence	= 20 shillings	= 100 new pence

Length

1 inch		= 2.54cm
1 foot	= 12 inches	= 0.3048m
1 yard	= 3 feet	= 0.9144m
1 rod	= 5.5 yards	= 5.0292m
1 chain	= 22 yards	= 20.117m
1 mile	= 1,760 yards	= 1.6093km

To convert	Multiply by
Feet to metres	0.3048
Yards to metres	0.9144
Miles to kilometres	1.6093

Surface or Area

1 sq. inch		= 6.4516cm²
1 sq. foot	= 144 sq. inches	= 0.0929m²
1 sq. yard	= 9 sq. feet	= 0.8361m²
1 acre	= 4,840 sq. yards	= 4046.9m²
1 sq. mile	= 640 acres	= 259.0 hectares

To convert	Multiply by
Square feet to square metres	0.0929
Square yards to square metres	0.8361
Square miles to square kilometres	2.5899
Acres to hectares	0.4047

Capacity or Volume

1 cu. inch		= 16.387cm³
1 cu. foot	= 1,728 cu. inches	= 0.0283m³
1 cu. yard	= 27 cu. feet	= 0.7645m³

To convert	Multiply by
Cubic feet to cubic metres	0.0283
Cubic yards to cubic metres	0.7646

Weight

1 pound	= 16 ounces	= 0.4536 kg
1 stone	= 14 pounds	= 6.3503 kg
1 hundredweight	= 112 pounds	= 50.802 kg
1 ton	= 20 cwt	= 1.0161 tonne

To convert	Multiply by
Pounds to kilograms	0.4536
Tons to kilograms	1,016.05
Tons to tonnes	1.016

INDEX

Note: the contents of the Appendices have not been included in this index.